SEVEN DAYS IN JULY

A Historic Account of the Battle of Atlanta

BY KENNETH A. GRIFFITHS

INDIGORIVER
PUBLISHING

SEVEN DAYS IN JULY

A HISTORIC ACCOUNT OF THE BATTLE OF ATLANTA

Seven Days in July: The Historic Account of the Battle of Atlanta

Editors: Kathryn Middleton, April Miller, Christian Pacheco, Donna Melillo
Cover and Interior Design: Kevin Williamson / kevinwilliamsondesign.com
Map Design: John Douglas Brown, Ken Griffiths

Indigo River Publishing
3 West Garden Street Ste. 352
Pensacola, FL 32502
www.indigoriverpublishing.com

Ordering Information:
Quantity sales: Special discounts are available on quantity purchases by corporations, associations, and others. For details, contact the publisher at the address above.

Orders by U.S. trade bookstores and wholesalers: Please contact the publisher at the address above.

Printed in the United States of America

Publisher's Cataloging-in-Publication Data is available upon request.

Library of Congress Control Number: 2014942507

ISBN: 978-0-9904857-0-4

First Edition

With Indigo River Publishing, you can always expect great books, strong voices, and meaningful messages. Most importantly, you'll always find . . . words worth reading.

This book is dedicated to my wife, Brenda. She helped with countless drafts, put up with my lack of word processor skills, accepted my long hours of research, and never lost her cheerfulness or stopped encouraging me.

To. Karen
John and I hope you read
this with pleasur
Ken Griffiths

CONTENTS

PREFACE

President Abraham Lincoln always seemed to possess a grand vision. He wanted the nation to remain a Union—in effect, the "status-quo antebellum." As time and the hard realities of war progressed, it became obvious that this unity could not be achieved. Too many men were dead and wounded, too much treasure was gone, too much honor was lost, and too many slaves were freed. There was too much imbalance where some sort of regional balance had existed earlier. Nonetheless, for Lincoln, the guiding concept—however flawed it was—was the restoration of the Union.

Although each state had entered the nation on a voluntary basis, the Union was thereafter perpetual in Lincoln's eyes. Lincoln loved the idea of implied powers and the implication that the Union of states was permanent since there was no formal method by which states could withdraw from the express contract that bound the states together. After all, this type of permanence is the fundamental organizing principle of all national governments. Governments are formed to last forever. Lincoln thought that if the forefathers intended the Union last only for a specific term of years, or that it could be terminated at will, they would have said so. In the absence of such a constitutional provision, such an act was impossible. The forefathers would not have omitted such an important provision. The framers were smart, well-informed men of the world. Many of them were lawyers. To allow slave states or any other state to leave would destroy the Union originally contemplated and end man's last best hope on earth.

The President believed his oath to preserve and protect the Constitution ordained and mandated his upholding the country. This whole North/South dispute related to the Union, or rather to the lack of it. Lincoln knew in his heart and in his mind that it was this issue—preserving the United States—and not the abolition of slavery that was the basis of his oath. Slavery, although the word was never used, was after all a part of the Constitution—not once, but over and over. Nonetheless, it would be difficult for anyone to think that in the absence of slavery, constitutional or not, the nation would now be facing its potential dissolution. Stopping this constitutional destruction was important enough to go to war over—or at least to get one started.

Lincoln needed a conclusion to make the war worthwhile and provide a valid justification for all that had transpired. Lincoln understood, as few others did, that the only way the Union, which had been ripped apart by conflict and military force, could be restored was to crush the Confederates' considerable military. So long as that force operated, it would be sufficient to maintain the existing state of disunion, as it was the South's most obvious and potent manifestation of sovereignty. Winning peace, or whatever arose, would have to come later.

However, that conclusion needed to come quickly. Time was a Confederate ally. It was unlikely that the United States would accept a war going on forever, or even for four more years. Americans grow tired of objectives viewed as unobtainable and move on to more mundane, personal opportunities. They let the movements of history sort themselves out.

At times, it seemed Lincoln alone understood this. He sometimes doubted, however, that he was really up to the task. Was there no general that could understand, and upon understanding, execute the strategy with a plan and then accomplish it? Ambrose Burnside, George McClellan, Henry Halleck, and George Meade had certainly failed to do so.

Even Ulysses S. Grant—who among all those who had tried seemed to understand the need to come to grips with and defeat the Southern forces—somehow still got tied to geography. He moved toward Richmond. He was, as he had said he would be to Lincoln, where Lee was. With Lee protecting Richmond, Grant was tied there.

Lincoln knew that place or geography exerts a powerful force on humans. We are generally organized by geography. We own land, and we vote according to where we live. Our friends are local people. Our children and other family members often live nearby. We cheer for the home team. Place, especially home, is a substantial part of being a person. It shapes our view of right and wrong; it shapes our politics and our outrage. It creates its own worldview and its unique sense of honor. Even the great division of the war itself was sorted out as the North versus the South.

The shorthand terms of place and geography are a ready substitute for all the untold philosophy and truth about the war. Place represents ideals and beliefs, but place can be seen. It is real, and it can be found on a map. It is a concept that one can grapple with. Place is powerful, and generals and their armies have long known their purpose can often be understood as taking and holding a piece of ground—certainly a piece of ground that others have deemed important enough to defend and call a capital.

Because Richmond and Atlanta were bound up in that powerful connection, taking them might disconcert or even damage the armies of Jefferson Davis. It would be a big step on the way to destroy the entire Confederate army. Of course, the converse was also true. If the South could capture Washington, D.C., it would be a blow to the Union. It would be a *heavy* blow.

Grant also understood this. He could articulate and intellectually believe this was true. He could *explain* it to Sherman, his subordinate and the commander of the armies seeking to take Atlanta, but was he really able to *convince* Sherman? Did the defeat of Johnston's western army, the Army of Tennessee, burn as an article of faith with Sherman? Was it something that had become a part of Sherman's makeup or constitution? Did Sherman truly feel the importance of ripping Atlanta and Richmond out of Confederate control?

People are imperfect. A grand scheme to defeat the Army of Tennessee was going to be hard for a new commander to execute. Grant would not be there to stand by him. In fact, Grant had his hands full with Bobby Lee's Army of Northern Virginia and the Washington government. Lincoln wanted to believe movement and maneuver might be the same as direct combat since movement was, or appeared to be, easier than combat. Sherman would have to be most resolute to remain motivated to push for the hard, bloody, tough end that could bring conclusion to the conflict. No one had done it yet. Could it be done?

DESIGN NOTES

The cover features an image from a Library of Congress stereograph showing Union soldiers standing by the mounted cannons inside a Confederate fort. The photo was attributed to George N. Barnard in 1864. We felt the image captures the tension and anticipation that so often characterizes war. Battles often are followed by unclear silence and the strategists are left to ponder if the enemy has been defeated or is merely regrouping.

Anywhere this symbol occurs in the text, the number references additional information in an appendix the reader will appreciate. Rather than obstruct the flow of the narrative with numerous footnote interruptions, we felt this would make the material fully available for those who are interested and yet not create barriers for the casual reader.

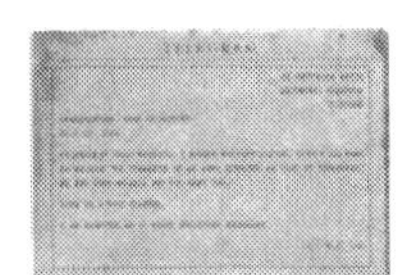

Telegrams are depicted in the text by a consistent image for readability and recognition. Telegrams were generally received on a teletype and the strips were cut into shorter lines and mounted on a card. Sometimes the text was delivered as is or retyped onto a preprinted form with the telegraph company name at the top or even sometimes hastily rewritten and delivered to the intended recipient.

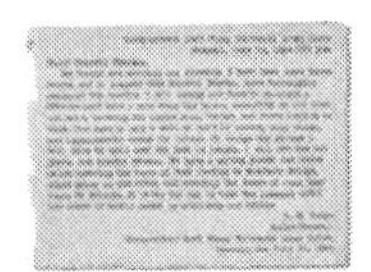

Likewise, letters are shown as either typewritten or handwritten. When depicted as handwritten, a consistent script font was used for the sake of readability rather than literally depicting a letter, which in some cases might be nearly impossible for the modern eye to read.

FOREWORD

Northwest Georgia has four distinct parts: the Cumberland Plateau, the Chickamauga Valley, the Armuchee Ridge, and the Great Valley.

The northwest corner of Georgia is where the strange, flat-topped plateau known as Lookout Mountain begins and continues for eighty-four miles. The landscape of Lookout Mountain is fantastic. Huge square-shaped, house-sized sandstone boulders have fallen off the sides of the mountain to their final resting places like the calving of icebergs from northern glaciers. The comparatively soft limestone provides the medium in which springs run and caves form. The soil supports huge, colorful rhododendrons, hardwood forests, and pines.

Swinging along the base of Lookout Mountain, one encounters the city of Chattanooga, Tennessee. To the south of the city are Missionary Ridge and the entrance to the Chickamauga Valley. This limestone-floored area has ridges rising 200 to 300 feet. Here, screened from interested eyes, hidden movement can take place until the imposing Armuchee Ridge hinders that movement. Sink holes, red cedar, hickory, willow, and dense undergrowth make the area difficult to traverse.

Beyond the valley lies Taylor Ridge, one of the most impressive of those making up the Armuchee system. It is composed of sandstone with rock-walled caves and outcroppings, and it is cut by gaps. Close observation reveals fossils in the rock. Huge white oak trees with their exposed roots seem to hold the world together. Sugar maple, beech, and hickory trees join the oaks in their task.

The massive Armuchee Ridges are about fifteen miles across—if one could move in a straight line from the west to the east. Ordinarily, however, one cannot, as the Great Valley unfolds on the eastern face of the ridge. The Coosa River and her sister rivers, the Conasagua, Coosawattee and the Etowah, all water a fertile and natural garden place.

This unique northwest corner of Georgia was untroubled by the presence of man for millions of years. The first people we know inhabited the land were the Paleo-Indians, and all they left were their Clovis, hand-shaped flint points. These early inhabitants were in place about

12,000 years ago; and although they probably lived full and interesting lives, we know very little about them.

As the climate began warming, the hunters and gatherers of the Archaic people flourished. Then, about 3,000 years ago, the beginning of agriculture took place in what is now called the Woodland Period. This was followed by the Mississippian Period, which ended about the time the first pale-skinned European explorers arrived on the American continent. During this period, the people of this area farmed, created large towns, and built impressive, large mounds.

Organized groups of men had walked and ridden through this region before. But in 1864, the land was host to the largest, most highly organized, most technologically abundant, best equipped, and best fed group ever: a force of about 100,000 men. All of these men belonged to one of three Federal armies within the Military Division of the Mississippi, named for the large river to the west. These were the Army of the Cumberland, the Army of the Ohio, and the Army of the Tennessee (named after the river, not the state). The men of those forces would march, fight, bleed, and die in Georgia.

Opposing this Federal force was a smaller in number, slightly less fed, less technologically equipped, and less supported group: the proud, rebellious Southerners. They, too, were organized into an army with a remarkably similar name—the Army of Tennessee (named for the state, not the river).

On May 3, 1864, about 324 years after Hernando de Soto moved his exploratory military force through this region, these two much larger military instrumentalities were on the move. They were locked together in a blue and gray waltz, the steps dictated by the same ridges and mountains and by the rivers, hills, and gaps.

Man-made objects played an important role in the lethal dance as well. In this case, it was the railroads that both were bound to out of necessity. Both required the things the railroad could deliver. The troops were never much farther from the tracks than a man could walk in a day. The graceful linear movement of the soldiers was tempered by cool mornings and furnace-like afternoons. It was dampened by rain, rivers, streams, and always by blood. The embracing pair moved on a dance floor that stretched for more than a hundred miles from Chattanooga to Atlanta. They entwined in a grip that killed, maimed, and wounded thousands of young patriotic men. During this time, our nation experimented with which way to go in a historic military contest called the Atlanta Campaign, one that would have a pivotal effect on the spirit of either the people of the Union or the people of the Confederacy.

A battle occurred on what is now the east side of Atlanta in July of 1864. There was a good deal of small unit combat and skirmishing, along with three large-scale actions that are now called the Battle of Peachtree Creek, the Battle of Atlanta, and the Battle of Ezra Church. At the time, the results were interpreted differently by the leaders of each side and, no doubt, by the ordinary participant.

History is not a science, and participants often see the same event in different ways. Vantage points differ and communication skills vary. Even recollections recorded immediately are hampered by the fog of war. Men involved in the Southern assault on the Francis DeGress' battery can't agree on the exact time the assault began, so historic accuracy is difficult and sometimes impossible. Fictionalized elements allow me to be specific. However, I have tried to stay true to the events, conversations, and personalities.

My book is largely a work of non-fiction, but it contains fictional elements. I have endeavored to place my story on the bedrock—or the hard red clay, as it were—of good history. Sometimes I had to choose between conflicting historical sources, and sometimes I had to make an educated guess. If you suspect that I am in error, please let me know, and I will attempt to correct it in a later printing.

Most of the people mentioned in the book existed, but my interpretation of them is a work of fiction. The goal of my fiction was to make the historical men more real to the reader.

Time and the prevailing culture both combine to make people separated by a hundred years or more different. Nonetheless, I assume for all the differences, men have certain fundamental aspects that remain more or less consistent. As a result of endless reading and thinking, I believe I have come to truly know the people who were previously only names to me. Telling the story of these historical realities is what I tried to do. You can be the judge.

This is a story, mostly factual, about the events that took place during seven important days in July that began with July 16 and culminated on July 22 of 1864 along with the relevant days that preceded the seven-day event.

"The military power must be destroyed, that is, reduced to a state as not to be able to prosecute the war. That is the sense in which we wish to be understood here-after, whenever we use the expression, 'destruction of the enemy's military power.'"
—*On War* by Carl Von Clausewitz

CHAPTER ONE

Union | WILLIAM SHERMAN

BURNETT HOUSE

CINCINNATI, OHIO

MARCH 18, 1864

4:00 P.M.

Generals William Sherman and Ulysses S. Grant had been together since Sherman had arrived the night before. Sherman touched the stars on Grant's epaulets.

"Those stars sure make that poor coat look proud, General," Sherman said. "Not sure I've ever beheld such a galaxy at such a close distance, and you sure deserve them. No one has done a better job, and no one will get this war over quicker than you."

Grant, never much for words, smiled just a bit, his eyes twinkling. Sherman's presence always seemed to put Grant at ease.

It had been a whirlwind of activity over the last two weeks. The telegram ordering Grant to Washington had arrived on March 3. He knew that the three stars of a lieutenant general awaited him, and on March 4, with his son Frederick and friend Brigadier General John Rawlins, he began his trip. He arrived in the Capitol on March 8 after stopping to see his parents, and he received his commission as lieutenant general at the White House on March 10. He next visited George Meade in the field and quickly decided that Meade should remain as the Commander of the Army of the Potomac. Upon returning to Washington, Grant had a long meeting with the President and determined the new chain of command for the Department of the Mississippi. William Sherman, James McPherson, and John Logan all moved up to fill the places created by his promotion. Then, he ordered Sherman to meet him at Cincinnati, where he outlined his strategy for the campaign and the decisions he had made about each commander's part in the effort to defeat the Confederate forces.

"Well, General, if you will, let me sum this up and see if you think I have it right." Sherman shifted the cigar in his mouth and cleared his throat. He pointed at the map with a bony index finger. "I am going to push Joe Johnston's Army of Tennessee with McPherson, Thomas, and Schofield while you and General Meade go after Bobby Lee in Northern Virginia. General Banks will move toward Mobile, and Butler will move on Richmond."

The grand design of this plan and its execution was to eliminate the advantage of the South's interior lines and coordinate the Union's superior numbers to keep Lee from sending reinforcements to help Johnston, like Lee had done for Braxton Bragg at Chickamauga. Grant wanted to keep constant pressure on the Confederate armies and force something to let go or break apart.

"Truth to tell, it probably doesn't matter where the dam breaks as long as it does prior to the elections this fall," Sherman said. "I wish there was a way to make all this happen by guile or maneuver, but I suspect you will deal with Lee by keeping on him day after day."

Grant drew on his cigar and expelled the blue smoke. Bringing the cigar back to his mouth, he chewed on the stub of his cigar and felt the warm tobacco juice begin its passage down his throat.

He then said, "I think you have said it back to me better than I told you in the first place." He permitted himself a smile. He knew Sherman was smart and articulate. Sherman had a quick mind and a vivid imagination that had always impressed Grant. Grant wasn't sure all this effort could be coordinated, but he knew it was a good plan, and he knew Sherman would carry it out. Sherman would probably carry the plan out better because it was Grant's, not Sherman's. Sherman was a hell of a number two, and together, Grant knew they could end the misery of the country. He also knew that his friendship and backing had been placed in such a way as to create a commander who could see this spring's offensive through to its conclusion. The suffering and hate the North and South both felt could be brought to an end, and the Union could be preserved.

The relationship between the two western generals was complex, but it could be summed up in very human terms. As Sherman would remark later, "I stood by Grant when he was drunk, and he stood by me when I was crazy." Neither seemed overwhelmed by the other or, more importantly, by themselves. And they didn't seem surprised about the positions they found themselves in.

Less than two years separated them. Sherman was older than Grant and was in his third year at West Point when Grant arrived for his first. Grant was an expert only in horsemanship at the academy while Sherman's marks were high nearly across the board. Grant graduated twenty-first out of thirty-nine while Sherman was sixth, despite his standing of 216 out of 233 in the Cadet Corps in behavior.

Grant was more direct in his personal behavior and his fighting techniques while Sherman was more indirect, intellectual, and sophisticated in his approach. While unlikely to admit it, both were intelligent, but Sherman worked his to an edge more often than did Grant. Sherman was a superbly educated man who constantly devoured all reading material available.

Sherman spent thirteen years in the army, rising to the rank of captain, and missed the war with Mexico. Grant stayed in twelve years and was brevetted to first lieutenant during the hard fighting in Mexico. Grant's time out of the army was dominated by a lack of success. Failure, with some highlights of success, characterized Sherman's time after his initial service as well. Sherman aimed higher than Grant though, with forays into banking, law, management, and a period as president and professor at the newly formed Louisiana State Seminary of Learning and Military Academy. This failure prior to the Civil War seemed to have provided an attitude of self-reliance and an approach based on a willingness to take risks and an understanding that they, as individuals, had little or nothing to lose. Both had taken risks and had seen failure as the result, and they were no longer paralyzed by it as some men were.

Both were men of the West and were American to the core. In the field, onlookers were often surprised to learn that the plainly dressed, average-looking men were general officers. There was no dash or pomp or circumstance. They both had goals and saw their endeavor as a hard job of basic work, and they had their plan and goals. All that was left was the execution.

Not long after this meeting, General Grant and his wife left Cincinnati on a train back to Washington while Sherman stayed another day. It would be eighteen months before the two blue-clad generals would see each other again. As Grant left, Sherman couldn't help but wonder what the enemy forces would do, yet he wasn't the least bit worried about how Grant would handle the enemy. Sherman knew Grant would always hold up his end of the deal.

Hence, on May 4, 1864, as the Commander in Chief of all the Union Armies, Grant would cross the Rapidan River with George Meade to find, fix, and fight the skilled and lucky Robert E. Lee and his hardened veterans from the Army of Northern Virginia.

On May 5, 1864, Sherman left Ringgold, Georgia, in command of the Union Military Division of the Mississippi to confront Joe Johnston's smaller but rested, refitted, and rejuvenated Army of Tennessee. Sherman's Military Division of the Mississippi had nearly 100,000 men while Johnston had fewer than 65,000.

With that, the spring offensive was underway. A new phase of the war begun, bringing changes neither the men of the North nor the South had contemplated.

CHAPTER TWO

NORTHWEST GEORGIA

May 1864

Early in May 1864, the Union Army of the Tennessee marched from its winter quarters and passed by storied Lookout Mountain. In this same area, during the previous fall, the veteran Union troops had pushed General Bragg's hard Army of Tennessee off the heights of the mountain and then pushed it hard again from the Missionary Ridge south of Chattanooga.

Following their victory at Chickamauga the previous fall, the Confederate force had successfully bottled up the defeated and demoralized Union army and nearly starved it into death or submission. This state of affairs changed upon Grant's arrival. Grant had moved quickly to feed Chattanooga by opening the river for riverboats to establish a supply line, the "cracker line." Then, in the battles of Lookout Mountain and Missionary Ridge, national Federal forces sent Bragg and his men south in defeat and then sent just Bragg himself to Richmond, Virginia, where he relinquished his command to Joe Johnston.

During that May, after wintering in Alabama and Tennessee, the newly provisioned, augmented, and organized Union forces led by Sherman moved to Chattanooga. From there, Sherman's forces moved into north Georgia, through towering Taylor Ridge via Snake Creek Gap, and then into Resaca. In June, the soldiers pursued the Confederates through Dallas, New Hope Church, Kennesaw Mountain, and Marietta, and then to the River Line at the Chattahoochee.

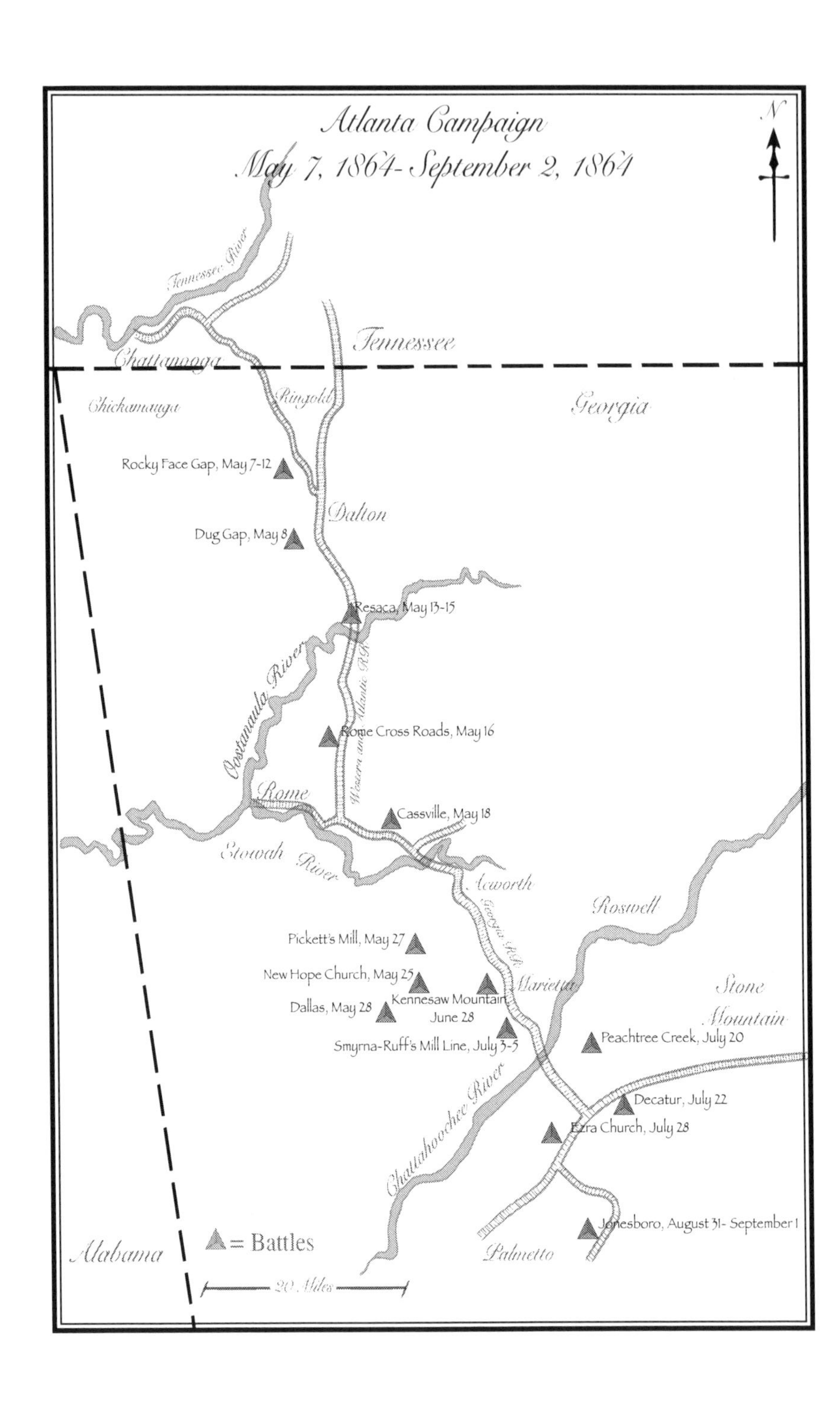
Atlanta Campaign
May 7, 1864- September 2, 1864
N
Tennessee River
Chattanooga
Tennessee
Chickamauga
Ringold
Georgia
Rocky Face Gap, May 7-12
Dalton
Dug Gap, May 8
Resaca, May 13-15
Oostanaula River
Western and Atlantic RR
Rome Cross Roads, May 16
Rome
Cassville, May 18
Etowah River
Acworth
Georgia RR
Roswell
Pickett's Mill, May 27
New Hope Church, May 25
Kennesaw Mountain
June 28
Marietta
Dallas, May 28
Stone
Mountain
Smyrna-Ruff's Mill Line, July 3-5
Peachtree Creek, July 20
Chattahoochee River
Decatur, July 22
Ezra Church, July 28
Jonesboro, August 31- September 1
Alabama
= Battles
Palmetto
20 Miles

July 10 - 14, 1864

CHAPTER THREE

Union | GRENVILLE DODGE

North Bank of the Chattahoochee

July 10, 1864

8:00 p.m.

Major General Grenville Dodge was everywhere, supervising the hundreds of men at his command. Dodge was thirty-three years old and of slight build and average height. His full head of dark hair crossed his forehead in a straight line, running parallel with his lips. He wore it parted on the left with nearly engineered precision. His hair often extended over his ears and was joined with a neat, full beard. He had dark, intelligent eyes and an almost patrician nose.

He stood at the bank of the Chattahoochee. On the eve of the war, two bridges stood over the Chattahoochee River in front of him, but by July 10, only one bridge remained, the one northeast of Dodge. The bridge at Roswell, where Dodge now stood, had been burned by the fleeing detachment of Joe Wheeler's 4th Tennessee on July 5, 1864. The river had been crossed there for a long time. The Creek Indians and the Cherokee had crossed at the Shallow Ford, which formed part of the Etowah—or as it was later renamed by white settlers, the Hightower Trail. Between the Shallow Ford and Vickery Creek, a bridge had been erected over the river in 1857. It provided a direct means whereby people could transport mill goods across the river and to Atlanta.

Now, only the stone piers remained of the former structure. Dodge had thrown a footbridge across the Shallow Ford and followed that with a light float bridge, and so the troops from Dodge's Sixteenth Army Corps had crossed the last substantial barrier protecting Atlanta.

Currently, his bridge builders were salvaging lumber and felling trees to create a new, more substantial bridge. Dodge already had two light artillery batteries part way up the road, which climbed the long slope from the riverbank to the ridgeline on the south side of the river. So far, no Confederate opposition had revealed itself.

Dodge possessed the need to always be doing something and exhibited the hands-on trait that is common in many engineers. He believed in substance before form, but he was sensitive to what others might think. He also had a deep interest in railroads. The railroad was a natural object for Dodge's imagination and expertise. It was an enormous user of engineering talent and was constantly moving. There was a symbiotic relationship between the railroad's needs and Dodge's own desire to be in control of the future, which neatly combined with an opportunity for wealth and success. Surveying for the railroads demanded an inquiring mind like his. It rewarded his enthusiasm for exploration and, in turn, fulfilled the unspoken need he had to be a pathfinder and hero. The railroad fulfilled his need to be a part of something bigger than himself.

Headquarters, Left Wing, Sixteenth Army Corps
Roswell, July 10, 1864 1:30 p.m.

Major General Sherman,

My troops are arriving and crossing. I have been here three hours, and in company with General Newton, have thoroughly examined the country. I will occupy and fortify to-night a tête-de-pont half a mile from the river, extending up and down one mile, covering the entire ford, bridge, and roads leading to them. The ford is half a mile or more in extent, very rough, and impracticable except for troops. To bridge the stream I will have to build over 650 feet in length. I will use the old piers, and trestle between. We have a strong picket out three miles covering the forks of road leading to McAfee's Bridge, eight miles up the river, and covering the forks of road that leads to Atlanta. It is too far out to take the command until the river is easily passed by artillery and trains.

G. M. Dodge
Major-General
Headquarters Left Wing, Sixteenth Army Corps,
Roswell, Ga. July 11, 1864

Dodge epitomized the idea of a "railroad man." As others said, Sherman *looked* like an American, but Dodge *acted* like one. In Dodge resided a democratic embrace of competition. He believed the person who *did* the most should *reap* the most in pursuit of the greater good. There was an acceptance that big, important things like the railroad and the war were jobs to be done quickly. He felt that a finished product need not be a thing of beauty or done with perfection, but it must be started and then finished fast. The result could be improved later, but the main thing was to get it done so it could begin to deliver its promise. Speed was almost as important as the task. The advent of railroads changed concepts of time and speed in a revolutionary manner. Dodge sought to do the same in the war.

Maj. Gen. J.B. McPherson,
Commanding Department and Army of the Tennessee:

General: I arrived here yesterday at noon, the command crossed and the troops were all in position before night, and now have entrenchments up. I have over a mile of ford and bridges to cover, and cannot make a tête-de-pont very far out that will cover it. I have taken and extended the line selected by General Newton. Our trains are all on the north side of the river. The ford is very rough, but shallow, and the bridge we will build is 650 feet long and 14 feet high. I put a footbridge across last night so that troops can pass. It is very difficult for them to wade, the water is swift and the bottom full of holes. The enemy's pickets are near Buck Head, and men out of Atlanta to-day say that there is no infantry after you get four miles this side of Atlanta, and that Stewart is on their right. Johnston's headquarters are at a little house three miles this side of Atlanta, on the railroad. Atlanta papers on the 10th instant say that a council of war was held that day, and that it is rumored that Johnston will make a fight for the city. This would tend to show that it is not their intention. All trains belonging to the army have gone toward Augusta, and everybody fleeing. Eight miles up the river from here is a good bridge that is not destroyed. I will work hard on the bridge here and finish it as soon as possible. It is a big job as you will perceive from the length. Everything was burned up here that we could use—houses, mills, lumber, and all.

I am, very respectfully, your obedient servant,
G.M. Dodge,
Major-General, Commanding.

CHAPTER FOUR

Confederacy | ROBERT E. LEE

HEADQUARTERS OF ARMY OF NORTHERN VIRGINIA

NEAR PETERSBURG, VIRGINIA, ABOUT THIRTY MILES SOUTH OF RICHMOND

JULY 12, 1864

Deep in his heart, Robert E. Lee knew that the near-siege operations his army was now engaged in were going to end in a predictable and disastrous manner. He had told Lieutenant General Jubal Early as much before Early had been sent to clean up the Shenandoah Valley. Petersburg—with its railroad, turnpike, and location on the Appomattox River—was essential to the defense of Richmond. In Lee's mind, being forced by Grant's persistence to remain within his extensive fortifications and, as a consequence, be deprived of the ability to maneuver doomed Lee to an almost certain defeat. The one bright spot was Early's victory at the Monocracy River against General Lew Wallace's 6,000 Federals.

With a few flicks of his pen, Lee finished drafting a message to President Davis:

To Jefferson Davis
Richmond, Virginia
Camp
July 12, 1864
9:12 p.m.
Mr. President:
I send you a paper of the 10th instant containing Mr. Secretary Stanton's bulletin to Genl. Dix,

acknowledging a defeat of Genl. Wallace at Monocacy by Genl. Early. I have also received a dispatch from Genl. Fitz Lee this evening reporting that he met Genl. Gregg with his division advancing toward Reams' Station, charged him with three of his regiments & drove him back, capturing some 30 men & two officers. His loss small. The enemy's not known. He thinks he was moving against the railroad. We have only had it in operation for two days, but have got through several trains of corn & provisions.

I am distressed at the intelligence conveyed in your telegram of today. It is a grievous thing to change commander of an army situated as is that of the Tennessee. Still if necessary it ought to be done. I know nothing of the necessity. I had hoped that Johnston was strong enough to deliver battle. We must risk much to save Alabama, Mobile & communication with the Trans Mississippi. It would be better to concentrate all the cavalry in Mississippi & Tennessee on Sherman's communications. If Johnston abandons Atlanta I suppose he will fall back on Augusta. This loses us Mississippi & communication with Trans Mississippi. We had better therefore hazard that communication to retain the country. Hood is a good fighter, very industrious on the battle field, careless off, & I have had no opportunity of judging of his action, when the whole responsibility rested upon him. I have a high opinion of his gallantry, earnestness & zeal. Genl. Hardee has more experience in managing an army.

May God give you wisdom to decide in this momentous matter.

Truly & resply yours
R.E. Lee

P.S. Today we could get no papers from the enemy, from which I inferred there was some good news they wished to withhold. The one sent was captured. You must excuse its condition.

R.E. Lee

Lee then looked down at the copy of the telegram he had sent earlier in the day to the President. He wanted to be honest in his comments about John Hood. He knew what to do in a fight, but responsibility for the war in Georgia was much more than just a fight.

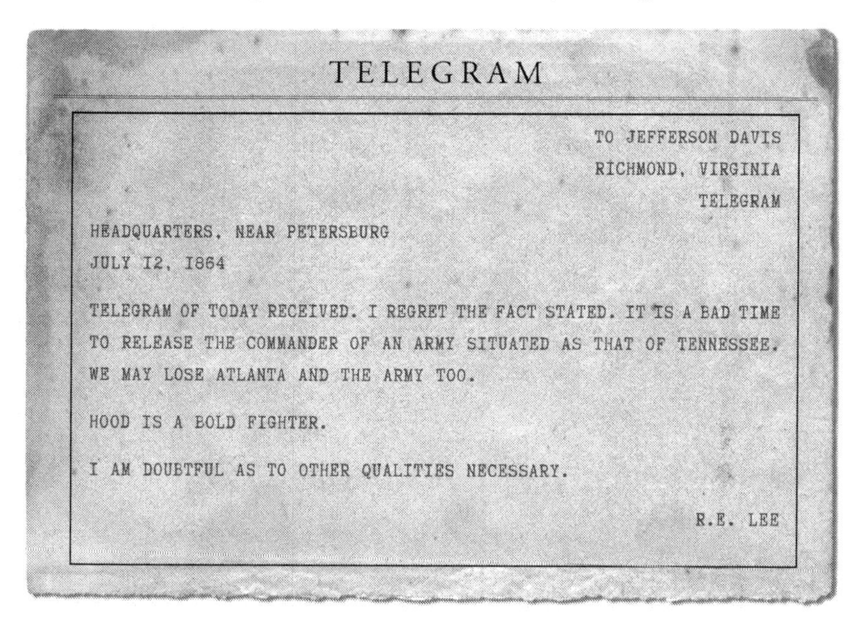

TELEGRAM

TO JEFFERSON DAVIS
RICHMOND, VIRGINIA
TELEGRAM

HEADQUARTERS, NEAR PETERSBURG
JULY 12, 1864

TELEGRAM OF TODAY RECEIVED. I REGRET THE FACT STATED. IT IS A BAD TIME TO RELEASE THE COMMANDER OF AN ARMY SITUATED AS THAT OF TENNESSEE. WE MAY LOSE ATLANTA AND THE ARMY TOO.

HOOD IS A BOLD FIGHTER.

I AM DOUBTFUL AS TO OTHER QUALITIES NECESSARY.

R.E. LEE

Lee knew Davis was fond of Hood and that his appreciation of Johnston's best qualities was often overlooked. Lee could only pray that God would provide wisdom and direction to the President. He closed his eyes, and his heart fluttered as it often did these days. A kind of otherworldliness washed over his head. He hoped sleep would come easily that night.

CHAPTER FIVE

Union | WILLIAM SHERMAN

FIFTEENTH ARMY CORPS

OLD SANDTOWN

Red-tailed hawks are large birds with a curved, red tail and broad, strong wings with cruel eyes and an arrogant, regal look. These birds can be found over most of North America. They habitually soar in high, wide circles as they scan the land below for prey. Hawks in search of prey over north Georgia during 1864 would have seen sights they had never seen before. The land was alive with men, horses, mules, wagons, and guns.

To the hawk circling above this day, the landscape appeared as a length of colored ribbon and bolts of cloth. The hawk's eyes were drawn to the Chattahoochee River, which moved as if it were alive. Here, the river ran southwest. As the river flowed to the Gulf, it became more of a north–south watercourse, separating Georgia and Alabama. The river was green and blue in the middle and dark under the trees' branches at the river's edge, where shadows lay. On both sides of the river were summer-green hardwoods in full leaf with the shimmering green pines, providing proof of the red clay that they grew in. The hills on both sides of the river rose 150 feet above the water at their peaks.

What was new to the hawk was the red dust, which rose like a red cloud from the road. That Georgia clay was baked as hard as a brick; nonetheless, it grudgingly released tiny particles of itself as men, mules, and horses trod the road, and the wheels of ambulances, wagons, caissons, limbers, and cannons rolled over and over. The combined action created by all this movement was a great deal like a hammer mill run in conjunction with grinding wheels.

The fine particles climbed in the air and settled on everything. This devil's flour was in the men's noses and in their hair and on the backs of the animals, caking when it touched wet places. Thousands of boots and shoes looked as though a woman's make-up purse had exploded over them. Sunlight caught and reflected off a million shiny metal and leather surfaces.

There was dust, dirt, and tons of manure. The red road swam with hot, stinking, miserable men. Those tired men in dark blue wool uniforms had sweat running down unshaven bearded faces and breath that reeked of coffee and tobacco, mixed with the odor of gun oil, axle grease, wood smoke, and the ripe aroma of crushed blueberries and blackberries. Under a July sun in Georgia, which built temperatures in excess of a hundred degrees, all this combined to manufacture a smell that was overpowering.

The Fifteenth Army Corps of the Army of the Tennessee was stretched out, in part to avoid the dust and in part because armies need great distance when they are on road marches.

Yet as they marched, they grew closer to the Confederate forces that lay within the River Line. The Chattahoochee River runs deep and wide in some places, yet it is easily fordable in others. It is an obstacle made all the more difficult because of the man-made fortifications south of Marietta called the River Line. This scientifically-designed fortress protected the railroad as it crossed the river. Used intelligently with its interlocking fields of fire, it would allow a small number of men to withstand the onslaught of many. Even now, the thin, slow-talking, sharp-eyed men inside the fort waited to kill the blue-clad Federal men who pressed down on them.

But so well-designed and built, the River Line was viewed as something to go around rather than attack directly. Where the River Line hadn't been extended, nature had done a pretty good job of creating a defensible river line of her own that could be used to do just that. On the Confederate's left was the river that was bordered by high hills, which would permit no flank attack.

A small group of gray-colored men appeared to mostly watch and wait on the southern shore, deep in the shade of the dense trees. The hawk knew they were there, and the men who looked skyward saw and envied the hawk. The men remarked on the bird's brilliant, orange, incandescent tail as the bird glided between them and the sun.

Sherman was learning again—if, in fact, the lesson was not already deeply etched in his mind—that it was easier to flank Joe Johnston on a map than it was on hilly, tree-crowned, river-and-stream-cut terrain. Johnston's Army of Tennessee retreated to prepared positions, and Sherman's men would flank them rather than attack them directly, saving Rebel and Federal lines.

Movement was a part of his western army. Given his lack of patience, he always preferred the straight line—the shortest distance between two points. Since early in May when the campaign began, however, the shortest distance could only be purchased at the expense of a huge butcher's bill. If flanking left or right accomplished the same thing, then that is what his army would do. The hot, fast marches were better than a direct assault any day, and the aggressive marching was having its effect. The continued flanking meant his Union army was closer and closer to its goal.

The Grand Federal Army of the Military Division of the Mississippi was made up of some 100,000 odd soldiers. These men were mostly volunteers from what was known as the West. They were organized pursuant to a formula used by both the Union and Confederate forces. First—or last, depending on your belief in the individual—was the organizational unit known as an army. This military hierarchy starts with a commanding general and is broken down in very specific steps right down to the soldier on the front line. Each layer is commanded by an officer, is designed for effective communication, and has a specific function within the army.[1]

The Union Army of the Tennessee alone had 35,245 men, of whom 1,561 were officers and 33,684 were soldiers. By July of 1864, the Army of the Tennessee would seem to be well knit, cohesive, and solid, but it had not always been so. It had changed several times. The bulk of the soldiers who made up this army had fought together at Shiloh, or Pittsburg Landing as it was sometimes called. In that fight, they were the Army of the District of Western Tennessee. It was formed into the Department of Tennessee on October 16, 1862 and commanded by Grant, who was a major general at the time.

Eight days later, the department was reorganized as the Thirteenth Army Corps. Then, on December 18, 1862, it was divided into four corps: the Thirteenth, Fifteenth, Sixteenth, and Seventeenth. Major General Sherman was selected to command this western force on October 27, 1863, just days short of a year since it had been merely the seminal Thirteenth Army Corps. By the time the Atlanta Campaign began, Major General McPherson had assumed its command. Along with the Union Armies of the Potomac, Virginia, and Cumberland, it was one of the major armies of the United States. It was without a doubt one of the most successful armies—and one of the most lethal, and it was ready for a fight.

CHAPTER SIX

Union | JOHN LOGAN

FIFTEENTH ARMY CORPS

HEADQUARTERS

BETWEEN ROSWELL AND MARIETTA

JULY 12, 1864

Like the lawyer he was, General Logan marked what he thought were the two most important paragraphs of the new order from McPherson as if he were studying a statute. He knew now where he was to go and where the hardtack and ammunition would be.

II. Maj. Gen. John A. Logan, commanding Fifteenth Army Corps, will march his command at 5 o'clock this p.m. toward the bridge across the Chattahoochee near Roswell Factory, making a distance of about ten miles to-night if practicable. He will resume his march at an early hour to-morrow morning, thus protecting his men and animals from the heat of the day.

III. Maj. Gen. F. P. Blair, commanding Seventeenth Army Corps, will remain in his present position until the return of General Stoneman, or until further orders, making such demonstrations about Sandtown, Howell's, and Turner's as may be made necessary, communicating in the mean time with Major General Sherman, and receiving from him instructions. Four days' rations will be issued to the men of the Seventeenth Corps, and the trains sent to Marietta with the general supply train.

IV. All the wagons and artillery will move by Marietta and fill up with provisions, forage, and ammunition.

WM. T. Clark,
Assistant Adjutant-General
Atlanta, July 13, 1864

His Excellency JEFFERSON DAVIS, Richmond:
Have just arrived without detention. Our army all south of the Chattahoochee, and indications seem to favor an entire evacuation of the place. Shall see General Johnston immediately.

BRAXTON BRAGG

ATLANTA, July 13, 1864—1 p.m.

His Excellency JEFFERSON DAVIS:
The enemy are reported by General Wheeler as having crossed two corps to this side of the river about nine miles above the railroad bridge. An official report has just reached General Wright that the enemy's cavalry, accompanied by artillery, crossed the Chattahoochee this evening nine miles from Newnan. Were at last accounts advancing on that place. Our army is sadly depleted, and now reports 10,000 less than the return of 10th June. I find but little encouraging.

B. BRAGG.

HDQRS. MILITARY DIVISION OF THE MISSISSIPPI,
In the Field, near Chattahoochee River, July 13, 1864.

General DODGE,
Roswell:
General McPherson left here about 10 a.m. for Marietta and Roswell. Report to me this evening his arrival and that of the Fifteenth Corps. All very quiet here.

W.T. SHERMAN,
Major-General, Commanding

ROSWELL, July 13, 1864—9 p.m.

Major-General SHERMAN:
Advance of Fifteenth Army Corps is camped near Roswell. General McPherson has not arrived. Men who left Atlanta yesterday, employees in Government shops, say all machinery, stores, &c., have been packed up and are being sent to Augusta. They came by way of Decatur. Report no force of enemy in that direction, or works. They think most of the infantry is west of railroad. They saw no works after leaving Atlanta. Bridge is built, is double track.

G.M. DODGE
Major-General

CHAPTER SEVEN

Confederacy | JOSEPH JOHNSTON

JULY 14, 1864

By early 1864, Jefferson Davis' original plan to fight the Union invaders as close to the borders of the Confederacy as possible was in substantial disarray. The borders had long since been violated, and in the Western Theater, the Union army was deep in the heart of the Southern states. The Army of Tennessee and Johnston had fought in a losing cause and now stood ready to receive and repel the invaders.

Johnston was competent in a number of areas. He had reorganized the army and restored the morale. It had become better rested, fed, and shod. Its drill improved. Horses had been fed up and could pull limbers and bear the weight of horsemen on their backs. Throughout the winter, the army healed. It became an organization of spirited, combative, loyal troops. Johnston was loved and admired because his soldiers sensed he cared for them, and the army was as well-prepared as it could be. These are important attributes to bring to bear on a broken, out-of-repair army. He largely fixed it during its winter in Dalton. Little fault could be found in Johnston's actions to renew the army, and the praise for his accomplishment was warranted.

Johnston's positive attributes had led to his selection as the first West Point graduate to reach the rank of general in the old army. His rise was based on intelligence, organization skills, personal bravery, and personal ambition. To this mix was added a personality that mistrusted others, especially Jefferson Davis, his commander-in-chief.

Johnston embraced secrecy. He was vain. He confused appearance with substance, or he hewed to appearance in the absence of substance and hoped no one noticed. While viewed nearly as a father to many of his troops, he also exhibited sensitivity to rank and its social consequences. Johnston, polished and difficult, sought to avoid failure and could, with little provocation, erupt in anger. He was quick to blame others and sometimes saw evidence of conspiracy where none existed. He did not receive criticism well and always sought self-justification. He was personally honest, but his lack of trust in others reflected a certain lack of self-confidence and personal security.

Some of these characteristics came back on themselves. By mistrusting others, he would fail to communicate the full concept of his plans and would make it difficult for others to attain the information they desired or sought. Without the full picture, subordinates often failed to carry out the mission entrusted to them. That resulted in failure, or at least less success, than was expected. In turn, that led Johnston to develop an even more restricted willingness to share or communicate plans with the same people.

Johnston, to his credit, had given lots of thought to the campaign he would wage. His intelligence led him to the conclusion that a defensive campaign presented the only realistic choice. He was sure he needed to stay close to the railroad and always between Sherman and Atlanta. To win, he would defend until an opportunity presented itself or Sherman made a mistake he and the Confederate Army of Tennessee could capitalize on. He thought a defensive, reactive posture could potentially allow him to defeat Sherman's much larger force and could buy time either for the upcoming fall elections in the North or for something good to happen on the ground.

Seizing the initiative never entered into Johnston's calculus, and somewhere in the past, the grasp on initiative had slipped away from the Southern Army of Tennessee. Initiative, in a warrior's context, must first reveal itself in a plan, find existence in march and maneuver, and manifest itself in attack or confrontation with the enemy.

Initiative can drive a defense. A strategic defense, as opposed to a reactive or responsive defense, may hide a grim determination to launch devastating counterattacks, or it may be part of an overall plan to allow forces to concentrate somewhere else, exhaust an enemy before beginning offensive operations, or force an enemy to meet on your own terms.

While moments of robust initiative in the Confederacy may exist, one must mine the evidence in a fine and diligent manner to gain a glimpse of it in the actions of the Army of Tennessee during the spring of 1864. In place of initiative was a pessimistic, safe, reactive, wait-and-see acceptance of the inevitable. Sherman's army was bigger, better equipped, more aggressive, more strategic, and more ambitious. In Johnston's eyes, little could be done but his selected course.

Of course, Johnston was not a coward. He was not physically afraid. If called on to meet Sherman face-to-face in a one-on-one duel with swords or pistols, Johnston would not flinch or falter. Duty, honor, and personal standing would demand his presence. For the South, unfortunately, that was not the issue.

Passion for the cause was just not part of Johnston. There was nothing in the current circumstance compelling him to act with fervor—nothing to motivate him to do something extra, to be bold, to take a risk. Rather, caution demanded that he focus on what he had to lose rather than on what could be gained. The will to win, the fire in the belly, and the passion that separates exceptional military leaders from others exists only in few and did not exist in Johnston. Ordinarily, a lack of passion makes no difference. Ordinary competence, especially in subordinates, is generally all that is needed or wanted. Of course, an extraordinary performance from an individual soldier, in small and large units, can tilt the outcome. Extraordinary or heroic action is always welcome on the battlefield when confronting a competent enemy in a more or less equal contest, as is luck. However, greater resources are usually predictive of outcome, and those events are viewed by history as merely commonplace in the annals of war. However, in this case, passion—or rather the lack of—made all the difference.

The physiological imperative and fire that drove Robert E. Lee to make an opportunity simply did not exist in Johnston, and the opportunity for the defense to provide the foundation for a bold counterstrike never seemed to be part of Johnston's decision making. Nothing in his past experience prepared him for this time. He knew he should plan and prepare his defenses so as to deny the advantages of the larger numbers and the offensive nature of Sherman's intentions, but Johnston's defensive posture was not born of higher strategic reasoning. It seemed right to him, at a basic personal level. It was comfortable. It was what came naturally to him and was, consequently, what he would rely on or fall back on when under stress. Johnston was skilled at tactical reaction, and defense was the ideal circumstance to employ it.

With the possible exception of First Manassas, it is impossible to find an example in Johnston's past of an aggressive plan designed to achieve victory. Rather, the enemy always appeared to be ten feet tall and to outnumber Johnston's own slender resources by multiples. The army settled for tired competency and a predisposition for the reactive and predictable.

As far as it went, when one's personal platform of success was dependent on another making a mistake and then capitalizing on it, as Johnston's was, a series of difficulties arose that made success dubious. First, Sherman had to make a mistake; second, Johnston would have to learn about it in a timely manner; third, circumstances must allow Johnston to be in a position to avail himself of the presented opportunity; and lastly, Johnston had to be successful in exploiting the mistake. This quartet of events—mistake, recognition, reactive ability, and successful execution—combined in a way that made it unlikely that Johnston's strategy would result in victory.

Johnston had not given much thought to the mid- and long-run, but had focused much of his effort on the immediate future. Subconsciously, he knew if retreat were to come, he would be retreating into friends since Georgia had been the military home for the entire army for several months. In a retreat, he would draw closer to his supply source, and at the same time, he would frustrate Sherman's goals. He would be content with that achievement.

He thought that as his lines of communication became shorter, Sherman's would become longer and more vulnerable. A longer line of communication should tie down the increasingly large numbers of blue-coated troops, and this should reduce the effective force confronting him. Johnston hoped he could get help from General Forrest, who was operating out west. Yet, he did little to think how he could use his own cavalry forces under "Fighting Joe" Wheeler to accomplish the same thing. Just because a man has risen in the old, mostly peacetime army to the rank of general did not mean he is a skilled strategic thinker or an innovative and successful commander. Extraordinary commanders may wear generals' stars, but wearing them is not the reason for their military genius. Most generals are average. In this case, average was the same as inadequate.

A plan predicated on being safe in the immediate short run of time, most of the time, will yield only average results. The Army of Tennessee was likely as strong as it would ever be. No plan existed to make it larger or to improve its fighting qualities. Sherman's Military Division of the Mississippi was probably never going to be much weaker. It was possible the Northern army would give up on the forceful reunification of the nation, that the will to win could blow away in the election of 1864. To thwart the impending Union thrust, Johnston needed more than a wait-and-see approach; he needed a great plan to surmount the Army of Tennessee's substantial, immediate disadvantage and the likelihood of Sherman's improving future. Yet no such plan existed from Johnston or anyone in Richmond or Dalton.

HDQRS, THIRD DIVISION, FOURTH ARMY CORPS
South of the Chattahoochee, July 14, 1862
Col. J.S. FULLERTON
Assistant Adjutant-General:
General:

COLONEL: Moore, a scout whom I sent out on the 13th at daylight, has just returned, and makes the following statement: He left Atlanta at 3p.m. yesterday. He came out of Atlanta, returning by the Peach Tree road. About a mile from the town on this road the Rebels were busily engaged in constructing four separate forts on the separate hills. The inhabitants of Atlanta are still leaving, going much farther south, and the town is pretty well cleaned out. All the valuable property, such as machinery and army stores, has been removed, and he heard toward Augusta. Moore says only a small supply of subsistence is kept in Atlanta, only so much as could be readily removed in case of a retreat. Moore says General Bragg arrived from Richmond on Tuesday evening and a brigade of four regiments from Pollard, Ala. Moore says it was reported in the rebel camps that this brigade was from Kirby Smith, but that he talked with the men of the brigade, who told him they were from Pollard, Ala., and had never been with Kirby Smith. Moore says in returning he came out by the Peach Tree road till he struck the Turner's Ferry road, which he took and went to the extreme left of the rebel infantry line. This point is a small church in sight of the ferry. General Manigault's brigade is on the extreme left; thence to Campbellton the river is watched by squads of cavalry. From the left of the rebel line Moore returned to Buck Head, where he found Wheeler's cavalry, and thence into our lines through General Dodge's command, to whom he reported. Moore brings an Atlanta paper of yesterday.

Respectfully, & c.,
TH.J. WOOD
Brigadier-General of Volunteers, Commanding

P.S.—Moore says as he passed along the rebel lines yesterday afternoon, Hardee's corps, which had been in the center for some time, was breaking up its camp, and is, he understood, to take position to the right of Stewart's corps, which would place Hardee's corps on the extreme rebel right, and Moore says it would be entirely to the right or east of the railroad.
WOOD

CHAPTER EIGHT

Confederacy | BRAXTON BRAGG

ON THE ROAD TO THE HEADQUARTERS OF HOOD'S CORPS

JULY 14, 1864

The day had been spent in meetings. All the meetings had taken place at the little white house Johnston had selected as the headquarters for the Army of Tennessee. The house was hot and airless, and thus far the meetings had accomplished little. Although Bragg had learned nothing that had changed his mind, he had reacquainted himself with the four men whose abilities the future of the Army of Tennessee rested on: Johnston, Stewart, Hardee, and John Hood.

He had not acted on the presumption his mission was based on. General Bragg still carried an order placing General Hardee in command of the army. That order was the product of long discussions, earnest communication, and anguished bouts of indecision on the part of Jefferson Davis. At times, Davis thought it would be best if he left the capitol and took charge of the army personally.

Bragg was forty-seven years old, and some days he believed he was too old for this work. He had a well-deserved reputation for being outspoken, grumpy, and hard to get along with. On top of that was the fact that he had lost the confidence of the senior leadership of this army when he had commanded it. As a result, he had sought to be relieved and had been replaced by the very man who had now lost the confidence of Jefferson Davis: Johnston. It could not be denied that Johnston had retreated from one position to the next, and now the army seemed ready to lose Atlanta too.

Bragg shifted on his horse. It was good to be out of that house and on the back of a horse. It had been a long train ride from Richmond in a jouncing car on rails, behind what had seemed to be a less than reliable engine, which could not have much life left. As he rode, he thought about the situation with Johnston.

There seemed to be four options. He could go back to President Davis and tell him that they had the best man in the job, but Bragg, despite his difficulties as a commander, did know about army organization and was certain for a number of reasons that Johnston was not the right commander. So, there really were only three options, and three possible replacements: A.P. Stewart, Hardee, and John Hood.

Bragg may have been a difficult human being, but he knew in his heart he wanted to do his best for his country, President Davis, and this loyal army. He had spent the day with the three corps commanders. Even if none of them were the perfect choice, it was sound decision making to limit the selection to men who knew the army and the position it found itself in. Right or not, little thought had been given to reaching below the corps level to put a division commander in the mix. The choice really was one of those three.

So far, no one knew why Bragg was here. "Consultation" and "observation" were words everyone had used. Still, it had been awkward to get the three men to discuss the past and their personal views. He had been impressed by Stewart. He knew what was expected and knew when it was not forthcoming. Bragg liked that in an officer. Stewart was from Tennessee and like many from that state, was conflicted about slavery, state rights, and secession itself. Exactly where he stood on all those matters now was perhaps not relevant, but it did make Bragg wonder. Notwithstanding his inner feelings, Stewart had shown himself a capable and aggressive commander. Still, he had held his new rank and position for less than a month following the death of Leonidas Polk. Bragg didn't think Polk was a great loss to the service, but his replacement was too tender in time and in grade to be placed in command of the army. In Bragg's mind, that left only two candidates: Hood and Hardee.

Hardee was viewed as reliable by many, but Bragg felt that he was only reliable as a backstabber, as Bragg thought Hardee had sowed discontent and disloyalty for a long time when Hardee worked for him.

Both Lee and Davis thought Hardee could run the army. That is, they thought he was competent.

Still, Bragg really liked Hood. Where Hardee was old, Hood was young. Hood had a reputation as a leader and a fighter, and Bragg felt that Hardee didn't inspire much at all. Hardee had already turned down the command of this army before Johnston was selected. Hood wanted the position.

"Oh, Hardee would be fit to be tied if he had to report to Hood," Bragg said to himself. Hood was damn young, but Bragg liked his spirit. Though badly wounded, Hood seemed to be up to the task.

Bragg wondered if this were his decision, what he would do? He knew he couldn't make the decision on the basis of which one he liked the best—that was one thing Davis taught him. Davis had been willing to promote Bragg even though they had gotten off on the wrong foot way back in Mexico. The position was important and needed the best man for the job, and Bragg hoped he could get the true measure of Hood's worth when he met him at Hood's quarters, where Hood would feel the most comfortable.

One thing was clear to Bragg: Hood was the most vocal about the morale loss that the steady diet of retreat had engendered. He believed the men's spirits would soar if they were presented with a genuine leader. Of course, Hood thought he should be that leader. Victory was needed, and a new leader was needed to achieve it.

Bragg knew history. George Washington may have won by keeping the army together while the British slowly lost their zest for the conflict, but Bragg knew Bill Sherman, too. His old friend was not one to go home when the game was in his grasp.

Later that day, after a friendly meeting, Hood and Bragg sat across from each other. It had been an enjoyable hour and an enjoyable encounter in which Hood had talked about what lay to his front. Hood explained the layers of defense, Nancy Creek, the north and south branches of Peachtree Creek, any prepared defenses, and lastly the earthworks running east and west. Despite his lack of leg and working arm, Bragg thought Hood seemed rigorous and energetic.

Bragg felt that Hood still had something to say and was just unable to bring himself to deliver it. As Bragg stood to go though, Hood spoke, "General, before you leave, I spent a lot of time preparing this letter. I hope it will be helpful."

Bragg reached for the letter and put it away. Now, he had two letters in his pocket. One was the order from Jefferson Davis appointing Hardee to command of the army, and now this one from the man who wanted the job. He would read it when he returned to his quarters.

For now, he said, "Thank you, General. I'm sure it will be interesting to read. Good evening."

Once on his horse on the way back to his quarters, Bragg found himself to be too impatient. He pulled Hood's letter from his pocket, opened it, and read:

Near Atlanta, GA., July 14, 1864
General Braxton Bragg
Commanding Armies Confederate States, Richmond, VA.:
General: During the campaign from Dalton to the Chattahoochee River it is natural to suppose that we have had several chances to strike the enemy a decisive blow. We have failed to take advantage of such opportunities, and find our army south of the Chattahoochee, very much decreased in strength. Our loss cannot be less than 20,000, without having fought a decisive battle. I deem it of the greatest importance that General Kirby Smith should be ordered at once, with at least half, if not a larger portion, of his army, on this side of the Mississippi River. Our success west of the Mississippi River has proven a disad-vantage to us, since the enemy has re-enforced his army on this side, and we have failed to do so. The strength of the Army of Tennessee is such at this time as to render it necessary to have aid from General Kirby Smith - allowing that we should gain a victory over Sherman - to follow up our success and regain our lost territory. Our present position is a very difficult one, and we should not, under any circumstances, allow the enemy to gain possession of Atlanta, and deem it excessively important, should we find the enemy intends establishing the Chattahoochee as their line, relying upon interrupting our communications and again virtually dividing our country, that we should attack him, even if we should have to recross the river to do so. I have, General, so often urged that we should force the enemy to give us battle as to almost be regarded reckless

by the officers high in rank in this army, since their views have been so directly opposite. I regard it as a great misfortune to our country that we failed to give battle to the enemy many miles north of our present position. Please say to the President that I shall continue to do my duty cheerfully and faithfully, and strive to do what I think is best for our country, as my constant prayer is for our success.

Respectfully,
J.B. Hood,
Lieutenant-General

Had Bragg been a man of greater introspection, he would have seen in this letter the same disloyalty to Johnston that he believed he personally had so richly received from Hardee, but between him and Hardee was a chasm never to be filled. Instead, for Hood, the letter formed the foundation for promotion.

CHAPTER NINE

Union | WILLIAM SHERMAN

SHERMAN'S HEADQUARTERS OF THE MILITARY DIVISION OF THE MISSISSIPPI

JULY 14, 1864

While senior command changes in the Army of Tennessee were front and center, Sherman was occupied with reviewing the changes he had made to his newest special field order:

Special Field Orders No. 35
HDQRS. MIL. DIV. OF THE MISS.,
In the Field, near Chattahoochee River,
July 14, 1864.

Preliminary steps having already begun, the following general plan will be observed and adhered to:

I. Major-General Thomas will prepare to cross his army at Powers' and Pace's Ferries, and take position out from the Chattahoochee River, until he controls the country from Island Creek to Kyle's Bridge, over Nancy's Creek, but will not move the whole of General Palmer's and General Hooker's corps across until he hears that General Stoneman is back from his present expedition. He will endeavor to provide General Stoneman enough pontoon boats, balks, and chesses to make one bridge. He will dispose of General McCook's cavalry and detachments of his own infantry to watch the Chattahoochee about the old railroad crossing.

II. As soon as General Stoneman returns he will dispose his cavalry to watch the Chattahoochee at Turner's Ferry and about the mouth of Nickajack, connecting by patrols with General McCook, and will, if possible, procure enough pontoons to make a bridge ready on the first chance to cross the river about Howell's or Sandtown, and break the Atlanta and West Point railroad and telegraph.

III. Major-General Schofield, after having well secured his crossing-place at Phillips', will move out toward Cross Keys until he controls the ridge between Island and Nancy's Creeks and the road represented as leading from Roswell to Buck Head.

IV. Major-General Blair will immediately, on the return of Major-General Stoneman, move rapidly to Roswell and join his army. Major-General McPherson will then move his command out, either by the Cross Keys road or the old Hightower trial, until he is abreast of Major-General Schofield, amid General Garrard, with his cavalry, will scout from McAfee's Bridge toward Pinckneyville, and if no enemy is there in force will picket McAfee's Bridge and take post on General McPherson's left, about Buchanan's.

V. The whole army will thus form a concave line behind Nancy's Creek, extending from Kyle's Bridge to Buchanan's, but no attempt will be made to form a line of battle. Each army will form a unit and connect with its neighbor by a line of pickets. Should the enemy assume the offensive at any point, which is not expected until we reach below Peach Tree Creek, the neighboring army will at once assist the one attacked. All preliminary steps may at once be made, but no corps need move to any great distance from the river until advised that General Stoneman is back.

VI. Major-General Thomas will study well the country toward Decatur via Buck Head, Major-General Schofield to a point of the railroad four miles northeast of Decatur, and Major-General McPherson and General Garrard that toward Stone Mountain. Each army should leave behind the Chattahoochee River, at its bridge

or at Marietta, all wagons or encumbrances not absolutely needed for battle. A week's work after crossing the Chattahoochee should determine the first object aimed at, viz, the possession of the Atlanta and Augusta road past of Decatur, or of Atlanta itself.
By order of Maj. Gen. W. T. Sherman:
L.M. Dayton,
Aide-de-Camp

Sherman called for Dayton, his aide-de-camp, and said, "Let's get this out as soon as possible."

Sherman's interests ranged from his immediate combat front to the front where victory seemed to never be possible—Washington, D.C. He reflected in his nervous manner on the issue of state recruiter. He moved his hand across the field table and pulled a telegram message from the stack. "Maybe Halleck can, or will, do something about this," he began to write.

"If State recruiting agents must come into the limits of my command under the law, I have the honor to request that the commanding officers or adjutants be constituted such agents, and that States be entitled to a credit for recruits they may enlist. This will obviate the difficulty I apprehend from civilian agents."

"*There,*" thought Sherman to himself, "*a pretty lawyer-like way to deal with that issue.*" It was simply wrong to send a civilian into the Rebel states looking for recruits. It seemed folly. Anyway, they would spend their time hanging about his headquarters slowing up the entire war effort.

CHAPTER TEN

Union | JAMES MCPHERSON

McPherson's Headquarters near Roswell Bridge,

Army of the Tennessee

July 14, 1864

6:30 p.m.

North of the city, McPherson sat composing an order. He had earlier received and read Sherman's order and was setting his lead corps in action.

HQRS. DEPARTMENT AND ARMY OF THE TENNESSEE
Near Roswell Bridge, July 14, 1864
Mjr. Gen JOHN A. LOGAN
Commanding Fifteenth Corps:

GENERAL; You will move your command across the Chattahoochee on the bridge just finished by Major-General Dodge's command and take up a position on the Roswell and Atlanta road in the vicinity of a man's house named Beaver, about two miles from the river. Captain Reese, of the Engineers will indicate the position.

Very respectfully, your obedient servant,
JAS.B. MCPHERSON,
Major-General

July 15, 1864

CHAPTER ELEVEN

Confederacy | JOSEPH JOHNSTON

JULY 15, 1864

HEADQUARTERS OF THE ARMY OF TENNESSEE

Though not as passionate as always needed, Johnston believed in the Southern cause. He believed in it fully. The cause was enough for him to stake his life and career on it. Simply put, he thought the Confederacy had a right—an obligation—to leave the inhospitable Union. It was clear to him that the South had the right to be left alone and was entitled to use self-defense to combat a relentless North. Nonetheless, he could feel their forces all slipping away. It was sliding slowly, just starting to gain momentum, but still moving like a glacier, a bit at a time.

Johnston knew how the war would most likely end, but he also knew that he couldn't quit now. There was still a chance that Sherman could make a bad mistake that Johnston could pounce on and use to destroy the enemy. Johnston thought that he could only do it on the sly and only if he had as much of the Army of Tennessee as he was able to preserve. It had been seventy days or so since this campaign began in late May, and he still had nearly all the men he started out with. He still had a supply line, and he had hurt Sherman. There was no choice but to fight the poor man's war. He knew he must keep this army together in order to be ready to take the grand chance if it were offered.

Johnston felt that there was no need to explain this to his subordinates or to President Davis—or, least of all, to Bragg. He thought Davis should let him run the army *his* way, especially since every time he explained the situation, it ended up in the newspapers.

"*Lee has retreated more than I,*" Johnston thought, "*and at greater cost against a less formidable foe. Can't Davis see that?*" Yet Johnston also knew that with Bragg there, he had to observe correct protocol, as not to upset Bragg and Davis too much. He had to explain what was happening.

July 15, 1864
General Bragg:
General; General Wheeler reported only this morning that the enemy's corps at Isham's Ferry advanced eastwardly three or four miles in the afternoon and entrenched. I did not give you this information sooner because I expected you here. I have not visited you because absolutely afraid to leave my quarters.
Respectfully and truly, yours,
J.E. Johnston

CHAPTER TWELVE

Confederacy | JEFFERSON DAVIS

OFFICE OF THE PRESIDENT

RICHMOND, VIRGINIA

JULY 15, 1864

Jefferson Davis despaired. He was tired—unbelievably tired—and he was sick. His head pounded, his one good eye watered, and he felt entirely alone. He sat reading the telegram he had just received from his personal military aide, Bragg. The telegram from Atlanta lay on his desk on a sea of paper, which it would soon disappear under.

ALANTA, July 15, 1864
His Excellency JEFFERSON DAVIS,
Richmond
I have made General Johnston two visits, and been received courteously and kindly. He has not sought my advice, and it was not volunteered. I cannot learn that he has any more plan for the future than he has had in the past. It is expected that he will await the enemy on a line some three miles from here, and the impression prevails that he is now more inclined to fight. The enemy is very cautious, and entrenches immediately on taking a new position. His force, like our own, is greatly reduced by the hard campaign. His infantry now very little over 60,000. The morale of our army is still reported good.
BRAXTON BRAGG

His quick mind rebelled at the idea that two of his most senior generals, Johnston and Bragg, could come away from two meetings, one on the thirteenth and the next on the following day, with so little to show for it. He had sent Bragg to find out what Johnston intended.

Bragg was to explain the nation's deep need for Johnston's best stroke to defeat Sherman's army, which was now nearly at Atlanta's gates.

Johnston never seemed to communicate upwards to Richmond. "*Sometimes, I think if he hadn't been wounded, and if I hadn't had Lee to take over the Army of Northern Virginia, then Richmond would've been lost before Johnston told me any problem even existed,*" Davis thought.

Davis knew Johnston was hard to talk to, but Bragg had a mission to accomplish. Johnston had a duty to explain his plans once and for all. Bragg was not a fool nor was he an intruder, as Bragg was there on Davis' behalf. It was no social call or garden party where all the niceties must be observed. The two men had an obligation to review the plans, debate the choices, convince each other of the right path, and communicate it to Davis, who was waiting worried in Virginia.

"Will he fight or not?" Davis said out loud. Surely, if a fight was to be forthcoming, he would have been told. What other conclusion could one reasonably draw other than that no fight for the city was intended? Where was the reassurance that Johnston even understood the importance of the situation and that he would try to do something more than retreat?

As he reflected, Davis concluded maybe retreating was all Johnston could ever do. Had Johnston ever done otherwise? Sherman had paid time after time on the way south from Chattanooga because of Johnston's actions, but payment from Federal forces was not good enough. That kind of payment came too easily. A hard and smashing victory, a result that stopped Sherman was needed. Could no one see it but him?

His mind reeled. His eye twitched and watered. Davis picked up a pen, addressed a letter to Johnston, and scrawled, "A telegram of yesterday announces that the enemy is extending entrenchments from river toward railroad to Augusta. I wish to hear from you as to present situation and your plan of operations as specifically as will enable me to anticipate events."

CHAPTER THIRTEEN

Union | HENRY GRIFFITHS

FIFTEENTH ARMY CORPS

COBB COUNTY GEORGIA, MIDWAY BETWEEN MARIETTA AND ROSWELL

JULY 15, 1864

The afternoon was just as hot as the day before. The twenty days of rain in June had brought its own wet, sticky red clay gumbo, which was hell to the animals, equipment, and 150,000 or so soldiers of the two armies. Now the wet was over, and it had been replaced by the miserable, dust-filled, still, and oven-like air that worked on men and beasts even if all they did were stand. The clutching air seemed to leak from the hardwood trees. Iowa could have been, and no doubt was, hot right then, but Georgia's heat was more like a moist wool blanket with its high humidity.

Henry Griffiths leaned forward in his saddle to ease his lean, forty-year-old body into a more comfortable position. Griffiths watched as the men and animals of the Fifteenth Army Corps passed by. The Fifteenth Army Corps was the maneuver element of the Army of the Tennessee. At least, it was planned that the men maneuver unless overwhelmed by the fog and friction of war, at which point they often loaded, pointed, and fired and then loaded, pointed, and fired until one side or the other could do it no more and left the field with a victory or defeat, depending on how the tale was told. The Fifteenth Army Corps had both infantry regiments and seven artillery batteries with thirty-eight guns.

As the horse stopped, Griffiths looked forward and then back over his right shoulder at the long column of men, wagons, limbers, caissons, and his six guns. The four-wheeled units of limbers and caissons and the No. 2 field gun carriages rolling by were an impressive thing to see.

He thought the army had done one thing right: once they decided on what a wheel should be, they put it on everything the artillery owned, from gun carriages to the wagons and the rolling forges. They carried extra wheels, and it was nice to know extras were close at hand when someone needed a spare.

Each of the wheeled units was pulled by six good-sized horses. For pulling, most men who had worked both horses and mules would rather have a good mule than a good horse. Mules would pull more on less or poorer food than a horse would. Hard experience in the din and the noise of battle, however, had taught that while horses would rear and lash out with their hooves, a damn fool mule would buck and often as not roll on the ground. This would tangle harnesses, limber poles, and anything else around into a mess. Sometimes, such a mess could lead to disaster if the battery was overrun since nothing moved without mules or horses in the traces. Thrashing on the ground created a danger to the other animals and to the men detailed to keep charge of them. On top of the potential danger, mules provided a heightened sense of uncertainty on the battlefield. One would think the horse would be of higher spirit and hence more excitable under fire than the mule, but it just wasn't so.

The 1st Illinois Battery F had pulled away from camp ahead of its sister battery, the 1st Iowa. The guns managed by the boys from Illinois were the useful 12-pound Napoleons. The guns of the Iowa battery were six of the new model 1863 10-pound Parrott rifles. They had 70-inch tubes with rifling, consisting of three right-handed sets of lands and grooves. This rifling imparted a spin to the projectiles, which produced an amazing accuracy.[2] It was a joy to behold, and Griffiths believed in those guns.

Griffiths still thought of these Parrott rifles as his. By right, however, they were under the direct command of young Lieutenant Gay, and the 12-pounders were under Captain Burton. Griffiths' role was that of the Chief of Artillery for the 4th Division of the Fifteenth Army Corps. He was on the Division Commander's staff, but his duties extended to the control and placement of the twelve guns, and Gay and Burton looked to Griffiths for orders and direction.

As he watched the column move along, he could see only the men, animals, and equipment that rolled nearby. The dust made it impossible to see very far—and certainly not from the beginning of the first horse to end of the last wagon—but he knew that the long line was there. If everything was properly spaced, the distance occupied by each battery should be about 200 yards. With today's heat and dust, the total line probably stretched out for more than 500 yards—more than a quarter of a mile.

As each gun came by, Griffiths contemplated the unit as though it was a unique living thing. An unknowing person would see the lead, swing, and wheel teams, each of their drivers, and the caisson or gun and think each team was interchangeable with another. In reality, each gun crew had its own intelligence, attitude, and way of doing things. Subtle differences existed between one gun and another and one battery to the next, but all Griffiths' guns could put iron on the target. Griffiths bragged to others that if his gunners could see the target, they could hit it. His own eyes may be the least bit hazy, but these fine young gunners were blessed with keen eyesight that meant little could escape them.

Those 890-pound pieces looked lethal somehow even with their tubes angled downward as the road march continued. The twelve pounders of the Illinois battery and the rifled pieces of the 1st Iowa provided the best of both worlds to the men of Harrow's 4th Division. The Napoleons were wonderfully deadly at close range with canister and grapeshot, and the Parrotts were accurate at great distance. Sherman maintained a good battery was worth 1,000 rifles, so between the two batteries existed the equivalent of 2,000 men who were deadly at any range. Given the size of a now-typical regiment, the 2,000 men in effect constituted a force equal to a brigade.

Until two days ago, Logan's Fifteenth Army Corps as well as McPherson's Sixteenth and Seventeenth Army Corps had been encamped along the bank of the Chattahoochee River. The army had crossed Nickajack Creek and moved over the substantial Confederate River Line. The River Line had been designed and built at considerable effort but was hardly used since Johnston and his Army of Tennessee had stopped there only briefly before retreating across the river.

That had been a welcome rest as the men, including General Sherman, had bathed in the slow-moving river. Soldiers from both armies washed themselves and their clothing and removed all the gray backs or lice they could and tried to wash off the coating of red dust. The men ate, slept, and performed the private camp activities, which in the absence of combat and marching seemed to take all day. The Federal soldiers received new shoes from their long railway supply line, which ran nearly a hundred miles north to Chattanooga and then back to Nashville.

It had been nearly peaceful as both sides waited for the next phase of the contest. Sherman, with the initiative and the momentum, awaited more supplies before his three armies would feint to the right and then cross the Chattahoochee at Pace's Ferry, Power's Ferry, Sope Creek, and Roswell.

The Army of the Tennessee, under McPherson, was on the move across the bottom of Cobb County near where the border was formed by the Chattahoochee. The army constituted the left wing of Sherman's even larger force. The three corps under the volunteer generals Logan, Dodge, and Blair contained 23,000 men. The men in Logan's Fifteenth Army Corps were veteran troops who came from the western states of Illinois, Iowa, Ohio, and Michigan. They were mostly a volunteer force who had joined to preserve the Union as they knew it. These men generally believed that the fall of Fort Sumter in Charleston Harbor, South Carolina, endangered the Union their forbearers had created, and that act of defiance by the South galvanized these men and served as a catalyst for their grand adventure. Like Lincoln, these men thought that the lack of a means to withdraw from the Union cried out that succession was not intended to exist.

The Fifteenth Army Corps headed north to Marietta two days before when they had gotten their orders to move and camped a few miles south of it the next day. On this day, they moved through the village, which had not fared well over the past several weeks. Troops from both armies had surged through it, moving first one way and then another. It would remain a busy place since the railway ran alongside its western flank, and it had homes and buildings in which wounded men lay awaiting death and bloody soldiers with a limb or two gone lay in private agony from the loss and the thought of a future as shattered as their bodies.

Some of the men marching by Griffiths were veterans of the old Army of the Southwest under General Curtis. They had marched through snow. They had won the battle at Pea Ridge and then survived a harsh march to the Mississippi. They had then joined the forces under General Grant as he failed and then finally succeeded in capturing Vicksburg in the summer of 1863. They had walked and ridden trains, horses, and steamboats across the country to reach the Union army surrounded in Chattanooga and to confront the Southern army under Braxton Bragg on Lookout Mountain and Missionary Ridge. Now, a hundred miles south, tied to the winding tracks of the Western and Atlantic railroad, the city of Atlanta was less than fifteen miles away. It had been a lifetime for thousands of young men in butternut and blue, who lay in marked and unmarked shallow ditches from Resaca to Marietta.

As the last of the six guns moved through the once-charming streets of Marietta and out onto Roswell Road, Griffiths thought it was good to be moving again, as moving seemed to be natural for this army. It seemed to grow as a result of its movement and to do it in a natural way. Maybe it was because its members all had to move to the West or had to walk to farm something in their lives before the war, but it just seemed right.

Movement, as hard and endless as it seemed, was the only thing that could bring this horrible war to a proper conclusion. Sherman's pursuit of Johnston and the pressure on his ragged, tough army prevented troops from Georgia from joining Lee as he fought to save Richmond. Lee was locked in a more geographically constant but deadly dance with Meade's Army of the Potomac with Grant pushing, pushing, always pushing on the Union forces in both Virginia and Georgia. It was as Lincoln's story went: if you can't do the skinning, at least hold a leg. Meade and Sherman were both doing a little skinning and a little leg holding.

Dodge's Sixteenth Army Corps had preceded the Fifteenth, and Blair's Seventeenth Army Corps was following them in turn. The order to march had General Harrow's 4th Division leading the way for the Fifteenth, followed by the other two divisions. The road from Marietta to Roswell was about ten miles long. The distance would be less if the road were straight, but little in the area went straight.

Along the road were blackberries—warm, ripe, and juicy. They had been picked and eaten by the men who marched before them. Even so, there were still more for the eager hands and mouths of the Fifteenth. The berries, however, didn't come free. The brambles that they grew on extracted a bloody price. The sweet smell of the berries also attracted the yellow jackets from their holes in the ground, and these demons buzzed and stung. Most of the soldiers thought the berries were worth it.

Finally, the columns were halted to rest. At these times, canteens were never big enough or full enough for the thirsty men, and wells were too slow to quench the thirst of the more than 150 animals that pulled the wagons and guns. Orders had been to start early, rest during the heat of the day, and resume the march in the afternoon. On paper, the order made sense, but as far as Griffiths could see, it was hot all day long.

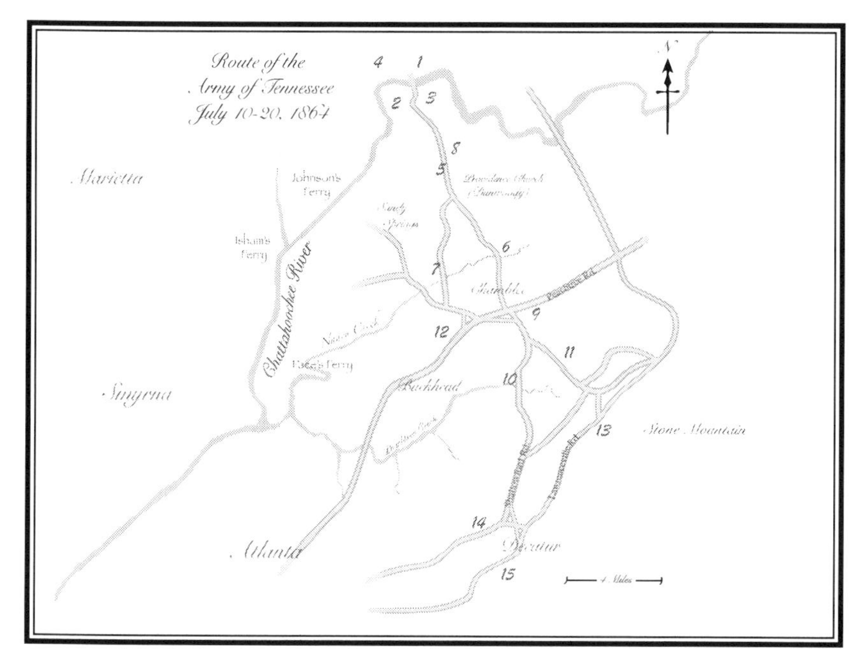

Route of the Army of the Tennessee, July 10-20, 1864

1. The Army of the Tennessee was under the command of Major General McPherson and was made up of three corps: the Fifteenth Army Corps under Logan, the Sixteenth Army Corps under Dodge, and the Seventeenth Army Corps under Frank Blair. All three corps had marched from Marietta after having left the siege of the River Line. Confederates burned the bridge over the Chattahoochee at Roswell on July 5, 1864. Men from Dodge's Sixteenth Army Corps built a footbridge at the Shallow Ford on July 10 and then completed a bridge that was 18 feet wide by 710 feet long by the evening of July 13.
2. The Sixteenth Army Corps entrenched on the ridge south of the Chattahoochee River from July 10 to 17.
3. The Fifteenth Army Corps crossed the river on July 15 through 17 and entrenched on the south bank.
4. Blair's Seventeenth Army Corps arrived in Roswell and went into camp on July 16.
5. The Fifteenth Army Corps moved toward Decatur, via Dunwoody, on July 17 on today's Roswell Road,and then on Roberts Drive.
6. The Fifteenth Army Corps passed through Dunwoody and followed the Shallowford Road to Nancy Creek, where they camped for the night.
7. The Sixteenth Army Corps likewise marched toward Decatur, via Dunwoody, on July 17 and took the right fork on today's Ashford Dunwoody Road and camped for the night where the road crossed Nancy Creek.
8. The Seventeenth Army Corps began the march to Decatur, following the same route as the Fifteenth Army Corps on July 17.

9. Contact was established between the Fifteenth and Sixteenth Army Corps at Old Cross Keys and later at the Rainey Plantation, where the Sixteenth Army Corps camped on the night of July 18.
10. The Seventeenth Army Corps camped at Blake's Mill on the night of July 18. McPherson had his headquarters there, too.
11. Logan's Fifteenth Army Corps traveled down a cut road, probably today's Chamblee Tucker Road. Then, the corps traveled right on Henderson Mill Road, moved to Browning's Courthouse (today's Tucker, Georgia), and returned to Henderson Mill Road to camp for the night of July 18.
12. Sherman's headquarters on July 18 were at the plantation of Samuel House.
13. The Fifteenth Army Corps moved closer to Decatur on July 19, followed by the Seventeenth Army Corps.
14. The Fifteenth and Sixteenth Army Corps took this route, today's DeKalb Avenue, on July 20.
15. The Seventeenth Army Corps traveled on today's Ansley Street and Oakview Road on July 20.

CHAPTER FOURTEEN

Union

ARMY OF THE TENNESSEE

LOWER COBB COUNTY

JULY 15, 1864

The citizens of Atlanta and the government in Richmond had never really believed Sherman and his soldiers would get so near Atlanta. Fear and deep disbelief replaced the conviction Johnston would stop Sherman long before Kennesaw Mountain. Of the 20,000 people in Atlanta, those who were able had already fled. Those who could get on the train to Augusta or Macon had done so or were making preparation to do so. The vacuum created by the departing civilians was sucking both Johnston's force as well as the boys in blue into the city behind them. General Johnston had kept his army together, but Sherman was as relentless as ever. Destruction of the Federal army was necessary for the survival of the Southern government, and that destruction was as remote now as it had been in May.

As the dust-covered Union army moved along the road between Marietta and Roswell, they sometimes saw barefoot women and children who displayed a mix of fear, curiosity, and sullenness. The houses they saw reflected the variety of people who lived along the road. Most of the dwellings were rough log cabins, low and mean-looking behind split-rail fences. The homes were deserted of the hard, narrow-faced, and severe-looking women. Most had run away with everything of value that they could prod, ride, or carry to avoid this blue-clad army.

To the marching soldiers from the West, there was a likeness to how the land and its boundaries ran. Federal lands in Iowa, like here, had also been surveyed into huge squares, though here in Cobb County, it was on a smaller scale. Each lucky winner in the state land lottery got either 160 acres of land that had belonged to the Cherokees or 40 acres if gold were believed to be present on the land. Although hampered by trees and forests, this lottery meant there was a regular north-south, east-west aspect to the farms and homesteads and their boundaries. One could easily tell where one farm began and another ended.

Soldiers who were farmers, or had been raised on a farm, recognized that this was good farming country. It had hot summers, rainfall, and dark brown soil above red, pink, and orange clay. The heavy soils supported hardwoods, which had flourished in the hot, wet summers. There wasn't as much of a winter here in Georgia, meaning there was a possibility for a longer growing season.

July 16, 1864

First Day of
the Seven-Day Event

CHAPTER FIFTEEN

Confederacy | JOSEPH JOHNSTON

HEADQUARTERS OF THE ARMY OF TENNESSEE

DEXTER NILES' HOUSE

MARIETTA ROAD, ABOUT THREE MILES FROM ATLANTA

JULY 16, 1864

7:10 P.M.

Though the heat of the day was slowly ebbing, the inside of the little white weatherboard house seemed like an oven. General Johnston felt his own temperature rise as he fingered and reread the telegram he had just received from Davis. Though the fact that the enemy had extended its entrenchments near the railroad to Augusta required some concern, Johnston found himself focusing on Davis' request for his present situation and plan of operations.

Johnston preferred not to communicate with Davis. The two men never really had understood each other, and time had modified their relationship in a negative manner. Davis still simply didn't understand the situation or its importance, Johnston reflected. But Johnston couldn't ignore the telegram. He had to tell Davis something. After all, Johnston knew that Davis had a right to know, and it was his duty to tell Davis.

Though the temperature stayed the same, Johnston felt the heat and pressure slowly drain away from him. He closed his eyes. In a strange way, his Georgia campaign was playing out the opposite of his first campaign in the summer of 1847. As a lieutenant in the U.S. Army, he had served under General Winfield Scott in the Mexican War. He had observed General Antonio Lopez de Santa Anna move from defensive position to defensive position, often moving as a result of a flanking maneuver by the U.S. soldiers.

There were differences in scale. The distance from Veracruz to Mexico City was nearly 200 miles while the distance from Chattanooga to Atlanta was half that. He had been a lieutenant then, not a lieutenant general. The opposing forces then were smaller, numbering in the thousands, not the tens of thousands. Yet the stakes in both were important and somewhat the same. The Southern nation in both cases had the possibility to lose the battle, the war, and its existence as a sovereign nation. Here, the war was more total, and the combatants spoke the same language.

There, buried in all the differences, was a similarity: continuous defensive positions by the home army and the drum head—a summertime dance of the pursuer pulled and pushed by the magnetic attraction to a place, be it Atlanta or Mexico City.

He understood General Santa Anna better today than he had seventeen years earlier. Sometimes, circumstances made the undesirable path of retreat the only path available. The undesirable was necessary.

Suddenly, he was tired. Johnston knew Davis wanted to be rid of him, and sometimes, he supposed that it would be all right with him if Davis did. But Johnston was afraid Davis had run out of commanders for this army, so Johnston supposed they were stuck with each other until the end of the dance.

He thought for a moment, composed his thoughts, and began his reply.

Near Atlanta, July 16, 1864.
His Excellency the President.
Richmond:
Your dispatch of to-day received. The slight change in the enemy's dispositions made since my dispatch of the 14th to General Cooper was reported to General Bragg yesterday. It was a report from General Wheeler that Schofield's corps had advanced eastwardly about three miles from Isham's Ford and entrenched. As the enemy has double our number, we must be on the defensive. My plan of operations must, therefore, depend upon that of the enemy. It is mainly to watch for an opportunity to fight to advantage. We are trying to put Atlanta in condition to be held for a day or two by the Georgia militia, that army movements may be freer and wider.
J.E. Johnston

Of course, Johnston knew Davis and doubted his message would make much of a difference, and he was right. The telegram sealed Johnston's fate in the mind of Davis.

CHAPTER SIXTEEN

Confederacy | JOHN HOOD

HEADQUARTERS OF HOOD'S CORPS

JULY 16, 1864

Sometimes, it was difficult for even Hood to believe this promotion—a tall order since he often believed things that were not supported by facts. He knew himself to be a romantic, and that quality generally aided belief in matters deemed fantastic by others. His life, West Point, the army, three years of war, his wounds, and his responsibilities—in another man, it would have created a realist, maybe a cynic—but not in him. His new circumstances were tremendous, so much so that it was next to impossible for him to get his mind completely around it. Hood had just learned he was to become the commander of the Army of Tennessee.

In July of 1849, around fifteen years ago, John Bell Hood was appointed a cadet at the United States Military Academy at West Point. For part of that time, he roomed with another cadet, James B. McPherson, who often helped him with his academics and who he now considered an enemy. The academy was, at that time, under the command of one of the nation's foremost soldiers, Robert E. Lee. Upon graduation, Hood became a brevet second lieutenant in the U.S. Army. He stood six feet and two inches tall, looked like a modern Norse warrior, and had straight blonde hair and serious eyes that would light up from time to time. He served in Texas as a lieutenant in the famed 2nd Cavalry and fought Comanches. In April 1861, a few months before his thirtieth birthday, he resigned his army commission and became a young captain of the Confederate cavalry.

Promotion then came quickly. In this, he was not unusual. Many junior officers from the "old army" were jumped several grades as armies on both sides expanded rapidly. To compound this, many of those who had risen to command regiments, brigades, and division in the earliest days had been killed or wounded in the devastatingly destructive meat grinder of the early battles. Those who had survived of this initial group quickly found themselves wearing general's stars where they had recently been wearing bars or oak leaves.

Hood wore the bars of a captain in 1861 and then wore the insignia of a brigadier general in March of 1862 when he was still shy of his thirty-second birthday. It had been heady stuff to move from a company of a hundred men to a regiment of nearly 1,000 and then to a brigade with four regiments.

Everyone said it: Hood had earned his promotions on the battlefield. At Gaines' Mill in Virginia, on June 27, 1862, Hood's brigade of Texans had smashed into and routed the center of the Federal line in conjunction with another brigade. That day, they won the battle, the glory, and the reputation of Lee's best.

Then, on August 30, 1862, as part of James Longstreet's right wing, Hood was one of six division commanders and led his troops in Longstreet's attack at Second Manassas. This attack routed Pope's panicked Army of Virginia, which retreated across Bull Run Creek.

Early in the morning, north of the village of Sharpsburg, Maryland, and east of winding Antietam Creek, Hood led his reserve division in its counterattack against the Federal right and center. Hood's troops drove the Union force back to the northern edge of the cornfield. This timely action saved Jackson's corps, which had nearly been overwhelmed. Successful as it was, Hood's advantage only lasted until 7:30 that morning when his division was forced back to the high ground near the Dunker Church. In a battle in which one of every four men was a casualty, Hood's star rose and shone brightly. Hood was promoted to the rank of major general at the age of thirty-two. The combination of Hood and Longstreet had worked well.

Midsummer of 1863 found the ever-restless Hood part of Lee's campaign into Pennsylvania. On the far right of the Confederate line, Hood conceived an envelopment of the left end of the opposing Union line that was "in the air," meaning the line simply ended rather than turning back onto itself to create a better protected end. On July 2,

Hood's left arm stopped a round. The ball struck his arm with enough force to knock him from his saddle. His left arm, which he had feared he would lose to the surgeon's knife, was not amputated but was essentially useless thereafter. He recuperated in Richmond and was much made over by an admiring city.

Only a little more than two months later, Hood had recovered enough to lead a corps of three divisions again under Longstreet. Hood's corps was part of Longstreet's left wing, which in turn was part of Bragg's 66,000-man Army of Tennessee. Hood arrived on the afternoon of September 19 in time to send their blue-jacketed enemy reeling back to Chattanooga. His luck ran out early in this endeavor when his right leg was hit hard and destroyed. It was later removed near his hip. He was promoted to lieutenant general, the equivalent of three stars in the Union army while he was recovering in Richmond.

Upon his return to the Army of Tennessee, he became one of three corps commanders under Johnston. General Johnston seemed very pleased to have this storied fighting general with him. The army, some 60,000 strong, waited in and around the northwest Georgia town of Dalton as the situation after Bragg's disastrous generalship at Lookout Mountain and Missionary Ridge slowly improved.

These promotions in position and rank were all based, Hood was confident, on his personal courage, dash, bravery, skill, advanced education, natural leadership, and military genius. He would have thought that this trail of advancement was only incidentally fueled if he had he been so inclined to reflect on it, on his unbridled ambition, on his demand for recognition, and on his embrace of power.

During the Civil War, the military system was hierarchical in nature and pulled men upward as spaces became available. This was especially true if one demonstrated personal bravery and coolness under fire and if it were seen and reported. If these reports fell within the view of those seeking able men to promote, especially if they knew or had an acquaintanceship with the candidate presented for selection, the outcome was entirely human and predictable. There simply was no time, nor resources, for an objective and systematic selection process to take hold. The selection system was driven by crises and was chaotic. Troops needed officers and leaders. If chance put average men into positions that they were wholly inadequate for, those men served as best they could, and soldiers died. There was a war on, and natural selection provided an expeditious remedy.

Sometimes, the job made the man, and he grew into it and filled it in an extraordinary manner. Sometimes, a man was found who served with élan and distinction in each role that he found himself in, but not often. The extraordinary man was often the product of luck and fortune and was highly unusual.

The system plucked men up and placed them at the next higher level, at which the skills that had served that man so well formerly were now entirely inadequate to the task. If not that, then the task was so different or the time to learn so compressed or the experience curve too steep that success at the new level was impossible. The transition from company and regimental tactical mastery under the guidance of skilled senior leadership to mastery of developing a grand strategic vision was a river too wide for all but the most talented. That hard truth existed regardless of the exalted opinion of self that most men who arrived at that riverbank possessed.

Hood was a battlefield commander and had worked well and sometimes even brilliantly. His commands almost always fought, and their primary means of fighting was to attack. Attack, in this strange and changing contest, was generally murderous to those taking the offense, and this was the case in the attacks carried out by Hood's brave soldiers.

It had been a whirlwind in the days since Dalton, as the three corps of the Army of Tennessee inched back, fought, and inched back again—maneuvers that were troublesome to Hood. Hood thus abandoned his obligation of loyalty to General Johnston, and in a calculated political move, he began to complain and criticize the action of his commander. He bypassed the chain of command and wrote letters to his highly positioned friends in Richmond, including Bragg and President Davis.

Hood was an active man—a fighting general. He was the youngest lieutenant general in the Southern army. He was a bright star in a bright galaxy. He knew beautiful women, took carriage rides with President Davis, and received the praise and adulation of the capitol. It was clear to him that he was special, unique, and gifted. He was certain other highly placed officers and political leaders knew and admired his unique and special gifts. In ways he only little understood, even if he had given it much thought (which he had not), his ideas seemed to roll out of him, unburdened by any effort of concentration or internal debate.

Attacks, especially those composed of direct assaults, won battles, and winning battles won the war. Hood felt that retreats would only result in defeat. His proven talents convinced him, in an ironclad way, of this idea, which left little room for other possibilities. His concept was direct and straightforward: you can't win the wars by retreat.

Crisis and hard times push men down into their fundamental character and beliefs. Hood was no exception. His basic instinct, just as he had with the Indians in Texas, was to take the battle to his opponent. His special talents powered his belief that he would and should lead a resurgent Army of Tennessee into battle with the relentless Federals. Buoyed by success, heady in his youth, disdainful of his superiors, and only five years from being a seasoned lieutenant, Hood was clear about his destiny.

Hood was at best an imperfect vessel for holding all the South's military ambitions here in Georgia. Hood himself might not hold to that view, but those with understanding and some objectivity could recognize it. At that moment, however, Hood's ambition and personal motivation coincided nearly perfectly with the desire working in Davis' head: Do something. Strike now before it is too late.

Hood was bitterly opposed to digging, cutting, and trench warfare, which had become a way of life to the Army of Tennessee. He was sure, and probably right, that an army that became accustomed to retreat and defensive entrenchments would find it next to impossible to assault the Federals, who were likewise past masters of the defensive arts. Once a soldier had learned that he was protected in his earthworks and that he could defend against many times his number, the knowledge works in a vicious, emotional, and intellectual way when he is then demanded to load his musket, affix his bayonet, and assault others who were so safely ensconced in well-constructed earthworks. It becomes damned difficult.

Hood knew he could not win by backing up and surrendering Atlanta. If sheer willpower, bold plans, timely leadership, and the indomitable spirit of the soldiers of the Army of Tennessee could all be combined, then maybe victory could be achieved by assault. It would be best, in an ideal world, to lead men in an attack who had never enjoyed the comfort, cover, and protection those earthen walls and head logs afforded. But such was not the case. Even with all the taming a hundred days of defense had inculcated, he believed that valor, dignity, honor, and fearlessness would rise and be present in the inspired Southern soldiers when called upon. Certainly, it would be present when he called on them.

As events would prove, valor was present in each portion of the battlefield around Atlanta, but other important ingredients for victory were lacking.

SPECIAL FIELD ORDERS No. 69
ROSWELL BRIDGE, GA.
July 16, 1864.

* * * * * * * * * * * *

VII. In order to carry out the spirit and intention of Special Field Orders, No. 35, Headquarters Military Division of the Mississippi, the following movements shall take place:

1. The Fifteenth Army Corps, Maj. Gen. John A. Logan commanding, will move out from its present position at 5:30 a.m. to-morrow on the road leading to Cross Keys, following this road to a point near Providence Church, where he will take a left-hand road (sometimes called the upper Decatur road) and proceed on this road until he reaches Nancy's Creek, where he will take up a good position on each side of the road and go into bivouac.

2. The Left Wing, Sixteenth Army Corps, Maj. Gen. G.M. Dodge commanding, will follow immediately after the Fifteenth Corps on the Cross Keys road to Nancy's Creek, where he will take up a good position on each side of the road and go into bivouac. He will direct the Ninth Illinois Mounted Infantry to feel out from his right for Major-General Schofield's command, and will endeavor to keep open a line of communication by means of vedettes. The pickets of the Fifteenth and Sixteenth Corps should connect.

3. Maj. Gen. F.P. Blair, on his arrival at the bridge with his command, will follow the rest of the army, and report to the major-general commanding for special instructions.

4. Brigadier-General Garrard, commanding cavalry division, will move his command at 5:30 a.m. to-morrow, crossing McAfee's Bridge, and will push out to the vicinity of Buchanan's, near the headwaters of Nancy's Creek, and take up a position covering the roads to his left and front. He will feel to the right and open communication with the Fifteenth Army Corps. He will also leave a sufficient guard for McAfee's Bridge, and one regiment to be stationed near Roswell to form part of the guard for trains and to patrol the country in the vicinity. The trains will be compactly parked, in the most secure position which can be found, as near the bridge as practicable.

5. Each Corps commander will leave one good regiment of infantry to form the guard for the train. The regiment from the Sixteenth Corps will take post at the bridge on the west side, and the other two regiments, one from the Fifteenth and one from the Seventeenth, will remain immediately with the trains.

6. Great Vigilance must be exercised by the guard to prevent the train from being surprised by the enemy's cavalry.

7. All wagons and encumbrances not needed for battle must be left behind.

8. The supply train of the cavalry division will be parked with the infantry trains.

By order of Maj. Gen. James B. McPherson:
WM.T. CLARK,
Assistant Adjutant-General.

SPECIAL FIELD ORDERS No.54
HDQRS. 15th ARMY CORPS
Near Roswell Factory, Ga., July 16, 1864

IV. Division Commanders will have their commands in readiness to move to-morrow morning, provided with three days' rations and forage and 100 rounds per man of ammunition, in addition to that already in cartridge-boxes.

VI. This command will move out to-morrow morning at 5:30 o'clock on the road leading to Cross Keyes, following that road to a point near Providence Church, where it will take a left-hand road, sometimes called the upper Decatur road, and proceed on this until Nancy's Creek is reached, when a good position on each side of the road will be chosen and the troops ordered into bivouac.

VII. Brig. Gen. William Harrow, commanding Fourth Division, will have the advance, and will be followed by the divisions of Brigadier-Generals Woods and M.L. Smith, respectively.

VIII. The ammunition wagons which are intended to transport the additional 100 rounds referred to in paragraph IV of the order will follow each division, and the ambulance train of each division will likewise follow. Fifteenth Army Corps headquarters train will follow in the rear of the First Division. All other wagon of the command will follow in rear of the entire command in the order of march. Two regiments of infantry will follow in the rear of the entire train as rear guard.

IX. The general supply train will be left and parked as near the river bridge as practicable, on the west side, under the direction of the chief quartermaster of the corps.

By order of Maj. Gen. John A. Logan
R.R. TOWNES,
Assistant Adjutant-General

SPECIAL ORDERS No. 175
HDQRS. SEVENTEENTH ARMY CORPS,
In the Field, July 16, 1864

Brig. Gen. M.D. Leggett will have the advance to-morrow, and will move his command promptly at 4 a.m. on the road to Roswell Ferry.

Brig. Gen. W.Q. Gresham, commanding Fourth Division, will hold his command in readiness to move at 4:30 a.m., and will follow immediately in the rear of the Third Division.

The trains of this command have been ordered to move at 2 a.m. on the road before indicated in advance of the troops.

By command of Maj. Gen. Frank P. Blair:
A.J. ALEXANDER,

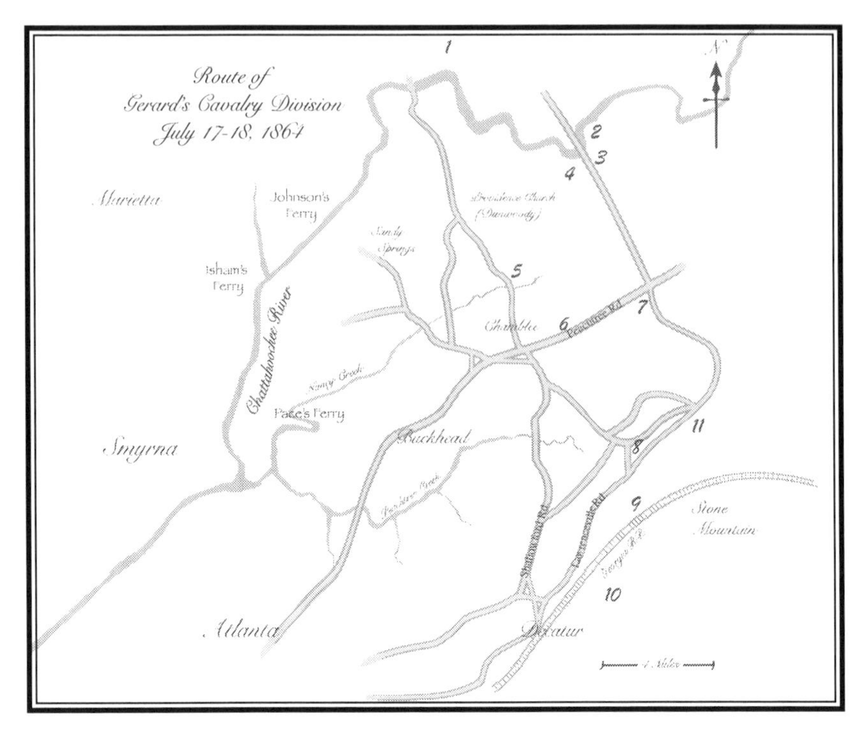

Route of Garrard's Cavalry Division, July 17-18, 1864

1. On July 17, 1864, the division left on Old Alabama Road at about 9:00 a.m. with orders to tear up the Georgia Railroad east of Decatur.
2. Miller's brigade led the way to McAfee Bridge.
3. Crossing the bridge, the column passed through the picket line of Colonel Eli Long's brigade about one mile south of the river.
4. The line of march turned right and proceeded until it crossed Nancy Creek near New Cross Keys.
5. The Seventeenth camped here for the night with Garrard's right about one mile east of Logan's Fifteenth Army Corps' left and a line back to Buchanan's house, which was occupied by Robert Minty's men.
6. At 5:00 a.m. on the morning of July 18, troopers moved toward Buchanan's house.
7. The line of march turned right at Buchanan's, heading toward Stone Mountain Depot.
8. The lead elements confronted some forty to fifty dismounted Confederate cavalry at Browning's Courthouse. Skirmishing ensued.
9. Union troops struck the Georgia Railroad about one mile west of Stone Mountain Depot and began tearing up the track.
10. Lightburn's brigade of the 2nd Division of the Fifteenth Army Corps arrived to aid in the destruction of the tracks, and together, they destroy two miles of track west toward Decatur.
11. Garrard's troopers returned to camp south of Browning's Courthouse.

July 17, 1864

CHAPTER SEVENTEEN

SOUTH OF THE CHATTAHOOCHEE

JULY 17, 1864

MORNING

On July 17, for the first time, the commanders of the two competing armies were both on the Atlanta side of the Chattahoochee River. This fact was known only to one of them: the Union. General Johnston's headquarters were at the home of Dexter Niles, and that dwelling was outside the city's fortifications, about six miles due south of Sherman's location.

Johnston's mind and troops were focused on the area around Montgomery's Ferry. Sherman's troops, meanwhile, were moving toward Atlanta from three widely separate points, none of which was Montgomery's Ferry. Sherman and his subordinate commanders were busy sending and receiving messages and orders.

SPECIAL FIELD ORDERS No. 36.
HDQRS. MIL. DIV. OF THE MISS.
In the Field, Chattahoochee, July 17, 1864.

The operations of the army for to-morrow, the 18th July, will be as follows:

Major-General Thomas will move forward, occupy Buck Head and the ridge between Nancy's Creek and Peach Tree, also all the roads toward Atlanta, as far as Peach Tree Creek.

II. Major-General Schofield will pass through Cross Keys and occupy the Peach Tree road where intersected by the road from Cross Keys to Decatur.

III. Major-General McPherson will move toward Stone Mountain to secure strong ground within four miles of General

Schofield's position, and push Brigadier-General Garrard's cavalry to the railroad, and destroy some section of the road, and then resume position to the front and left of General McPherson.

All armies will communicate with their neighbors. The General-in-Chief will be near General Thomas' left, or near General Schofield.

By order of Maj. Gen. W. T. Sherman:

L.M. DAYTON

Aide-de-Camp

July 17, 1864

Memoranda to Special Field Orders, No. 36:

The map composed of two parts of the official compilation made at Marietta July 5 and 11, 1864, is the best and will be standard for orders issued from these headquarters. As a general rule, old roads will be found to lead to Decatur, but new roads to Atlanta. The general country is very hilly and stony, but improves south and east as we approach the head of the Ocmulgee. Peach Tree Creek is considerable of a stream, but ford-able at all points east of the main road from Buck Head to Atlanta. The first real lines will be found on the Old Peach Tree trail, which starts at Turner's Ferry, keeps near the Chattahoochee, crosses Peach Tree at Moore's Mill and on a main ridge by Buck Head, Buchanan's and Pinckneyville. Our first line must be in front of this road, leaving it clear for communication; General Thomas the right, General Schofield the center, and General McPherson the left. General Thomas will move substantially on Atlanta, General Schofield on Decatur, and General McPherson, with General Garrard's cavalry, is charged with the destruction of the railroad between Decatur and Stone Mountain. As soon as the road is broken all the armies will close on General Thomas, occupying the main roads east of Atlanta, or, in other words, the line swung across the railroad near Decatur. General Thomas will press close on Atlanta, but not assault real works, but not be deterred by cavalry or light defenses. General Schofield will threaten the neighborhood of Decatur, but Generals McPherson and Garrard will risk much and break the railroad during the 18th or 19th.

W.T. SHERMAN,

Major-General, Commanding

CHAPTER EIGHTEEN

Atlanta

By 1862, Atlanta had become the location of the Confederate arsenal and the Quartermaster Department under the command of Colonel Moses H. Wright. Within the new building, completed in 1863, were the facilities for manufacturing saddles and harnesses and machine shops for creating percussion caps and ammunition ranging from .57 caliber rounds for rifles to ten-inch artillery shells. More ordinary products were the cartridge boxes, canteens, belts, small arms ammunition, and friction primers. In addition, a huge repair shop was created to refurbish gun carriages, caissons, rifles, cannons, pistols, bayonets, and swords. As time passed, the primary function of the Atlanta arsenal was to supply the Army of Tennessee. To accomplish this task, the arsenal employed over 5,400 men and women by 1864.

The Quartermaster Department in Atlanta was established in 1861 under the command of Major G.W. Cunningham. The products of the department, while seemingly less warlike, were every bit as important. It produced shoes, jackets, pants, shirts, undergarments, and wool hats. It produced the leather and cloth used in the manufacturing of the ready-to-wear goods.

The rolling mill on the east side of the city, adjacent to Oakland Cemetery, produced two-inch naval armor plates for the ironclads of the Confederate Navy. Private and government factories found Atlanta to be a place in which production could occur in apparent safety and which raw materials could flow in and finished goods could flow out on the railroad network.

In the period before the railroad, Samuel Mitchell owned the area. Later, Mitchell gave five acres to the state to be used by the railroad and then laid out the rest of his tract as town lots. These lots were laid out perpendicular and parallel to the tracks of the Western Atlantic Railroad. This arrangement did not conform well to the primary roadways and resulted in an octopus-like series of arms radiating from the center to the major points of the compass. This scheme was well established by 1860 and still persists over a hundred years later.

By 1860, there were 9,554 people living in Atlanta. By the summer of 1864, the number had swelled to around 20,000, not including the Army of Tennessee.

In 1860, the manufacturing, construction, commerce, and transportation formed the reason for the existence of the city. They were the same reasons that were given for Union's pursuit of Atlanta.

SPECIAL FIELD ORDERS No. 70
HDQRS. DEPT.OF THE TENNESSEE,
Near Nancy's Creek, Ga., July 17, 1864

VI. To carry out Special Field Orders, No. 36. Headquarters Military Division of the Mississippi, a copy of which is enclosed herewith the following movements will take place to-morrow:

The Fifteenth Army Corps, Major General Logan commanding will march at 5a.m. on the Decatur road to Widow Rainey's, thence on the Stone Mountain road, by Blake's Mill to Browing's Court House, at the intersection of the Stone Mountain and Lawrenceville and Decatur roads, where he will hold his command in readiness to assist Brigadier-General Garrard, if he requires it, in his effort to make a break in the railroad.

Major-General Dodge will move his command at 6 a.m., taking the road to his left in rear of his advance division, by Adams' across Nancy's Creek to the Peach Tree road, thence eastward on the Peach Tree road to the Decatur road from Roswell, thence Decatur road toward Peach Tree Creek, engaging the attention of the enemy, and keeping his command well in hand for any emergency.

Maj-Gen. F.P. Blair will move his command at 6 a.m. the Decatur road to Widow Rainey's, thence on the Stone Mountain road to Peach Tree Creek at Blake's Mill, following the Fifteenth Army Corps.

Brig. Gen. K. Garrard will move his command at 5 a.m. by the most practicable road or roads in his front to the railroad, and do what damage he can to it by burning bridges and culverts, piling rails on the track and setting them on fire so as to heat and warp the iron, tearing up the ties, piling them up, putting the iron rails on top, and setting the ties on fire.

The importance of making a break in the railroad cannot be overestimated, and the general commanding trusts that all will act with spirit and determination which is the best guarantee of success.

* * * * * * * * * * * *

By order of Maj. Gen. James B. McPherson:
WM.T. CLARK,
Assistant Adjutant-General

CHAPTER NINETEEN

Confederacy | WASHINGTON IVES

4TH FLORIDA INFANTRY REGIMENT, ARMY OF TENNESSEE

NEAR ATLANTA

JULY 17, 1864

8:00 P.M.

Sergeant Major Washington Ives of the combined 1st Florida Cavalry (dismounted) and 4th Florida was twenty years old. He had been with the 4th Florida since he had joined Company C on April 12, 1861. He had seen the regiment at its newly organized strength, some 926 men and 47 officers, and he saw its tattered remnants now. They had come out of the battle at Missionary Ridge with only eighteen men available for action, after having started the fight with 172. One hundred and fifty-four men had been killed, wounded, or captured in the poorly planned, but hard fought defense of Chattanooga.

After the battle, as the Confederate Army of Tennessee took up its defensive position for the winter, the 4th Florida was consolidated with the 1st Florida Cavalry (dismounted), which by then had only thirty-three effective men. The consolidated regiment was, in truth, not even half a regular company. Some men would return, but the two once-substantial Florida units could muster only about fifty men. Three years of war—with its death, wounds, camp life, and desertion—had nearly used up 2,000 effective Florida soldiers.

The 1st and 4th Florida with two other Florida regiments, the Kentucky Orphan Brigade, and the Georgia and Tennessee boys in Brigadier General Smith's brigade made up the division commanded by William Bate. This division was one of four that made up Hardee's corps.

Ives had just finished writing a letter to his father and was consuming the last of his dinner of bacon, cornbread, and cabbage. Ives wished

Lieutenant Billy Roberts and Steve Knowles were there to talk to, but they had left earlier in the day. The talk was that they had had enough and were on their way home.

He glanced at his new Pattern 53 Enfield rifled musket. He and the rest of the Florida boys had received the weapons on June 26 and had wanted to use them against the boys in blue at the defense at Cheatham's Hill on June 27, but they had arrived after the hard fighting and dying was done.

While Ives' gun was no longer brand new as it had been last month, it gleamed like the well-oiled machine it was. Ives' weapon was one of nearly 900,000 Pattern 53 Enfields that saw service on both sides of the conflict between 1861 and 1865. The Enfield had a .577 caliber barrel, which allowed troops to load and fire either the .577 caliber round made in England or the South or the .58 caliber round made by the Federals for the 1861 and 1863 Springfield rifled musket. The Enfield was deadly accurate in the hands of a marksman with ranges in excess of 300 yards, although most of the time the range men tried to kill one another at was considerably less than 300 yards. The weapon weighed about nine pounds and was 55.3 inches long. It had a deep- blue-colored barrel and bands with a beautiful brass butt plate and trigger assembly. Ives liked his new piece as it came, but some of the Florida boys began to sand away the blue color to reveal the shiny silver underneath. Sunlight on shiny metal did not seem like the smartest of ideas to Ives, so his barrel remained blue.

Enfield Lock of England, which developed the Pattern 53 rifle, produced weapons for the British government. Over time, three levels of quality came to be recognized with the popular weapon. The number one Enfield was a weapon with machine-made parts of the highest quality, and they were interchangeable. These guns were all made to meet the British government's gauges. Not only would the parts work well together, but also the interchangeability meant a soldier could repair the gun in the field. Parts of this high quality could be used in any repair and work as well as the original. This interchangeability was shared with the Federal Springfield rifle, which was derived from the original Pattern 53 Enfield. The Springfield reached levels of manufacturing excellence that the parts made in one location were interchangeable with those made elsewhere.

The number two Enfields were made by hand rather than by machine. They were good but of somewhat lesser quality. The number three's were often stamped with fraudulent inspection stamps and were made to take advantage of foreign buyers. Unfortunately, the one-two-three numbering classification system was never made official to serve as a guide to buyers and as a reassurance to the quality actually being purchased. Rather, the quality was discovered in the field long after the fact of purchase.

For men on both sides of the line, shooting was as fluid as a well-practiced dance.[4] It was natural and smooth, as the mind disengaged from the process. The carnage, on the other hand, took lots of mental control to ignore. If one thought about what the men behind the walnut stocks and the bright steel or blued barrels were intent upon doing from the other side, it would be impossible to live with. Disengaged, numb, professional performance was what allowed and sustained the killing.

Ives chewed the last of his meal. He knew he would not put his thoughts about the attack and defense in writing to his father. Some things were better told at home once he was out of the war, or maybe they would be better never told. Nonetheless, he would write to his father tonight and bring him up-to-date with the men from north Florida. He knew his father treasured his letters. He knew he saved them.

CHAPTER TWENTY

Confederacy | JOSEPH JOHNSTON

HEADQUARTERS OF THE ARMY OF TENNESSEE

DEXTER NILES' HOUSE

JULY 17, 1864

10:15 P.M.

One moment, Johnston had been in earnest discussion with his chief engineer, Lieutenant Colonel Stephen W. Pressman, about the five and a half miles of earthworks that constituted the Confederate outer lines of defense around the city. He was engaged in planning for the future. The next moment, he was presented with a message that held no future whatsoever.

Major Charles Huber had entered the room containing the two officers and, at a glance, saw the map that both men were looking over. Johnston, somewhat surprised at the interruption, especially so late in the evening, said, "What is it, Major?"

"General, sir, begging your pardon, sir. This message just came for you." Outside, the military band broke into the tune "Dixie."

Johnston held in his hand the standard four-inch by eight-inch telegraph form and a sheet of paper on which Huber had handwritten the deciphered telegram. He discarded the telegraph form, which read:

TELEGRAM

THE SOUTHERN TELEGRAPH COMPANIES

TERMS AND CONDITIONS ON WHICH MESSAGES ARE RECEIVED BY THESE COMPANIES FOR TRANSMISSION.

TELEGRAM

THE PUBLIC ARE NOTIFIED THAT IN ORDER TO GUARD AGAINST MISTAKES IN THE TRANSMISSION OF MESSAGES EVERY MESSAGE OF IMPORTANCE OUGHT TO BE REPEATED BY BEING SENT BACK FROM THE STATION AT WHICH IT IS TO BE RECEIVED TO THE STATION FROM WHICH IT IS ORIGINALLY SENT. HALF THE USUAL PRICE FOR TRANSMISSION WILL BE CHARGED FOR REPEATING THE MESSAGE, AND WHILE THESE COMPANIES WILL AS HERETOFORE USE EVERY PRECAUTION TO INSURE CORRECTNESS, THEY WILL NOT BE RESPONSIBLE FOR MISTAKES OR DELAYS IN THE TRANSMISSION OR DELIVERY OF REPEATED MESSAGES BEYOND FIVE AND ONE HALF TIMES THE AMOUNT PAID FOR SENDING THE MESSAGE, NOR WILL THEY BE RESPONSIBLE FOR MISTAKES OR DELAYS IN THE TRANSMISSION OF UNREPEATED MESSAGES FROM WHATEVER CAUSES THEY MAY ARISE, NOR THE DELAY ARISING FROM INTERRUPTION IN THE WORKINGS OF THEIR TELEGRAPHS, NOR FOR ANY MISTAKES OR OMISSIONS OF ANY OTHER COMPANY OVER WHOSE LINES A MESSAGE IS TO BE SENT TO REACH THE PLACE OF DESTINATION. ALL MESSAGES WILL HEREAFTER BE RECEIVED BY THOSE COMPANIES FOR TRANSMISSION SUBJECT TO THE ABOVE STIPULATIONS.

J.R. DOWELL, GEN'L SUP'T RICHMOND, VA.
W.S. MORRIS, PRES'T, RICHMOND, VA.

He then read the deciphered telegram:

TELEGRAM

RICHMOND, JULY 17, 1864
GENERAL J.E. JOHNSTON:

LIEUT. GEN. J.B. HOOD HAS BEEN COMMISSIONED TO THE TEMPORARY RANK OF GENERAL UNDER THE LATE LAW OF CONGRESS. I AM DIRECTED BY THE SECRETARY OF WAR TO INFORM YOU THAT AS YOU HAVE FAILED TO ARREST THE ADVANCE OF THE ENEMY TO THE VICINITY OF ATLANTA, FAR IN THE INTERIOR OF GEORGIA, AND EXPRESS NO CONFIDENCE THAT YOU CAN DEFEAT OR REPEL HIM, YOU ARE HEREBY RELIEVED FROM THE COMMAND OF THE ARMY AND DEPARTMENT OF TENNESSEE, WHICH YOU WILL IMMEDIATELY TURN OVER TO GENERAL HOOD.

S.COOPER,
ADJUTANT AND INSPECTOR GENERAL.

Well, he had known it would come to this. It was wrong-headed as usual—as those fools in Richmond often were—but he also felt a small nibbling of relief. His name would not be on the lips of those discussing the fall of Atlanta. Instead, let that name be "Hood."

Johnston, always correct as to military administration, sat to carefully write his acceptance on the message form. Near at hand, he found paper and pen. Without haste and with an orderly mind and an eye toward future historians, he composed:

General Orders No. 4
Headquarter Army Of Tennessee,
July 17, 1864
In obedience to orders of the War Department, I turn over to General Hood the command of the Army and Department of Tennessee. I cannot leave this noble army without expressing my admiration of the high military qualities it has displayed. A long and arduous campaign has made conspicuous every soldierly virtue, endurance of toil, obedience to orders, brilliant courage. The enemy has never attacked but to be repulsed and severely punished. You, soldiers, have never argued but from your courage, and never counted your foes. No longer your leader, I will still watch your career, and will rejoice in your victories. To one and all I offer assurances of my friendship, and bid an affectionate farewell.
J.E. Johnston,
General

Johnston finished penning the last order that he ever expected to write.

"Hold on to this until I tell you to publish it. That will be all for the time being," he said to Huber. He turned and left the room to walk in the quiet of the night.

CHAPTER TWENTY-ONE

Confederacy | JAMES W. RATCHFORD

HEADQUARTERS OF HOOD'S CORPS

TENT OF THE ADJUTANT GENERAL

JULY 17, 1864

11:00 P.M.

"Come in. Come in, Sergeant. What do you have for me?" Major James W. Ratchford asked as he looked up from his desk. The tent was illuminated by only one lantern, and it seemed to produce more shadow than light. The young courier appeared less composed than he normally did when delivering dispatches and telegrams. He stood at attention briefly and said, "Telegrams from Richmond, Major."

As was his practice upon receiving messages, Ratchford opened it immediately and read its contents.

Ratchford found the telegrams compelling. One contained orders appointing Hood to the temporary rank of full general in the Provisional Army of the Confederate States. The second was a copy of the telegram from Cooper, the Adjutant and Inspector General of the Confederacy to General Johnson relieving him of command, and the third was a short wire from the Secretary of War, Seddon. Seddon's message was scrawled on a strip of paper about eight inches long by about three and a quarter inches:

Gen. John B Hood
You are charged
With a great trust,
You will I know test
To the utmost your
Capacities to discharge
It. Be wary no less
Than bold. It may yet
Be practicable to cut
The communication of the
Enemy or find or make
An opportunity of equal
Encounter whether he
Move east or west.
God be with you
James A Seddon

Ratchford thought that the words were strong and filled with possibilities. The message had good advice, but Ratchford was also certain that Hood would disregard it without thought.

In Ratchford's mind, Johnston was a great man, and those in Richmond didn't understand that no one could take Johnston's place right now. Hood was a great battlefield commander, especially in the thick of it and most especially at the division level, but he wasn't big enough for army command. Those thoughts tumbled through his mind as he raced toward Hood's tent.

Hood was sound asleep and took some waking. He seemed as startled as Ratchford was when he read the messages.

Hood looked up and said, "Major, say nothing of this to anyone." Ratchford left Hood with a careful salute, which Hood returned.

There would be no outward manifestation of Hood's promotion—unlike a full Union general, who wore two epaulettes with four stars on each. Of course, at the time, there were no Union generals wearing four stars. Grant wore only three.

The insignia of the Confederacy was, in some ways, as confusing as the highly individualized method employed for naming military units. Military units were identified by the name of the current or past commander. In the more industrialized North, units had numbers that more or less remained the same regardless of the comings and goings of the individual officer in command.

For insignias, all Southern general officers from brigadier to full general were entitled to wear a device on the collar: a wreath and three stars. In addition, frogging or a gold braid of four wales or ridges wide was worn on the sleeve. There was no outward differentiation between the four levels of general officers. To complicate matters, a full colonel wore the same three stars on his collar as generals did, just without the wreath. A colonel in the Union army wore a silver eagle. In a gathering of senior Southern officers, the rank order could only be determined if one knew each officer by sight. In the Union army, each grade of general officer wore an additional star as he advanced from brigadier to major general to lieutenant general until arriving as a full general with four stars.

An hour later, at about one in the morning, Ratchford—wearing the single star that designated his rank—returned with a congratulatory message from General Joe Johnston.

CHAPTER TWENTY-TWO

Confederacy | CHARLES SMITH

COMPANY I, 32ND OHIO, ARMY OF THE TENNESSEE

SOUTH OF THE CHATTAHOOCHEE RIVER

JULY 17, 1864

EVENING

It had been a long day of marching through the thick, dry, red dust. The day had begun at 3:00 a.m. and didn't end until 10:30 that night. Beginning in the dark with cooking fires and ending the same way after having covered some twenty miles was a plenty. The 32nd Ohio had waded across three streams and then crossed the long bridge over the Chattahoochee. Breakfast had been taken in a pasture about a mile south of Marietta. It had been a good breakfast: a tin of freshly picked, sweetened blackberries on top of coffee, fried pork, and hardtack, a type of cracker.

Corporal Charles Smith liked blackberries, and he ate them as often as he found himself able to pick them. Smith was just twenty-eight years old. He had been a farmer in the summer and a school teacher in the winter. He had attended the local college but was certain he would spend his life as a farmer. The war had intervened, however, and now he was a soldier and a member of the 32nd Ohio Infantry Regiment. He had been in lots of fights in his nearly three years in the army and had thus far not suffered a wound. He carried his diary with him and was generally able to find time to record the day's events before he dropped off to sleep.

His immediate view of the war was limited to the small area to his front and sides. He was usually very aware of what was ahead of him and what was going on to his right and left. In addition, it was his practice to read everything he could get his hands on, especially newspapers, so he was able to keep up with the overall course of the war and the several campaigns.

The previous night, he had only two hours of sleep. He had been soaked with sweat when he lay down on his gum blanket, and he had been wet from heavy dew when he was awakened by the noise of the rousing camp. Since arising, he and the rest of his division had marched through Marietta, Georgia, where the Union Fifteenth Army Corps and the rest of the men had marched through two days before. It was a nice village with a courthouse, railway depot, hotels, warehouses, and several pleasant homes. In Marietta, he had visited with several friends he had happened to see.

From Marietta, he had marched in the dust and the heat all the way to Roswell. His toes were blistered so that each step was agony, and his clothing chaffed to add additional torment. The sun and the physical exertion had exhausted Smith. During the day as he trudged along, he had imagined several times that death would be sweeter than his current hardship. Pressure from his peers and fellow soldiers was the only thing that kept him moving painfully forward.

Before crossing the newly prepared bridge, the unit had passed through the pretty village of Roswell. It had some imposing homes, and some other fine residences surrounded by groves and evergreens. Before the sun and the road had exhausted him, Smith had enjoyed seeing the corn fields that dotted the rolling hills.

Corporal Smith knew the men in the 3rd Division better than those in the 4th, his current division. His regiment, the 32nd Ohio, had been part of the 3rd Division until July 10, about a week ago when it had been moved to the current division. Anyone who was interested in such organizational shuffles knew the change was to position Colonel Benjamin Potts to take command of the brigade, which he did just a week after the 32nd Ohio was transferred. Smith remember the day they had changed divisions, as it had been a Sunday and Chaplain Bennett, who was both a warrior and preacher, had preached to any man who wished to hear him.

In the temporary encampment, Smith had a cold wash, drank some coffee, wrote a few lines in his diary, and soon fell asleep. He hoped tomorrow would be easier than today.

July 18, 1864

CHAPTER TWENTY-THREE

Confederacy | JOHN HOOD

JULY 18, 1864

BEFORE 1 A.M.

Hood sat in the hard wooden chair with his left foot on the floor. His mind was a jumble of racing thoughts. From time to time, he would flex his leg and move a bit in the chair. Right now, it was a blessed relief to have the artificial leg off for a while.

Hood's injuries caused him much pain and struggle. His arm, or what was left of it, hurt sometimes. It almost burned and hurt to touch it. The remaining portion of his right leg would often itch and sometimes hurt, too, so much that the pain would distort his mind and he would become angry. Hood found it maddening to be unable to move in the eager, graceful way he could before the minie ball and Doctor Richardson had done their hard handiwork on his upper thigh. Now, Hood couldn't get around much by himself, needing a crutch and an able-bodied helper. Hood would get so tired just trying to move around. It was hard to do, but he knew he must go where the fight was.

Of course, Hood was lucky to be alive. More than half those with the same surgical treatment had died, but he still longed to walk and ride as he once did. Though he could still ride, he had to be strapped into the saddle—an indignity to Hood. Riding, an activity he used to love the most, became a chore, but Hood would ride just to prove that he could, as he did when he rode with President Davis in Richmond.

Hood reached over to take a spoonful of laudanum, something he often used to soothe his pain. He thought a spoonful might distract him from the physical pangs enough to let him get his mind back around to the grand opportunity that General Johnston's departure opened for him.

Hood also thought a spoonful would take the edge off both the jumble in his mind and the sting and occasional hammer blow where his leg used to be. He sat back, closed his eyes, and waited for the laudanum to work. It reminded him of the chloroform they knocked him out with the day they took his leg.

After being wounded, he didn't have to wait long to get on the operating table. The boys had him back to that little farmhouse pretty damn quick. Doctor Richardson even told him he had a new saw, sharp and clean. A minie ball—or two—had shattered Hood's thighbone, and Richardson had felt the leg had to go. The muscle was torn away, and no repair was possible—at least not without Hood dying.

That ride down to Colonel Little's folk's place in the ambulance seemed to take forever. Hood hated to depend on another man, but Doctor Darby had the magic juice for him when he needed it. There were two deep scalpel cuts with a flap of good skin left after cutting and sawing the meat down to the bone and then through the bone, cutting everything free.

The severed limb should have been discarded into a pile of parts, but out of respect or a sense that death was close, they saved it, wrapped his leg up, and took it with them so Hood and his leg could be together in burial. Later, once it was obvious Hood was not going to die, the leg got buried in its own ceremony in its own little grave, without Hood.

The end of the fresh cut bone was filed, scraped, and rounded so no sharp edges would cut the flap of skin. A drain was left, and the stump was bandaged. It all went so fast—fast was better than slow for a lot of reasons. No sawbones was as quick as a man with a rifle, but a good doctor could finish in ten minutes.

After the cutting, sawing, and rounding, surprisingly nothing had killed him. He got a little better each day. Nonetheless, he could remember it all—the sounds, the smells, and the pain. Some didn't think it was possible to remember it all, but Hood knew it was true regardless of the science.

The damage and the partial repair had left him with less than he started with. Oddly enough, if he had followed his father's advice and wishes, he would have probably done the cutting and sawing instead of providing a lump of meat for others to practice on.

Now, he didn't have much left to lose. Hood thought it just as well that he didn't need to be in front every time the army made a move. He would leave it to others. He had nothing left to prove and less to prove it with.

When his orders came to assume command of the Army of Tennessee, it was like lightning. They were hard pressed, now backed up within the fortress of Atlanta. They had been backed up for sixty-six days all the way from Dalton—more than a hundred miles.

Morale varied from company to company, brigade to brigade. Some of those boys were going to hate to see Johnston go, but Hood knew a lot of them were tired of retreating and never getting a chance to go on the offensive. Soldiers don't like to back up and hide, as it goes against everything a fighting man knows and believes. Maybe now they could go on the attack.

General Lee would find a way, and Hood knew he would, too. Hood thought that maybe Sherman would make a mistake and they could smash him. Maybe Sherman would separate that enormous army of his, and Hood could go after an isolated part. A million ideas flashed in Hood's head. Of course, he knew they must attack. The when and where were the questions.

July 18, 1864

By the President of the United States of America

A Proclamation

Whereas by the act approved July 4, 1864, entitled "an act further to regulate and provide for the enrolling and calling out the National forces and for other purposes," it is provided that the President of the United States may, "at his discretion, at any time hereafter, call for any number of men as volunteers, for the respective terms of one, two, and three years for military service," and "that in case the quota of (or) any part thereof, of any town, township, ward of a city, precinct, or election district, or of a county not so subdivided, shall not be filled within the space of fifty days after such call, then the President shall immediately order a draft for one year to fill such quota or any part thereof which may be unfilled."

And whereas, the new enrollment, heretofore ordered, is so far completed as that the aforementioned act of Congress may now be put in operation for recruiting and keeping up the strength of the armies in the field for garrisons, and such military operations as may be required for the purpose of suppressing the rebellion, and restoring the authority of the United States Government in the insurgent states:

Now, therefore, I Abraham Lincoln, President of the United States, do issue this my call for five hundred thousand volunteers for the military service, Provided, nevertheless, that this call shall be reduced by all credits which may be established under section 8 of the aforesaid act on account of persons who have entered the naval service during the present rebellion, and by credits for men furnished to the military service in excess of calls heretofore made. Volunteers will be accepted under this call for one, two, or three years, as they may elect, and will be entitled to the bounty provided by the law, for the period of service for which they enlist.

And I hereby proclaim, order and direct, that immediately after the fifth day of September, 1864, being fifty days from the date of this call, a draft for troops to serve one year shall be had in every town, township, ward of a city, precinct or election district or county not so subdivided to fill the quota which shall be assigned to it under this call, or any part thereof, which may be unfilled, by volunteers on the said fifth day of September 1864.

In testimony whereof, I have hereunto set my hand and caused the seal of the United States to be affixed.

Done at the city of Washington, this eighteenth day of July, in the year of our Lord one thousand eight hundred and sixty four, and of the Independence of the United States the eighty-ninth.

ABRAHAM LINCOLN

By the President:

WILLIAM H. SEWARD Secretary of State

NEAR ATLANTA, July 18,1864.
General S. Cooper
Richmond

Your dispatch of yesterday received and obeyed. Command of the Army and Department of Tennessee has been transferred to General Hood. As to the alleged cause of my removal, I assert that Sherman's army is much stronger compared with that of Tennessee than Grant's compared with that of Northern Virginia. Yet the enemy has been compelled to advance much more slowly to the vicinity of Atlanta than to that of Richmond and Petersburg, and has penetrated deeper into Virginia than into Georgia. Confident language by a military commander is not usually regarded as evidence of competency.

J.E. JOHNSTON

CHAPTER TWENTY-FOUR

Confederacy | JOHN HOOD

HEADQUARTERS OF HOOD'S CORPS

SOUTHSIDE OF THE CHATTAHOOCHEE RIVER

JULY 18, 1864

1 A.M.

Shortly before 1:00 a.m., a message of congratulation had come from Johnston for Hood. After he had read it, Hood thought for a few minutes and drafted his reply:

July 18, 1864—1 a.m.
General J.E. Johnston:
General: Much to my surprise I received the appointment you refer to. I accept your congratulations and without the concomitants it would have been more agreeable. I desire to have a conversation with you, and for that purpose will be over early in the morning.
Respectfully,
J.B. Hood

The night, or early morning, wore on and seemed endless to Hood, whose mind continued to race from topic to topic, all against a backdrop of imagined glory and a warm passionate welcome home in Richmond once he had won this battle.

At last, it was time to rise. Hood hobbled out to the breakfast with his staff and a Kentucky congressman, where Hood read the appointing telegram aloud. Stunned silence surrounded the breakfast group—the group who arguably knew him well. The congressman expressed reservations about Hood taking over from Johnston, who was held in such high regard by so many after all.

"*What else can I do but follow orders?*" thought Hood. "*In victory or failure, the blame or credit will go elsewhere.*" Hood knew that Johnston had been wrong since they started and that this was the time to really make a mark—to be bold and win. An active offense was needed. An army could not successfully attack by cowering behind earthworks, and he thought the man who led such a changed army would be recognized and lionized for the victory obtained. Each of his past assignments had almost always placed him in the center of attention. His personal leadership had been spoken of as brilliant. This time would be no different.

Winning this fight for Atlanta and joining up with Lee to defeat Grant would be terrific. This was not a horse race where the top three finishers were all in the money. This was war, meaning there was only one victor. The men needed to regain the habit of winning. They must attack, and Hood knew he could make that happen. Once Sherman was smashed, the Union would have to let them go, and they could rebuild their society in the manner they determined. He would do what Johnston could not for the soldiers and the Confederacy.

"*But,*" Hood thought, "*maybe the boys just like Johnston.*" Hood thought a moment on this before shaking his head. After Hood began his command, the men would see his personal sacrifice, and they would know that his winning attack would bring the end of this war. Hood believed the soldiers needed a commander like him—a hard, tough-minded leader, not merely a courtly aging gentleman like "Old Joe."

In Hood's mind, President Davis was right to make this change. Hood would give it his all to do the best for Davis and the country and make Davis proud. He knew he needed to keep this to himself for the next little while. He needed to see what General Johnston's plans were and then go from there. Johnston would make Hood's plan better, and the boys would make it work. These thoughts sped through Hood's head as he swung along with his crutches.

After being helped into his saddle, Hood left the corps headquarters near Turner's Ferry on the Chattahoochee. Soon, his path combined with that of Lieutenant General Stewart, the newest corps commander, who had been selected to run the corps formerly held by the unlucky Polk, who had been killed not long before.

The road connecting Marietta to Atlanta was known by those living in Atlanta as the Marietta Road and by those in Marietta as the Atlanta Road. Regardless of the name, it was the same road, and it ran from downtown Atlanta in a northwesterly direction. It followed essentially the same route as that of the Western Atlantic Railroad. Both the railroad and the wagon road passed through the northwest corner of the inner wall of the city fortification. That northwest corner lay about two miles from the city center.

Both generals and a few of the staff officers continued toward Montgomery Ferry near the site of Standing Peachtree, where the Chattahoochee River makes a turn toward the southeast and turns back hard to the west.

About a mile and a half outside the inner fortifications was the neat white-frame house that General Johnston had made the headquarters for his Army of Tennessee. The little house would be airless inside, but since it was still early, the temperature would at least be mild.

Almost immediately after Hood was ushered into Johnston's room, Johnston was on his feet coming to meet Hood. As Johnston came forward, he invited Hood to sit and ordered coffee for them both. To himself, Hood noted that Johnston remained always proper. His form was always precise.

The coffee arrived hot and black. It provided a little social lubricant and some breathing room as it was savored and enjoyed. Johnston held the saucer with one hand and his cup in the other. Under the circumstances, Johnston had maneuvered Hood into a chair with a small table next to it where Hood could place his saucer. By plan or otherwise, it allowed him to handle his cup appropriately with his one good hand.

Of course, now that Hood sat in front of Johnston, he was hit by the sudden doubt that many men experience when they see the reality of their new command. It's one thing to criticize a higher up and talk about what should have been done instead when the responsibility of the position is not on your shoulders. It's another to maintain that confidence when the responsibility—and any blame or praise—would be entirely on you. In that moment, Hood experienced a healthy dose of doubt and fear.

Hood began, "General Johnston, what is the cause of the order I received last night?"

"Sir, I don't know," Johnston said. "President Davis has seen fit to relieve me."

"Sir, the Army of Tennessee needs you. I implore you to pocket that Richmond dispatch, leave me in command of my corps, and fight the battle for Atlanta."

"The President has seen fit to relieve me, and I can do nothing—and will do nothing—unless the order is countermanded."

"But Sherman will have the city unless we check him soon."

"My response has not changed."

"General, let me see what can be done to remedy the matter," said Hood.

Hood struggled to get up and with his crutch steadied himself and withdrew from the room. He knew his continued presence would only exacerbate the matter.

As the door closed behind him, Hood looked up and saw Generals Stewart and Hardee. Hood spoke, "He is set on leaving and in following his orders to the letter. He will not merely disregard his orders but insists that he could comply only with an order countermanding his removal."

Hardee said, "Let's go out of here and to somewhere where we can talk." The other two generals agreed.

As Hood and he followed Hardee out into the dusty yard, Stewart said, "As we discussed and agreed earlier, let's—" He paused. "It's important to keep General Johnston in command until we can fight this impending battle."

"Let's get a telegram off to the War Office, and do it now," Hood said. The telegram was as follows:

ATLANTA, July 18, 1864.
General S. COOPER:
GENERAL; I have the honor to acknowledge the receipt of my appointment as General of the Army of Tennessee. There is now heavy skirmishing and indications of a general advance. I deem it dangerous to change commanders of this army at this particular time, and to be to the interest of the service that no change should be made until the fate of Atlanta is decided.
Respectfully,
J.B. HOOD,
General

Time passed, the heat rose, and the three generals kept company with each other, speaking little. Following a quiet lunch, Hood excused himself from Hardee and Stewart. As he hobbled away, he knew Hardee, Stewart, and he had some things in common, but their interests did not coincide perfectly. If these orders stood, Hood would be their commander. Hardee had declined that job after Chattanooga, but Hood knew that Hardee would rather take the position than let Hood have it. Hardee may be hard to deal with, but Stewart just wanted the matter settled so that his part and job could be made clear.

Crutch under his good arm, cork leg swinging forward, Hood made his way awkwardly back to the house and asked if he could see Johnston. Hood hoped that Johnston might share his plans since Hood knew Johnston must have some ideas about how to stop the fast-moving Union army.

He had waited only a short time when Johnston came out and invited him inside. Hood followed as Johnston led the way. Johnston looked worn and tired, probably because the days of his command were behind him. Hood knew his best days were yet to come with a past that was still hot and bright and pushing him forward.

On the table, a map of the Atlanta area was spread. Johnston oriented the map for Hood, pointing out their location and the general locations of the three corps along the outer lines of defenses. With a quiet voice, Johnston began to explain, as one would to a young soldier who knew little of the terrain or strategy, the opportunity he believed was unfolding.

"General Thomas with the Army of the Cumberland has crossed the Chattahoochee here and here." Johnston's thin index finger jabbed the map at Pace's Ferry Crossing and Power's Ferry, a little to the north. "Between him and our fortifications lies high ground on Peachtree Creek here."

Johnston continued, "It seems all the Federal forces are swinging like a gate with Thomas as the post. People toward the end have a longer distance to go. You can see Schofield's little army and McPherson swinging wide. Thomas is isolated from the rest of the army. My plan is to strike him while his army is separated from both Schofield's army and McPherson's. I figured both will be slow to react and too far away to be of much immediate help. We will strike as Thomas attempts to cross the creek. It isn't a huge stream, but the banks are steep in most places, and it is rough country all along it. The ground favors us, and the circumstances favor us. An attack should cause confusion, and the crossing units should lose some of their integrity in the process. There is a bridge on the main road which should act like a funnel and allow our strength to meet him while he is in only column strength.

"Surprise and numerical superiority and this terrain all favor us. Hood, your corps is here on the right. I would purpose to use you to sweep down, cross this little creek here, and then beyond, cross Peachtree Creek here. This should allow you to move west to strike Thomas in his preparations. If you can do that right, it should provide us with a clear and decisive victory. We should be able to push Thomas back to the river where his force would be trapped. We can add our corps in as Thomas is pushed to the west. Our fresh troops should be able to make life miserable as the Yankees retreat. This should work, and if not, we have a safe place to fall back to. This should get underway early in the day so that we have plenty of time to exploit the situation."

The plan made good sense to Hood. It was sound and seemed simple as plans go. Of course, all of war is bound up in chance, and nothing was ever as simple on the ground as it was on a piece of paper. There would be a stroke and a counterstroke. There would be the Union army moving and his army moving. The Army of Tennessee would need to be ready to move at the proper time. Hood had been around long enough to know that most plans, good as they are, seldom survive the first contact with the enemy. But one must still plan.

"General, thank you, sir, for preparing me in this manner. I have no questions but would be pleased to understand your ideas on the troops you think should be engaged. How will you use Hardee?" From there, the conversation continued, with Hood mostly listening.

After a few more comments, Hood was relieved to finally be able to dismiss himself from Johnston, as the interview had been stressful to both men. Hood left to wait for a reply from Richmond at his own headquarters.

The wait gave Hood time to reflect about the plan Johnston had outlined. Hood thought that if he were going to be in charge, he may be able to bring some spring back into the legs of these Confederate men and pull off the attack. But now all that relied on Davis' reply.

The sun beat down, and flies moved from one steaming pile of horse manure to the next. Then, without any warning, the reply was there. The paper was handed first to Hood and then to Hardee and Stewart:

RICHMOND, July 18, 1864.
General Hood:
Your telegram of this date received. A change of commanders, under existing circumstances, was regarded as so objectionable that I only accepted it as the alternative of continuing in a policy, which had proved so disastrous. Reluctance to make the change induced me to send a telegram of inquiry to the commanding general on the 16th instant. His reply but confirmed previous apprehensions. There can be but one question which you and I can entertain—that is, what will best promote the public good; and to each of you I confidently look for the sacrifice of every personal consideration in conflict with that object. The order has been executed, and I cannot suspend it without making the case worse than it was before the order was issued.
Jefferson Davis
(Same to Generals Hardee and Stewart.)

"Well, Hood, I suggest you go in and speak to General Johnston, don't you agree?" said Stewart.

Hood left without comment and sought another interview with General Johnston. As his aide left, Johnston suggested Hood sit.

Hood said, "General, the three of us—me, Hardee, and Stewart—appealed to President Davis to stay his order, but he has turned us down. Now, I appeal to you on my behalf and on behalf of the others. Put your orders in your pocket. Let's fight Sherman as you outlined earlier. You command the troops. Make this fight for the country, Atlanta, and the Army of Tennessee."

Johnston paused for a moment, seemingly thinking about Hood's request. "I will not. As I have said, the President has seen fit to relieve me from command. I will do nothing—nothing—unless the order is countermanded."

Hood leaned forward. "Sir, think of me and the great embarrassment I feel concerning this situation. I am nearly a stranger to this army. I don't even know the disposition of the various divisions. Outside of what you told me earlier, I do not know all of your immediate plans concerning us and the detailed strategy that you think can prevent Sherman from taking the city. Please, sir, stay here. Give me the benefit of your counsel and advice. Stay in command. The army needs you."

These were difficult words for Hood, and the thoughts were nearly impossible for him to express. General Johnston, in the emotion of the moment, nearly succumbed. But with moisture glistening in his eyes, he rejected Hood's plea.

"I will not," Johnston said as he rose. "Now, I must leave. My wife and I must go to Atlanta to see about getting to Macon. I will return."

After watching Johnston leave the room, Hood rejoined Hardee and Stewart and told them of his failure to convince Johnston to remain. Moments later, Johnston could be seen mounting his horse and moving off in the direction of Atlanta. Without a backward glance or a wave or salute, Johnston rode out of the yard. About 4:00 p.m., General and Mrs. Johnston boarded a train bound for Macon, some ninety miles to the south.

Hood and Johnston never saw each other again.

CHAPTER TWENTY-FIVE

Confederacy | THOMAS B. ROY

NEAR DEXTER NILES' HOUSE

JULY 18, 1864

LATE AFTERNOON

Thomas B. Roy had spent most of the afternoon waiting for his chief, Lieutenant General William Hardee, to complete his conference with the other two corps commanders and Johnston. Roy had come along with Hardee and some of the staff in case Hardee needed anything or thought it important to send a message to one of his division commanders.

Nothing of the sort had taken place, and little had interrupted the heat and near boredom that seemed to blanket the dusty yard. A couple of times during the long day, one or more of the generals had come out with a serious look. Exactly what was under discussion had not yet been shared with him, but the rumors of high command changes had snaked their way out onto the baked red clay where staff from all three corps as well as that of the Army of Tennessee sought shade and news.

Roy was no longer the clerk-turned-private-soldier who had left law school at the University of Virginia to join the Confederate army. As Hardee's chief of staff, he felt far more at ease than he ever did before. He had long since come to know that he had Hardee's complete confidence. Sometimes, he even wrote home to Hardee's new wife when Hardee ran out of time. Roy may be a colonel now, but regardless of his promotions, he still looked up to Hardee and admired him and always would.

Hardee was the first of the corps commanders out the door and came toward him with a hard, agitated look on his weathered face.

He held his black hat in his hand and slapped it against his leg as he moved rapidly away from the army headquarters.

"Let's go now," Hardee said as he placed his hat on his head and swung up onto the back of his horse Black Auster. The yard was now full of men standing at attention, horses snorting, and aides steadying mounts.

Roy thought it best to remain silent until he was asked to speak. Hardee broke the silence not a moment later. "You would not believe what has just occurred. President Davis has relieved General Johnston from command and appointed that pup Hood. Bragg had his hand in this. I know it, and this is little better than most of the rest of his decisions." Roughly, he urged his horse to walk. "Hood is largely a self-promoter, and I shall not serve under him."

Cutting off any possible reply, Hardee continued, "I am old enough to be Sam Hood's father and am well senior to him. This will not stand. It cannot."

"Sir, do you think they may recall you declined command of the army back in Dalton?"

"Maybe so, but by all that is holy, that was then, and now is now. Hood will grind this army up just to prove he is still the dashing and gallant Hood. It will get bloody with little to show for it—mark my words. This war is a hard row under the best of circumstances, which we haven't seen for some time now, and this will be the end of things. I will do my duty until I can be relieved, but this is a bad day for the cause."

CHAPTER TWENTY-SIX

Confederacy | JOHN HOOD

HEADQUARTERS ARMY OF TENNESSEE

LATE AFTERNOON

For the first time in his army career, Hood would not wait for orders—he had to prepare them. He could not complain about the content of the orders, for he alone was responsible. With this in mind, he wrote the following with his adjutant:

Headquarters Army of Tennessee,
In the Field, July 18, 1864

Soldiers: In obedience to orders from the War Department I assume command of the army and the department. I feel the weight of the responsibility so suddenly and unexpectedly devolved upon me by this position, and shall bend all my energies and employ all my skill to meet its requirements. I look with confidence to your patriotism to stand by me, and rely upon your prowess to wrest your country from the grasp of the invader, entitling yourselves to the proud distinction of being called the deliverers of an oppressed people.

Respectfully,

J.B. Hood,
General.

Hood then prepared a second message.

General Samual Cooper,
Adjutant and Inspector General:

I have assumed command of the Army and Department of Tennessee.

J.B. Hood.

(Same to President Davis.)

After, Hood was busy much of the afternoon and throughout the evening. He communicated with all three of the corps commanders, which now included Benjamin Franklin Cheatham. He felt his best accomplishment so far was keeping Hardee at Hardee's post and promoting Cheatham into the vacant corps command position of Hood's old corps. In addition, he spoke to Carter Stevenson and his cavalry commander, Wheeler. Hood began to feel increasingly confident about his readiness for the next day.

Hood retired to the beautiful twelve-column mansion belonging to William Herring. It was an appropriate place for the youngest and newest full general in the Confederacy—a grand headquarters for the gallant Hood. He was ambitious enough to enjoy the advantages of the position, whether he had won a battle yet or not.

With difficulty, he climbed the six brick steps. He smiled behind his beard, and a close observer would see a sparkle in his often-sad eyes. Standing on the veranda, he said, "Not much time to enjoy this—must get my plans together and communicated."

CHAPTER TWENTY-SEVEN

Confederacy | ISAIAH V. MOORE

COMPANY E, 37TH GEORGIA INFANTRY, TYLER'S BRIGADE, BATE'S DIVISION, HARDEE'S CORPS, EASTERN END OF THE CONFEDERATE TRENCHES OVERLOOKING CLEAR CREEK

JULY 18, 1864

LATE AFTERNOON

Sergeant Isaiah V. Moore was looking forward to the evening. It would be a little cooler then, and the light picket fighting off to his left and out in front of him would end, as long as everything went normally. It would be good to sit, put some food in his belly, and think of his sweet wife Elizabeth, his children, and his expanding farm back in Madison County, Georgia. Before it got dark, he would pen a few lines in his diary.

Sergeant Moore had enlisted on May 9, 1862, along with a number of men from his home county. There had been six companies originally. Together, the companies made up the 9th Battalion of Georgia Volunteers. They had gone into training camp in Knoxville, and by June of 1862, they were engaged in maneuvers and firefights in Tennessee. In those days, they knew little fear and shared a general belief that they would whip the Yanks and go home soon. Now, the volunteers knew death could come at any time and that the fight was going to be a long one.

Moore thought that perhaps he was not completely recovered from the severe sickness that had laid him low back on May 3. He had survived the hard fight at Dallas only to become sick just a day or two later. Sick was better than dead though. He had lost several friends in the charge his brigade had made around 4:00 p.m. on May 28. Griffith, Spurlock, Bill Wood, and one of the Dudleys had left this worldly life, and he would not see them again.

He had returned to duty via Macon, Atlanta, and Marietta from Eufaula, Alabama, where he had gone to recover. He had gotten back to Marietta in time to participate in the general retreat from Kennesaw Mountain back toward Smyrna and the River Line on the Chattahoochee. They had been moving pretty much all the time, interspersed with days of digging and some rest.

Of course, the big thing that had just happened was the removal of Johnston and the promotion of Hood. Moore wasn't certain the change marked an improvement. He had served under both Bragg and Johnston. From what Moore had seen, Johnston seemed to admire the advantage of the defense. There was something to be said for both Hood and Johnston, but it seemed to Moore that it was going to be hard, perhaps impossible, to send Billy Sherman and his well-fed Yankees back home if all they did was retreat.

Johnston had retreated for a long time. Moore's unit, the 37th Georgia, had been prepared to fight and move on April 29. Since that time, they had done just that. They had stood and fought and then backed up. They had crossed a lot of rivers since then and now lay on the north slope of the second ridgeline, south of Peachtree Creek. Clear Creek was on their right.

The army here was still essentially in the same order in line they had been in since they had crossed the Chattahoochee on July 9. Hardee's corps was still lined up with Bate's division on the right. Patrick Cleburne's boys were in the middle, and Walker was to Cleburne's left. Cheatham's division, under George Maney, was on the corps' far left.

Sergeant Moore was glad of the little shade that existed on the hillside. Later, maybe he could walk to the creek that ran down there to his right front and forget about the never-ending retreats. With Hood as commander, he thought that the ways of the past three months would change. Perhaps Hood would put them back into the fight. It would probably take Hood a while to feel competent to use the army in any meaningful manner, but with all the railroads meeting in Atlanta, the city had to be held. Hood would have to rise to the occasion, if he could.

This was a terrible war, especially from where Moore was standing. It seemed nearly certain to him that the Union, with all its advantages, would triumph in the end. He could see nothing of the enemy but knew they were moving toward Atlanta and would probably soon be on the banks of the Peachtree Creek. Moore could only hope that the

Yankees would make a mistake. Maybe they would be vulnerable when they were in the middle of crossing the creek.

When the war was over, he would be glad to get back to farming and raising his family and forgetting about all this death. He and Elizabeth wanted more children, and he hoped more would come. Lots of children were as important as lots of land. War was a young man's game, and while at thirty-three Moore didn't *feel* old, he was no longer young. He had seen too much and knew the fragility of human life.

CHAPTER TWENTY-EIGHT

Union | JOHN SCHOFIELD & WILLIAM SHERMAN

HEADQUARTERS OF THE MILITARY DIVISION OF THE MISSISSIPPI

HOME OF SAMUEL HOUSE AT THE INTERSECTION OF OLD CROSS KEYS AND PEACHTREE ROAD

JULY 18, 1864

Earlier in the day, the plump, short, and bald Major General John Schofield and his staff had arrived and established their headquarters at the plantation house of Samuel House. Schofield was only thirty-two years old and had been a classmate of both Hood and McPherson.

Schofield's keen, analytical mind was confident to a mathematical certainty that the Union was going to win this war, and if there were a subject he excelled in, it was mathematics. Schofield was ambitious, and he knew that confidence and ambition combined to create a calculus in which good performance and good friendship with the right people could form the foundation of a bright future in the army.

For these reasons, he had prodded Sherman to accept the hospitality he could offer at the fine red-brick mansion that was his headquarters. He had been waiting and was glad to see Sherman move to the veranda. Schofield keenly enjoyed the opportunity to rub elbows with his boss, and with their proximity, Schofield's own performance would be easy for Sherman to see. Beyond that though, Schofield genuinely admired Sherman and liked to be near him. He always learned something from Uncle Billy.

It was about mid-day when Sherman began sending and receiving messages after settling into the house. He wrote his first message to McPherson, whom he believed to be somewhere along Shallowford Road.

Sherman lit a cigar, sipped his coffee, and got down to writing to his friend.

Hdqrs. Military Division of the Mississippi
In the Field, on Peach Tree Road, July 18, 1864–12pm

General Mcpherson:

I am at Sam. House's, a brick house well known, and near Old Cross Keys. A sick negro the only human being left on the premise says we are eleven miles from Atlanta, five from Buck Head, and a sign board says ten miles to McAfee's Bridge and eleven to Roswell Factory. At this place the main Buck Head and Atlanta road is strongly marked and forks, the right–hand looking north going to McAfee's and the left to Roswell Factory. This left–hand road forks one mile from here, at Old Cross Keys, the main road going to Roswell and left–hand to Johnson's Ferry. The latter is the road traveled by us. I suppose all of Thomas' troops are at Buck Head, with advance guard down to Peach Tree Creek. I think I will move Schofield one mile and a half toward Buck Head, where the negro represents a road to Decatur and forward on that road a mile or so. I think Sam. House's is not far from the northwest corner of lot 273, and if I move him as contemplated he will be to–night about 202, 203. On our map a road comes from the direction of McAfee's toward Decatur, and if you can find position about 192, 191 it would best fulfill my purpose, but be careful to order Garrard to break the road to–day or to–night and report result. I will stay here or down at the forks of the road to–night. Schofield encountered nothing but cavalry, about 500, according to the negro's report, and all retreated toward Atlanta. Tell Garrard that it will be much easier to break the telegraph and road to–day and night than if he waits longer. This negro says there is a road leading to Stone Mountain from a Mr. Lively's, on the Decatur road, on which I suppose you to be. At any rate I will be here till evening and would like to hear from you.

Yours,

W.T. Sherman,

The afternoon wore on and became evening. It was still light, and the insect noises became more apparent as the camp noises began to subside. Sherman looked up at the incoming messenger. He knew from experience the message was from McPherson.

HDQRS. DEPARTMENT AND ARMY OF THE TENNESSEE,
Blake's Mill, Ga., July 18, 1864—9:30 p.m.

Maj. Gen. W. T. SHERMAN,

Commanding Military Division of the Mississippi:

GENERAL: Enclosed please find sketch of my position to-night and copy of Special Field Order, No. 70, paragraph VI, from these headquarters.

In pursuance of this order, the different commands were in motion promptly at the hour designated, the Seventeenth Corps closing up on the Fifteenth, and the Fifteenth and Sixteenth reaching a point about one mile from Bra-man's Court-House just as the last brigade of the cavalry was passing. The cavalry under Brigadier-General Garrard pushed on and struck the railroad, and five regiments were set to work to destroy it. A brigade of infantry of Morgan L. Smith's division, was also sent down, and the two forces together thoroughly destroyed over three miles of track, upsetting the ties, breaking the iron loose, piling up the ties, putting the iron on top, and setting fire to the pile. The whole of the Fifteenth Corps was marched to the immediate vicinity of Bra-man's Court-House, the Sixteenth to the point indicated on the map, and the Seventeenth to Blake's Mill, to be used as a reserve to re-enforce either flank in case the enemy advanced or was found in strong force. There being no water in the vicinity of Bra-man's Court-House just before dark, after the brigade returned from the railroad, the Fifteenth Corps marched to Henderson's Mill and went into camp.

There is no telegraph line along the railroad. During our operations we saw no indications of any heavy three of the enemy; nothing but cavalry, which fell back and disappeared readily on our approach.

Enclosed please find copy of report just received from General Garrard.

Very respectfully, your obedient servant,

JAS. B. McPHERSON,
Major-General

"Where is Blake's Mill located?" Sherman asked the messenger.

"Sir, the mill is two miles from the Rainey Plantation. It lies in the valley formed by the north part of Peachtree Creek," the messenger replied.

That plantation, Sherman knew, lay about three miles to the east of here.

"And which of his three corps is McPherson traveling with?"

"The Sixteenth Corps, sir."

"General Dodge then. Well, he is in good hands and in good company," Sherman said to no one in particular.

The messenger, nonetheless, felt compelled to reply, "Yes, sir. He certainly is."

"Go see my aide, Captain Dayton, and see if he has those orders finished. If so, why don't you take them back to General McPherson? Can you do that?"

"Yes, sir. I would be glad to do so. Thank you, sir."

HDQRS. MIL DIV. OF THE MISS.,
In the Field, near Cross Keys, GA
July 18, 1864.

The movements of the army to-morrow, July 19, will be as follows:

I. Major-General Thomas will press down from the north on Atlanta, holding in strength the line of Peach Tree, but crossing and threatening the enemy at all accessible points to hold him there, and also taking advantage of any ground gained, especially on the extreme right.

II. Major-General Schofield will move direct on Decatur and gain a footing on the railroad, holding it, and breaking the railroad and telegraph wire.

III. Major-General McPherson will move along the railroad toward Decatur and break the telegraph wires and the railroad. In case of the sounds of serious battle, he will close in on General Schofield, but otherwise will keep every man of his command at work in destroying the railroad by tearing up track, burning the ties and iron, and twisting the bars when hot. Officers should be instructed that bars simply bent may be used again, but if when red hot they are twisted out of line they cannot be used again. Pile the ties into shape for a bonfire, put the rails across and when red hot in the middle, let a man at each end twist the bar so that its source become spiral. General McPherson will dispatch General Garrard's cavalry eastward along the line of the railroad to continue the destruction as far as deemed prudent.

IV. All the troops should be in motion at 5 a.m., and should not lose a moment's time until night, when the lines should be closed on General Schofield about Pea Vine and Decatur.

By order of Maj. Gen. W.T. Sherman:
L.M. DAYTON
Aide-de Camp

CHAPTER TWENTY-NINE

Confederacy | JOHN HOOD

HEADQUARTERS OF THE ARMY OF TENNESSEE

JULY 18, 1864

LATE EVENING

Hood finished his report. It was short and to the point, but he knew it was important to keep Richmond informed. Information helped create trust, and trust—or the lack of it—was what had laid Johnston low. He would try to keep that from happening to him.

Near Atlanta, July 18, 1864.

Hon. Secretary of War:

The enemy advanced to-day on all the roads leading from Isham's Ford and Roswell, and established his line on Peach Tree Creek, his right resting on the Chattahoochee in the vicinity of the railroad, his left at Buck Head; our army about four miles from Atlanta, the creek intervening between the armies.

J. B. Hood,
General.

CHAPTER THIRTY

Union | JAMES MCPHERSON

Headquarters of the Army of the Tennessee

Blake's Mill, North Branch of Peachtree Creek

July 18, 1864

11:00 p.m.

It was pleasantly cool down in the valley by the running creek. There were the splashes of water from the mill wheel and the creaks and groans of the wood and metal mechanical devices that changed energy into usable goods. Frogs and insects were just beginning to grow silent.

McPherson had finished his correspondence with Sherman and had reviewed all the official matters and returns required of an army commander. His righteous sense of duty was satisfied. It was still possible he would hear from Sherman, but McPherson had done his part in communicating to him earlier. Right now, in the cool and quiet, the time was his.

His army was pushing hard toward Decatur and the Georgia railroad. He was executing a giant wheeling motion as he swung down and out to encompass Decatur and then back toward the west to reach Atlanta. Others might complain that his movement was too ordered, too meticulous. But, he knew there was a right way to move an army and a wrong way. It was especially important to move an army that was deep in enemy country and removed from any real support in a careful, planned way. His actions were based on his well-understood sense of organization.

Careful planning resulted in a strong personal sense of control. This control and the ability to think a problem through resulted in actions based on a plan. These predetermined actions were a simple, bright line in an otherwise confusing and complex world. As such, for him, events almost always ran smoothly, and major surprises were few.

The last three years had been a whirlwind of activity, mixed with the harsh reality of war and a very rapid rise through the ranks of his profession. He was a new captain in 1861. Then, he was pleased to become Halleck's aide-de-camp and assistant chief of engineers and was promoted to lieutenant colonel.

Early in 1862, McPherson became Grant's chief engineer, where he laid out deployment positions that aided in the taking of Fort Henry. McPherson also contributed to the ultimate victory at Shiloh and received praise from Grant for his activity and personal courage. Because of the backing of both Halleck and Grant, he was promoted to brigadier general of volunteers and placed in charge of the railroads in 1862.

McPherson had his first real chance to lead troops in the field near Corinth in October 1862. His display of strong leadership led to his promotion to major general. In December of that same year, Grant received permission to create five corps under his army. Thomas, Sherman, and McPherson were all selected to lead individual corps. In this role, McPherson participated in the attacks on Jackson and Vicksburg. He was the youngest and least experienced of the U.S. corps commanders, but nonetheless, he was often favorably compared to the best among them. Then came Grant's promotion to lieutenant general, Sherman's elevation to command the Western Theater, and McPherson's selection to command the Army of the Tennessee in early 1864. From captain to army commander in three years was spectacular to any standard.

In addition, McPherson was an extrovert. He ran his army in a more collegial manner than most commanders. He liked getting others' opinions and, as a result, heard from a lot of his subordinates. He liked people, and they liked him. This mutual regard included his superiors, such as Halleck, Sherman, and Grant.

Despite how busy he was, McPherson seldom missed a day in writing to Emily Hoffman, his fiancée. It was an exercise he cherished—the one personal bit of luxury he allowed himself to enjoy. Everything else was subordinate to doing the right thing and completing all of his professional military obligations.

Emily had entered his life in the spring of 1859. It was not just any spring. It had been spring in San Francisco at a party given by Senator

William Gwin and his wife. McPherson—thirty-one years old at the time, handsome, and often with a twinkle in his eyes—was having the time of his life. He had important work to do on the fortifications of San Francisco Bay, and a petite, vivacious, quick, beautiful, blue-eyed girl had captivated him. In his serious view of the world, she was a refined, generous, intelligent, Christian young lady. James and Emily spent considerable time together, and friendship became love.

These were unsettled times, however, and the great questions of the day—slavery and succession—were on everyone's mind and tongue. Even in far-away California, these great questions intruded on the couple and their plans. The Hoffman family was from Baltimore and displayed a strong, even rabid, Southern point of view. That Rebel spirit displayed itself in a letter to Emily from her mother, in which Emily's mother forbade Emily from marrying a man from the North.

Emily did not want to displease and upset her family, and McPherson was certain his prospects would soon improve. He had been selected for promotion to captain, and he would be able to provide more in the material way of things. But war had been on the horizon, and McPherson was ordered to return to the east. Despite their love, the young couple decided to postpone their marriage.

Now, McPherson sat dreaming, looking at Emily's picture. He wanted the war over, or at least suspended long enough for him to travel north to wed Emily. She had returned to Baltimore, and the marriage awaited only the presence of the groom. But duty always intervened. The letters sent and received had to substitute for the marriage and home they both desired.

In the quiet of the night, McPherson started his letter to Emily.

CHAPTER THIRTY-ONE

Confederacy | ABDA JOHNSON

40TH GEORGIA, CHEATHAM'S CORPS

TRENCHES NORTH OF ATLANTA

JULY 18, 1864

11:30 P.M.

The campfire burned down. Colonel Abda Johnson was tired and sleepy. He looked into the embers and supposed that the fire could be a metaphor for life: hot and bright at some point and cooling at the end. Life did not always go exactly as one might plan or desire. He knew a lot of what happened was in God's power, but he had never believed that a man couldn't influence the course one's life took—until the war.

He could remember all his plans and dreams about the good things to come when he was admitted to practice law in Georgia at the age of twenty-one. He had graduated from the University of Georgia and then read law for two years before admission. That was seventeen years ago.

War, as he had known even then, could rip the guts out of the future. He knew with certainty that it could literally kill one's life and, with it, all future. He had seen a mountain of ruined and killed futures over the last two years in the army. He prayed he and Fanny still had one though. Since their marriage in 1852, life for the two of them had been good and seemed often to be on an ever-improving plane.

Yet now he wondered where all this would be once the war was over. Would some military tribunal denounce him as a traitor to the United States? He had stood foursquare against secession, but it was impossible not to go along once the break came. His life was here in Georgia, for good or bad, and now he was deep in the war as a colonel.

If the truth be told, his natural ambition and competitiveness rejoiced at being promoted to colonel and at commanding the 40th Georgia.

Yet he did not enjoy the number of men and boys dead on both sides since the defense at Chickasaw Bayou, Vicksburg, Chattanooga, and now here on the north side of Atlanta.

If he understood it correctly, he was facing some of the same western Union troops he had seen at Vicksburg. The commanders may be different, but the units and the men were much the same. Those units must be thinned considerably, just as the Southern units were, but it seemed like the Union had a never-ending supply of men. Johnson felt their best chance was an attack earlier on, but that was gone now. Both sides had gotten better at killing, and it seemed there were a lot more soldiers on the other side.

With Brigadier General Marcellus Stovall sick so much of the time, Johnson was beginning to feel comfortable acting as the commander of the entire Georgia brigade, which his regiment was a part of. If he were able and kept putting himself forward, maybe in Stovall's absence, he would get promoted to brigadier general.

His thoughts turned homeward again, and he fastened his mind around his sweet wife Fanny. He was so close to home, but even now, the Union army lay between him and his wife. His eyes closed, and thirty-eight-year-old Abda Johnson slept.

CHAPTER THIRTY-TWO

Confederacy | SOLDIERS AT THE PICKET LINE

PICKETS FROM THE 1ST AND 27TH TENNESSEE

NORTH OF ATLANTA FORTIFICATIONS

NEAR PEACHTREE CREEK

JULY 18, 1864

The water gurgled as it passed over rocks and around snags on its way down the river. With so little rain, the watercourse was more than ample to take the flow of Peachtree Creek. Generally, pickets on both sides of the conflict choose permanent terrain features such as a creek to define the line between the warring parties. Peachtree Creek had been so chosen.

On the northern side, Yankee pickets sat and watched, and on the southern side, the ragtag Confederates did the same. Word of General Johnston's fall from grace traveled like wildfire through the Union soldiers. For some reason, the same news moved with less speed among the Confederate troops.

The normal exchange between the pickets was of a bantering and continuing nature and halted only when an officer of either army presented themselves. Then the formality of silence would take over until the officer left the picket line for a more important duty. The officers on both sides perhaps had more in common with each other than with the men they commanded.

"Johnny Reb, can you hear me?" said one Union soldier.

"Of course I can hear you. You blue boys sound like hogs looking for acorns over there."

"Well, we noisy hogs know something you boys don't, and we ain't going to tell."

"I doubt you know squat. Anyhow, you can't wait to tell me, if I am any judge."

"You boys are goners for sure now."

"Damn liar, we are right here."

"You may still be there, but General Johnston is gone home for good."

"What the hell y'all talkin' about?"

"I say Joe Johnston is relieved, and old one-legged Hood is the new commander of you Tennessee boys."

"Can't be true. Show yourself, Yank, so I can rid the world of one more liar. Step out, you lying coward."

Although pickets only infrequently exchanged shots across their no man's land, the preceding conversation was satisfactory reason for these two and their fellows to blaze away at each other for the rest of the day.

Time passed, evening fell, and noise was heard from the Confederate lines. A relief soldier was on his way with some food for the pickets. As he walked up to the first group, he said, "Boys, you will not believe it. All we have fought for is gone and lost. General Johnston has been relieved."

"That is what those damn lying Yanks told us," said one of the picketers.

"Well, this time, the blue bellies have gone and told the truth. Hood is now the head of the army."

"Well, goddamn. I quit. Tell Colonel Field I have gone home. I ain't about to fight for that crazy crippled bastard."

"Me too. I'll go with you," another picketer spoke.

Within minutes, three or four Tennesseans had dropped their rifles, gun tools, patches, and ammunition to the ground. "Give these to Hood or Jeff Davis. They will need all they can get with old Joe gone," said the first man as the group began to walk away.

No effort was made to stop the dispirited men. Within seconds, they had left the line and vanished into the trees.

Sentiment in favor of Johnston was uneven within the Army of Tennessee. Some men remembered the winter in Dalton and how things had improved once Johnston had arrived. New battle flags, new shoes, and new weapons had all pointed to a new day. Soldiers are often critical of their general's tactical and strategic decisions, but most in the Army of Tennessee believed the Union army had paid a higher price in blood and dead for the real estate they had won than had the retreating Southern army.

Each man had his own feelings. Some retained the high hopes they had held in the spring. Others watched the sickness, death, and wounds of their comrades and had slowly lost heart. Many who had been content to follow orders and keep their own counsel for the last two months were now questioning, sometimes silently and sometimes out loud to their fellows, as to whether a plan would work and if it were worth it. The army was still a formidable force, but desertion was an increasing problem.

It varied from unit to unit. Evidence now shows that desertion, the most advanced form of demoralization, was perhaps worse in those units who had surrendered earlier at Vicksburg and returned to the fray. Likewise, desertion was high among Georgia troops, many of whom probably thought they could get home and make a positive contribution to their families. Some days found as many as three hundred men leaving what seemed an impossible situation. For many, Johnston's departure was the nudge they needed.

July 19, 1864

CHAPTER THIRTY-THREE

Confederacy | FRANK CHEATHAM

HEADQUARTERS OF CHEATHAM'S CORPS

JULY 19, 1864

The situation seemed confusing to Frank Cheatham. Not only had Joe Johnston, a man Cheatham and his troops held in high regard, left, but Cheatham also was no longer with his Tennessee division under Hardee, the division he had been at home with. There, he had been confident that he understood Hardee and his expectations and that he knew what his boys from Tennessee could do in a fight. Within his previous division, Cheatham was "Old Frank," one of the boys. Now suddenly, Cheatham was in a new situation. The comfort of the familiar was behind him and now only made the new responsibilities as acting commander of Hood's old corps seem even more daunting.

Cheatham was forty-three years old upon this appointment. His had been a life of adventure. His family had been in America for eight generations and had arrived in Virginia and over time moved to Tennessee. Politics, business, farming, and the law were generally their endeavors, and it was on the plantation of Westover, created by his great-grandfather, that Frank Cheatham was born and raised. Cheatham attended college in Lebanon, Tennessee. With the outbreak of hostilities with Mexico, he had been elected captain of a company within the Nashville Blues, which ultimately became part of the 1st Tennessee. Fighting for Monterrey, Cheatham was in the center of the victorious action. He was also part of Winfield Scott's expedition to Vera Cruz.

Upon returning home, Cheatham organized a new regiment of volunteers and was elected colonel of the newly formed 3rd Tennessee. For a while, he was the acting commander of a brigade of three regiments. Much to Cheatham's disappointment, these activities were not recognized by promotion to brigadier general. Only twenty-eight at the time, Frank was ambitious and believed he would have made a most satisfactory brigadier general. Following the end of the war, California beckoned. Cheatham and a partner opened a store, hotel, and restaurant in Stockton, California. Cheatham was quite handy with a handgun and was part of a vigilante force in the wide-open California gold fields. He returned home and was recognized by promotion to major general in the Tennessee Militia. He also engaged farming.

At the outbreak of the Civil War, the state of Tennessee formed an army. Cheatham was appointed quartermaster and placed in charge of a training camp in Tennessee. Here, he organized nine regiments in the early days of the conflict. Then, under General Gideon Pillow, he took part in the invasion of Kentucky. At Belmont, Cheatham and some of the regiments he had trained tangled with some 3,000 troops under Grant, who he had known from their service in Mexico. In March of 1862, Cheatham assumed command of an entire division, which he led successfully at Shiloh against his friend Grant. Yet he was wounded and lost three horses in the battle, and his division lost nearly one-third of its operational strength.

Despite all his military accomplishments, Cheatham's lack of a West Point education, his near-charismatic leadership, and his well-known taste for liquor combined to place Cheatham at odds with one of his peers: Bragg, who was a more decorous, old-school commander. By his home state troopers, Cheatham was known as one of the boys and would occasionally become personally involved in the discipline of his soldiers. Rather than relying on the institutions established for the good order and discipline, Cheatham would offer to fight. He could cuss, ride a fast horse, drink, fight, and shoot, and his men held him in high regard. He led by example and took the same risks he ordered others to follow.

None of this sat well with Bragg, who was regarded as humorless and sour. The two commanders were nearly polar opposites, and the hearty, personal "Old Frank" was very nearly unfit for any command in Bragg's view. As for Hood, well, Hood and Bragg were generally together. The negative feelings between Bragg and Cheatham carried over to the relationship between Hood and Cheatham.

Nonetheless, merit and Hardee's recommendation resulted in Cheatham becoming the acting commander of Hood's old corps. Cheatham was, in many ways, an ideal and successful political or volunteer general. These generals were needed as much in the South as they were in the North, especially those who grew as they climbed from position to position. They were never viewed as quite satisfactory—not as good as a professional, West-Point-trained officer. However, they were the best available. Without them, the initial troops would never have been raised or trained, and the war would have been over before it started. Cheatham had been selected over Cleburne, and that said a lot.

Cheatham had always sought out new situations, but this one had found him. In his new corps, there were some 14,000 troops from Alabama, South Carolina, Mississippi, and Tennessee. On top of that, there were boys from Georgia, North Carolina, Virginia, and Louisiana—troops from nearly the entire Confederacy. It would continue to be Hood's corps until Cheatham made an imprint on it. That might take longer than it would for his old division to become known as Maney's division. It would have been an easier transition if his promotion had been to command the corps his division was a part of. Here, he was a complete stranger.

The corps was composed of three divisions. Thomas Hindman's division had been commanded by Brigadier General John C. Brown, a fellow Tennessean, since July 11, about eight days ago. Alexander Stewart's old division was headed by Henry Clayton, a lawyer active in Alabama politics and a Mexican War veteran. Then, there was Stevenson's division under forty-seven-year-old Carter Stevenson, who was a Virginian and regular army officer with a West Point education. Stevenson had been a major general since October of 1862 and had been captured, paroled, and exchanged at Vicksburg.

First impressions could be misleading Cheatham knew, but most of the men in Stevenson's four brigades had known defeat at Vicksburg, and to some degree, defeat seemed to cling to them still. The division was probably weaker than it should be. However, Stevenson's leadership and that of his subordinates had improved day by day. To Cheatham, the division had to be judged as at least average.

Since crossing the Chattahoochee on July 9, the Army of Tennessee had taken position along a nearly six-mile front. The line ran essentially from west to east, out about three and a half miles from the center of Atlanta. These entrenchments had been constructed sometime before and blocked advancement from the north. There were two lines of defense. The Confederate forces occupied the outermost northern line of works. Behind this line was a complete ring of earthworks that lay about one and a half miles from the center of Atlanta. This innermost ring could be besieged. The outermost line could be flanked. A line running toward the railroad provided a defense to the east of the city.

The fortifications lay to the south of Peachtree Creek and on the elevated ground above the valley. When Hood had left the corps, the operative plan had been to block the Union forces coming from the northwest. Accordingly, the three corps had spread out along the long east-west front. It was not until July 19 that most of the troops, who had crossed the Chattahoochee, were to be found facing the enemy, or at least the direction the enemy was expected from.

The enemy force, who were slowly moving in from Decatur off to the east, were not as close and were probably fewer in number, so the threat was seen as more notional than that posed by Thomas' Army of the Cumberland. The more notional the threat, the more apathetic the response. Hence the Confederate force, which should have shifted to confront Schofield and McPherson, was spread thin and was only now beginning to arrive.

Arthur Manigault's brigade was headquartered in the beautiful, nearly completed home of Troup Hurt. The two-story home sat facing the Decatur road and the railway, which ran beside it. The railway lay nearly three miles south from the point where the east-west line turned ninety degrees and began its southern run.

Forces grew by accretion from very little on July 18 to a line that extended from below the railroad to Bald Hill, about a mile and a half further south. This lengthened line would grow until it contained the three divisions belonging to Frank Cheatham, two divisions of Hardee's corps, and most of Wheeler's slender command of horsemen. Behind this formidable force were the Georgia Militia and a substantial number of cannons. The number of soldiers on this north-south line would peak on the night of July 21, nearly 72 hours from this point. Then, the number would dissipate to form for the next phase.

For now, Cheatham's forces were bunched from east of Clear Creek and around the defensive shoulder to the south. Stevenson's division adjoined Bate's division. Clayton's division with units from Brown's troops was to the right, trickling down toward the railroad. The density of men was the greatest on the east-west line with far fewer soldiers per running foot of trenches down toward the rail line.

Cheatham believed Wheeler was someplace on his right flank but well to the east. The mounted troopers were there to protect the eastern side of the city and Cheatham's right flank as well as to delay, harass, and hinder the advancing Federals.

Two Federal armies, the Army of the Ohio and the Army of the Tennessee, were both well on their way to doing just that. The Army of the Ohio was swinging down from Solomon Goodman's house and would soon tuck in north of Decatur. McPherson's army was moving further to the east to come into Decatur and then west toward Atlanta. As spread out as the three corps of McPherson's Army of the Tennessee were, if their advance were unchecked, they would pass the right flank of Cheatham's corps—where Cheatham's flank just petered out and was in the air.

CHAPTER THIRTY-FOUR

Union | WILLIAM SHERMAN

Headquarters of the Military Division of the Mississippi

Home of Sheriff James O. Powell

July 19, 1864

Sherman, moving with Schofield's Army of the Ohio, had ridden some eight to ten miles from the plantation mansion of Sam House to the house of James Powell, otherwise known as the county's sheriff. Both Sherman and Schofield had then established their headquarters at the home.

It had been an eventful day. Sherman's ordinary restlessness had been exacerbated after learning that Johnston had been relieved and Hood appointed in his place. In Sherman's mind, this action was a confirmation that conditions would soon change.

Sherman sent and received a substantial message flow as a result. Tied with the news came a greater level of uncertainty about how his right, under Thomas, was separated from the two smaller armies that made up the Federal left.

Sherman wanted something to happen and believed that a pent-up energy was building behind the fortification of the city. Sherman sent four messages to Thomas, explaining in detail the disposition of the Federal forces and encouraging Thomas to be in the position to help the left wing if the need arose. In addition, Sherman sent his twenty-nine-year-old Inspector General and Brigadier General John M. Corse to Thomas to personally explain the situation and to ensure that Thomas understood it with certainty. At the same time, he sent Thomas a message requesting information about the disposition of his Army of the Cumberland.

When Sherman finally heard from Thomas at 3:30 in the afternoon, Sherman was delighted but immediately peppered Thomas for more information. Sherman sent his last personal message to Thomas a little after eight in the evening. Satisfied that Thomas understood the line that his entire forces lay on, Sherman directed that Special Field Order No. 39 be published.

HDQRS. MIL. DIV. OF THE MISS.,
In the field near Decatur, Ga.,
July 19, 1864

The whole army will move on Atlanta by the most direct roads to-morrow, July 20, beginning at 5 a.m., as follows:

I. Major-General Thomas from the direction of Buck Head, his left to connect with General Schofield's right about two miles northeast of Atlanta, about lot 15, near the houses marked as "Hu" and "Col. Hoo."

II. Major-General Schofield by road leading from Doctor Powell's to Atlanta.

III. Major-General McPherson will follow one or more roads direct from Decatur to Atlanta, following substantially the railroad.

Each army commander will accept battle on anything like fair terms, but if the army reach within cannon-range of the city without receiving artillery or musketry fire he will halt, form a strong line, with batteries in position, and await orders. If fired on from forts or buildings of Atlanta no consideration must be paid to the fact that they are occupied by families, but the place must be cannonaded without the formality of a demand.

The General-in-chief will be with the center of the army, viz, with or near General Schofield.

By order of Maj-Gen. W.T. Sherman.
L.M. DAYTON,
Aide-de-Camp.

Throughout the day, the yard around the Powell Place was the scene of much activity. Messengers rode in and out, and staff officers moved as though the outcome of the war depended on them. Even during all this commotion, Sherman's staff found the time and the willingness to provide medical attention to Sheriff Powell's sick child, and the Powell family was treated with courtesy.

CHAPTER THIRTY-FIVE

Confederacy | JOSEPH WHEELER

HEADQUARTERS OF WHEELER'S CAVALRY CORPS

DECATUR

JULY 19, 1864

These were long, hot days. Even with his youthful energy, enthusiasm, and inexhaustible eagerness to please, Wheeler was tired. With only about 1,600 men in his command, he was stretched thin. The focus of his activities had shifted over the past two days from watching the river approaches to the west to delaying actions on Peachtree Road and on the roads leading to Decatur.

Sometimes, the engagements were hit-and-run affairs. Often, however, they were dismounted infantry actions that took hours. Generally, the hours were spent backing up from one position to another, with delaying the Yankees being the only realistic goal. There were always losses—ten men here, twenty-five men there. He knew his soldiers always gave as good as they got, but they were hard or nearly impossible to replace, and the Federal opposition seemed to grow a little each day.

It seemed as if the Federals were, nonetheless, battered by the end of each day. Yesterday was a good example. In fighting down Peachtree Road, they had charged and captured some sixty Union prisoners, and clearly, their actions slowed the Union tide. Despite that, by the time it was mid-day, the Yanks had managed to push across to the south bank of Peachtree Creek, and Wheeler had to move his slender command to the Confederate right, out around Decatur.

It was clear they were being pushed around, and their situation was made worse, in the minds of many, when the troops learned General Johnston had been replaced by Hood. By then, it had been a long day.

Wheeler had received messages from Hood from about noon onward. During all that time, he was warmly engaged with the lead elements of McPherson's Army of the Tennessee as it pushed its way slowly into Decatur.

The first message received read:

Headquarters Army of Tennessee
July 19th, 11 a.m.

Major-Gen. Wheeler
Commanding Cavalry Corps
General:

General Hood directs me to inform you that, unless circumstances now not seen should prevent, General Hardee and General Stewart have been ordered to attack the enemy at one o'clock p.m. to-day.

General Cheatham on the right is ordered to hold in check any force of the enemy which may advance in that direction, and you are desired to give all the aid in your power to General Cheatham to carry out this part.

Most respectfully,
A.P. MASON,
Maj. and A.A.G.

The second message arrived around 3:30 p.m. and read:

HEADQUARTERS ARMY OF TENNESSEE
Near Atlanta, July 19, 1864, 2:15 p.m.

Major-General Wheeler
Commanding Cavalry Corps:

General Hood directs me to acknowledge the receipt of your note in which you express the opinion that the extreme left of the enemy's infantry is moving toward Decatur. It is important to get exact information of the state of affairs in that vicinity at nightfall. He therefore requests you to send your best scouts close in, so as to ascertain whether the left of the enemy's infantry crosses Peachtree Creek, where it rests, and what is its strength, and notify him of the result.

Very respectfully,
T.B. MACKALL,
Aide-de-Camp.

Then, as the shadows became longer, Wheeler received another:

HEADQUARTERS, ARMY OF TENNESSEE.
July 19, 1864, 3:30 p.m.

Major—Gen. Wheeler
Commanding Cavalry Corps.
GENERAL:
Your dispatch about the force pressing you is received. General Hood directs that you will hold the enemy in check as much as possible and strike him as you think best.
Yours most respectfully,
A.P. Mason
Major and Assistant Adjutant General

Wheeler was disconcerted to some degree. He supposed it was difficult to understand fully what the national army was thrusting at him without their seeing it for themselves. This assault was no half-hearted attempt by the Union but the weight of several veteran corps. They were in Decatur, and from his own prepared positions, he knew tomorrow would be full of danger.

A last message arrived, directing Wheeler to meet with Hood and the other corps commanders as soon as he could. Several of his earlier communications from Hood had been confusing, but his summons was clear enough, so he moved down the Decatur road toward Atlanta.

CHAPTER THIRTY-SIX

Confederacy | PROSPER BOWE

SHALLOWFORD ROAD NEAR DECATUR

JULY 19, 1864

AFTERNOON

The ten companies of the 66th Illinois Infantry Regiment were all part of the 1st Brigade of the 2nd Division of the Sixteenth Army Corps of the Army of the Tennessee. When asked about their organization, the men in the 66th liked to say that they were in the 66th of the 1st of the 2nd of the 16th. It was particularly satisfying to say it very rapidly, and they practiced until it was natural. The regiment was made up of men from at least sixteen states. However, most of the men came from Illinois, and a substantial number came from Missouri. As sharpshooters, all carried the wonderful 16-shot Henry repeating rifle.

As private Prosper Bowe moved through the underbrush on this very hot afternoon, he remembered with a little humor the organizing advertisement that had lured him into the army. His friend Sergeant Lorenzo "Ren" Baker carried two of the advertisements with him, which he had cut out from the *Missouri Democrat*. He had picked them up from one of the soldiers in Company A and tried to convince Bowe that the two ads were of a historical nature and accordingly should be preserved. Bowe wasn't sure he agreed with his friend, but either way, he didn't much care. He mostly wanted to stay alive so that he could have a future. History didn't matter.

The advertisements had made the opportunity to join Birge's Western Sharpshooters seem more like a walk in the fall woods than how the adventure had turned out. He could see them in his mind's eye.

SHARP SHOOTERS!

WINCHESTER MODEL 1873

A REGIMENT OF SHARPSHOOTERS IS being organized in this Military Department to be commanded by Col. Birge. It is expected that this will be the crack Regiment of the West and those who are desirous of joining such a corps are requested to call at Headquarters corner of Fourth and Olive streets, where all information in relation to their distinct organization can be obtained.

This Regiment is to act upon its own responsibility, and each man for himself with his rifle as his companion. Let the SHARP SHOOTERS come on.

Birge's Western SHARP SHOOTERS!

THOSE WHO ARE ACCUSTOMED TO THE use of a Rifle, a fine chance is now open. A squad of ten men or more in any of the Western States will be transported to St. Louis. The Regiment will be furnished with the LONG RANGE AMERICAN RIFLE and a Navy Revolver. Backwoodsmen and Hunters desired. A prize of a fine Rifle will be given to the best shot in each company, and a Silver Medal to the second best. A splendid mounted Rifle worth one hundred dollars will be given to the best shot in the Regiment. Commissioned officers will not compete for any of the prizes. For further information address

Col. J. W. BIRGE
Sharp Shooters, St. Louis, MO., Box 3481
Western papers please copy.

When originally organized, the idea was that this unit was to be composed of those who were keen of sight and were able marksmen. These were to be men who understood the advantage of hitting what they aimed at and appreciated what the rifling in the barrel of a firearm did for accuracy. It was hard to believe some military professionals were convinced that the massed fire of unrifled muskets against infantry was superior to the aimed fire of a trained rifleman. It was true that one could load an unrifled musket a little faster than a rifled one since the rifled barrel gripped the round tighter, but rounds from rifled muskets tended to hit more people.

Men of demonstrated marksmanship were rare enough that no single state could come up with sufficient men to form an entire regiment. As a result, states sent companies. Most of the men came from the eight western states of Iowa, Illinois, Indiana, Michigan, Minnesota, Missouri, Ohio, and Wisconsin. The result was that the regiment was, on a small scale, much like the composition of the Army of the Tennessee. In addition, there were a small number of Union-loving men from Alabama, Georgia, and Tennessee.

In the beginning, the unit had been claimed by both Illinois and Missouri. It continued to be called Birge's Western Sharpshooters until the addition of Company K. With the addition of this tenth company, which had been organized as the 3rd Independent Company of Ohio Volunteer Sharpshooters under Captain George Taylor, the regiment became the 14th Missouri. Later, in 1862, it was transferred to Illinois and became the 66th Illinois. This was a regiment made up of veterans. They had been with Grant at Cairo, Illinois, and fought at Donelson and Shiloh. They were at the siege at Corinth and the battle of Iuka, and they had fought well against the guerrilla forces in Mississippi.

Bowe trudged onward. With grim humor, he thought about how this adventure was damn certain no walk in the fall woods. It was as hot as one could imagine, as it had to be a hundred degrees. It had been nearly as hot at Rome Cross Road back in May—not hot because of the weather, but hot because of the killing rifle and musket fire. He had seen Captain Taylor's body. Taylor had been hit square in the forehead. Colonel Buke and Major Campbell were also killed, and his friend Ren was hit hard in the left foot. That was the kind of wound a man wanted to get. It would keep him out of the brush along the road to Decatur.

"Not many Rebs out today. I guess they got the good sense to stay in the shade on a day like today," he said half to himself and half to anyone in earshot. He continued to move through the open area.

They had reached the river on July 10 and then crossed it and thrown up some earthworks on the south side of the river. In just two days, they had marched from Sandtown, on the extreme right of the army, to Roswell, now on the far end of the left. Sometimes, Bowe wished he were on horseback, but he was as used to walking as a man could be. That was a good thing because he still had some walking left to do.

CHAPTER THIRTY-SEVEN

Confederacy | JOHN HAGAN

COMPANY K, 29TH GEORGIA, HARDEE'S CORPS

CONFEDERATE TRENCHES SOUTH OF PEACHTREE CREEK ON THE HIGH GROUND

JULY 19, 1864

10:00 P.M.

On July 19, there had been two disappointments in the life of First Sergeant John Hagan of the K Company of the 29th Georgia. The first disappointment to befall him was the news that General Johnston had been removed from command of the Army of Tennessee. Hagan had experienced his first real combat about a year ago around Jackson, Mississippi, as part of Johnston's army. As he remembered it, Johnston had been full of confidence about "fixing Grant's Union army." Events conspired to modify Johnston's spirit and to cause him to retreat. For one, Vicksburg fell to that same Union army. Hagan believed that Johnston cared for his troops, but he did seem to go backwards more often than not, especially at what Hagan thought to be critical times. Still, it was a shock to learn that Johnston was gone from command and General Hood was in charge. To Hagan, it seemed like his own corps commander, Hardee, would have been a better choice.

The second disappointment was more personal and was a greater loss. He had convinced himself, and was now as certain as he could be, that the box that he so desired was either lost or stolen. Back on July 12, just one week before, he had written his wife Amanda about all the good things she should pack in a box and send to him to eat. He had requested, and since had thought about often, a bottle of syrup, some honey, rich cakes, and some vegetables. He explained in his letter that the box must be nailed and bound to survive its trip to him. He had even worked out a way for the box to make its way to him. It could reach him using his cousin, D.P. McDowell, who would bring the box upon his return from furlough.

The departure of Johnston and the failure of the box to arrive had combined to create a miserable condition for the normally curious and cheerful Hagan. He was covered in gloom as he relaxed in the trenches that defined the outer limits of Confederate authority around the city of Atlanta.

At his first opportunity, he would write Amanda and inquire about his cousin and as to the possible whereabouts of his much-anticipated box and all the good things to eat that no doubt it would contain. He was not hungry, but he was tired of cornbread and bacon. He longed for the sweet taste of the honey and syrup.

John Hagan was twenty-seven years old, and after his long stay in the hospital in LaGrange, he was now in good health. He had been in more serious fighting over the past several months than at any time since he had joined the army. In some strange way, he was enjoying himself. He had found he was good at fighting and liked running the company in the captain's absence. He was unsure if he had killed anyone yet, but if he hadn't, it was not for lack of effort or intent. On the other hand, he had been hit twice. Both times were by a spent round, so no real hurt came of it.

He knew the continuous falling back had been bad for the morale of some of his fellow soldiers, but now, with the entire corps drawn up together, he knew they were in great shape and wished the Yankees would attack them in their entrenchments. Those who were still despondent at this point, when the showdown seemed near at hand, were those who were always unhappy and always complaining. He was ready—not excited—but ready the way a veteran should be. If the fight came his way, he was confident he and his company of south Georgia boys would fight well.

His regiment and the other five Georgia units made up Steven's Georgia Brigade under the command of Brigadier General Clement H. Stevens. Stevens had led the brigade with success from Chickamauga until now. He was a fighter, and Hagan liked that.

There had been heavier firing than was normal in front of them during the day. One could feel that certain military tightness in the air that forecasted an impending clash. It was like the feeling in the air before a rainstorm. For a while before, Hagan had become concerned that the army would fall back and leave Atlanta to the Yankees. Then, his thoughts matured to the point that he figured Johnston had a plan to let a number of the Union forces cross the river, but only the number that the Confederates could defeat in detail. With Hood in command, Hagan just plain felt a hard fight coming.

He thought that he would write his good wife now. Adequate paper was hard to come by, but he had found some earlier. He enjoyed writing to Amanda and liked to tell her what was going on and to give her advice about the farm and finances. Writing put him in the mind of home, and it was a good way to end the day.

The camp was becoming quiet. The cook fires were now just bright beds of coals winking in competition with the lightning bugs. The sounds of the nocturnal summer concert performed by the tree frogs and a variety of insects swelled in volume as he finished his writing and spread his blanket.

CHAPTER THIRTY-EIGHT

Confederacy | HOMER HOWARD

COMPANY H, 43RD GEORGIA, STOVALL'S BRIGADE,

CLAYTON'S DIVISION

CHEATHAM'S SALIENT

JULY 19, 1864

EVENING

Captain Homer Howard sat with his back to a tree. Howard was thirty-four years old and, in his mind, no longer a young man. He didn't care for Lincoln's Yankee government one bit, especially that part that shot at him with such great regularity.

He was also accustomed to hard outdoor farm work. As a result, he was lean and strong. He stood about five feet and seven inches tall, was well muscled, and displayed a quiet dignity. He had been born in Georgia and was the youngest child of Hardy Howard. His father had moved from South Carolina in search of more and better dirt. The better dirt had been found in the rich bottomland along the Middle Oconee River, which ran through the southeastern part of Jackson County. The family prospered on the plantation, which lay only a few miles south of the town of Jefferson, Georgia. The old man had died some five years before at the ripe old age of eighty-two, and while Homer still missed his father, the old man had lived a full life. This was especially poignant to Homer when he watched young men, boys really, die on a nearly daily basis from wounds or disease. His father's life had not been easy, but he had left them with more than they had started with. And there were more Howards now than before. All in all, his father had plenty to be thankful for.

So far, the Howard family had been relatively fortunate in this war. Only his brother's son, John, had been lost, having died on September 11, 1862, at Second Manassas as a Confederate. If young John had lived, he would have been twenty-three on that day. John had grown up more as a kid brother to Homer since they had been raised in the same household. As a result, the loss was greater than it otherwise might have been. It was difficult to know that they would never again spend time together, and he wished John had not had to suffer and die with none of his family present.

He was left with a heavy sadness. John had been serving with the 18th Georgia as part of Hood's division in Longstreet's corps. On August 29, 1862, little more than two years ago, Hood's division had banged headlong into General John Hatch's Union soldiers, and his John was one of its casualties on the second day of that hard fight in Virginia. It seemed ironic to Howard that he had served in Hood's corps until yesterday, the same Hood whom his dead nephew had fought with when he died.

Two of Howard's other nephews were with him as part of his command in Company H of the 43rd Georgia. He liked being able to keep an eye on Green Duke and Harper Howard but was, at the same time, worried all three Howard males could die in one unlucky event. For that reason, and so as not to appear to show favoritism to family members, he tried to remain away from the two boys.

Company H, or Howard's Company as Homer liked to think of it, had been formed in March of 1862. To tell the truth, the day he was elected captain and commander was one of the proudest days of his life. He believed he had solid leadership, and he had learned to be a good soldier. His was one of eleven companies from Jackson County. In those less severe days, the men from the county had joined what they all called the Jackson Blues. It wasn't long before that idyllic name gave way to the more martial 43rd Georgia Volunteer Infantry. He and his company had been in every major battle of the Confederate Army of Tennessee.

The last ninety days or so had seemed to be a nearly continuous fight as Johnston had skillfully retreated. It had been fight and march, fight and march. Each step closer to Atlanta had worked at the men who hoped for an opportunity of a stand-up fight. The Federal force, which stayed after them, was massive and very well armed. From what he had seen, the Yanks across the way seemed a lot like the gray-clad boys he was with.

Even now, inside the outer defenses of Atlanta, the unit seemed to be constantly on the move. They had crossed the Chattahoochee River on the night of July 9, just ten days ago. They had marched down the road toward Atlanta and passed the little white house where General Johnston had his headquarters. They had moved about three miles south from the river that night before going into camp. Since then, they had moved to Walker's Mill near Peachtree Road, moving a little every day. On this day, they were about a mile east from Walker's Mill and beyond Clear Creek.

Their current outer defensive line, as best he could understand it, ran from Casey's Hill back to the west, near where they had crossed the river. It ran from there for about five and a half miles in an easterly direction. On that line, they had looked north to face the Yanks. His unit occupied the high ground and overlooked a shallow valley and another ridge beyond.

Rumor had it that somewhere out there was McPherson's army moving toward Atlanta. The ditches they found were only half finished. The regiment had set about improving the works along the portion of the line they occupied. It was clear that those who had dug the trenches had never intended to fight from them. They needed great improvement, and they received it.

There hadn't been much to eat for the past several days. Given all the marching, the digging, and the heat, Howard thought he weighed the least amount since that horrible starving time in Vicksburg. He wished the war would be over so that he could get back to eating vegetables and not being concerned with unnatural death every day. But he was in it until the end. A strong independent streak ran through Howard, as it did with many people who relied on themselves to prosper. Staying until the end was the right and honorable thing to do, and he could do no less. Men had to stand and be counted.

July 20, 1864

CHAPTER THIRTY-NINE

Confederacy | JOHN HOOD

HEADQUARTERS OF THE ARMY OF TENNESSEE

JULY 20, 1864

6:30 A.M.

Because of his old injuries, Hood did not rise to greet the four subordinate Southern generals as they entered. Custom of the service and his own personal code demanded he rise to meet his guests, but his lack of mobility prevented him. The generals understood, and he was excused from such customs. The sun had not yet risen, so there was coolness to the Georgia morning. Hot coffee was presented to the three infantry corps commanders and Wheeler, commander of the cavalry. Lips pursed and blew over the edges of the cups before the first tentative sips were taken. It was good. The coffee also helped start the meeting by sanding some of the roughness from the edges of personality and circumstance.

If there could have been more morning meetings like this between these five men, then the future may have been brighter. Perhaps the men could have learned to develop trust, appreciation, loyalty, and a smooth coordinated way of working together. With more time and more cool Georgia mornings, success may have been more likely.

Hood, who possessed the least amount of solid command time of the group, sat uncomfortably before them. Hood knew how he had gotten to this place. Even with his own somewhat flexible character, he knew what it had taken to feed his ambition. He also knew ambition could only take a man so far. Was there a hint of doubt lurking deep in his unconsciousness? He at least was less certain than he might have wished. Perhaps the same doubt he had felt when facing Johnston represented itself. Uncertainty caused his fundamental personality to assert itself, and the need to act began to dominate. He had a plan, and his hunger for action demanded the plan be executed.

Hood had received the intelligence from Wheeler to the effect that Sherman was on the move. Hood knew that the Union force had been split into three unequal parts, but not of Sherman's plans. To him, the most direct threat seemed to be the Yankee force moving toward Peachtree Creek. That force seemed to cover more than a mile and a half of his nearly six-mile north-facing front and lay only about two miles from his fortification.

The Union forces moving toward Atlanta from the east must also be confronted. To do this, he proposed Cheatham move the three divisions under his command to the right. In addition, the four brigades of Georgia Militia under Major General Gustavus Smith would cooperate with Cheatham. He felt that this force would be enough to hold back the secondary Union force. It was important, as he repeated to the commander, that Hardee remain in contact with Cheatham so that they present a seamless front.

Hood was unsure about the exact size and composition of the troops moving in from Decatur, but he was sure his former corps could repel the Union soldiers approaching from the northeast. Hood expressed the belief that the dismounted cavalry men and the old men and boys of the militia should be adequate to hold this smaller tide.

The primary Union force that Hood had to move against was under the command of Major General George Thomas, the same troops Johnston had urged him to attack earlier. Thomas was deemed slow by some, but few believed that his army would be easy to move, let alone rout, once it had time to position itself.

Hood looked up from the map and asked for comments from those standing around the table. Nothing was forthcoming, so he pressed ahead. His plan was not wholly different from the one Johnston had outlined to him. He would use the combined forces of the two corps, and they would begin the attack on their right. As the first troops moved out and made contact, their success would be followed by a smooth rippling attack by echelon. This meant that each brigade would rotate a bit to its left as it attacked and as a result would roll up Thomas' troops and drive them into the pocket created by the area where the Peachtree Creek and the river joined. Regiment followed by regiment, brigade after brigade, and division followed by division, over and over, the Confederate soldiers would flow down the slope and over the rise to descend upon and destroy the unsuspecting, confused, and isolated Federal force. Hood thought it would be a great victory, the first of many.

Questions were called for again. Each of the corps' commanders seemed to understand the plan. It was a simple and straightforward plan with nothing complicated or flashy. Their roles were plain, and the responsibilities of each were understood by the other. Understanding was substantial, but execution was speculative.

CHAPTER FORTY

Confederacy | WINFIELD SCOTT FEATHERSTON

MISSISSIPPI BRIGADE, LORING'S DIVISION

HEADQUARTERS OF

BRIGADIER GENERAL FEATHERSTON'S TROOPS

JULY 20, 1864

7:00 A.M.

Winfield Scott Featherston was by now an experienced warrior. He had started his military career as a seventeen-year-old volunteer in 1836 when the native Creek Indians rose up in Georgia. After the tribe was subdued, he left Georgia and returned to Tennessee to practice law, a form of combat generally believed to have less opportunity for death or serious injury than that of a military nature.

When the war of Northern aggression erupted, he was among the first to respond to the call for volunteers. He raised a company and served as its captain. His company became part of the 17th Mississippi Infantry Regiment. Shortly thereafter, Featherston was elected as its colonel and commander and then promoted to brigadier general in March of 1862.

As the Western Theater grew in importance, Featherston and his Mississippi brigade sought to be returned to their home state. At the request of Jefferson Davis, General Lee released him for duty under General John Pemberton. As part of General William Loring's division, Featherston's brigade escaped capture in the battle at Champion Hill. The division marched to Jackson and then joined the force commanded by first Johnston and now Hood.

Featherston stretched his slender six-foot frame and reflected. While there certainly were military and strategic problems with being backed up to the town of Atlanta, there were beneficial aspects as well. The first—and best to some—was plentiful coffee. The cup of it he held was full, strong, black, and very hot. He blew on his cup and made a tentative sip. Damn, it was hot. He looked forward to it being cooler.

As he understood it, the attack would get underway at 1:00 p.m., but from what Featherston knew of the military, it wouldn't start on time. Of course, with the Army of Tennessee now under Hood, they were all in for a difficult time. Featherston believed he could see things from an elevated perspective. He, after all, had a good grip on people, commanded a brigade, and had served as a division commander for three weeks. In his perspective, Hood was not in the position to win.

Depending on who did the counting or who asked, Hood had an army reduced from around 90,000 troops to closer to 60,000 facing a Federal force of over 110,000 men. Featherston knew that the army had few victories to unite it or allow it to boast because of Johnston's slow retreat since the spring campaign. Featherston also knew that it would be difficult for Hood to attack the enemy and bring them to heel even if the army were accustomed to the rigors of attack and assault. Going from the defense to the offense was not as simple as changing the direction of a locomotive. It would require planning based on accurate information about the enemy's disposition and location. To merely throw one's soldiers forward in hopes of smashing a breech to later exploit was to invite objectionable losses, loss of confidence in the command, retreat, surrender, and defeat.

On top of the good intelligence, Hood would need competent staff work and good decision making from his commanders. Plans needed to be communicated. Company, regimental, and brigade commanders needed to know how to execute the plan correctly. When plans went awry or the enemy responded in an unexpected manner, commanders at all levels would need to make decisions consistent with the mission.

Featherston didn't see that occurring. From what had been heard from around Hood's headquarters, it was apparent Johnston's former staff was disgruntled about the new commander. They were especially disgruntled that Stevenson commanded Hood's former corps only one day before being replaced by Cheatham and that Loring ran Polk's old corps for only about two weeks before being returned to his division and replaced by Alex Stewart, who was new to a command of that size. In addition, injuries and sickness required changes at the division level, not all of which were done in a sensitive manner and accordingly made some who were passed over angry and potentially less inclined to be helpful. Time and working together would probably repair much of the discord, but time was in limited supply. Sherman and his three army commanders were moving in a provocative manner and were calling the tune that both the blue and the gray would soon dance to.

The plan for the day was not overly complex, but it nonetheless required coordination between the brigades and divisions who stretched out along the entrenchments that made up the outer defensive line. It was a bold plan. It could work. Yet plans are static, and the battlefield is dynamic in a deadly fashion. Sometimes, the enemy stood and fought rather than being herded in a planned direction, the latter of which Hood needed. Featherston remembered hearing something to the effect that plans work well until contact with the enemy. Featherston knew from the battles he had seen that professionalism could carry the Confederate fighters only so far. To win this battle, they needed God to smile on them or frown on their opponents. More than leadership, skill, and courage were required. Fortune had to be present.

Looking north toward where he knew Peachtree Creek must be, he adjusted his gaze to what he estimated to be about two miles from where he stood. From his vantage point on the crest of a hill, he saw a dip in the terrain, then another ridgeline, and then what he believed was Peachtree Creek Valley and another ridgeline. The creek lay behind the valley to the north. Union Major General Thomas was probably getting ready to cross the creek at that very moment. It could be a long march to find and fix the Yankees, let alone defeat them.

Featherston's brigade, as a part of Stewart's corps, guarded the left of the line to Howell Mill Road as part of the seven to eight-mile Confederate line. Featherston's right would be next to Loring's division, which abutted the leftmost division of Hardee's corps. Continuity and cohesion often came apart where one organization or unit stopped and another began, and this seam worried Featherston.

That day, for the planned attack, Loring's division would consist of two brigades of about 3,000 men. The 3rd Brigade, under John Adams, had been contending with the Federal General John Palmer's Fourteenth Army Corps, who had crossed Peachtree Creek in small numbers at Moore's Mills, Howell Mill, and Greenbone Creek. Featherston hoped Adams would return in time to exploit any advantage the other brigades might create. He would prefer to defend this line than attack the one out at the valley.

CHAPTER FORTY-ONE

Union | JOHN GEARY

HEADQUARTERS OF THE ARMY OF THE CUMBERLAND

PEACHTREE CREEK

BETWEEN HOWELL MILL AND TANYARD CREEK

2ND DIVISION, TWENTIETH ARMY CORPS

JULY 20, 1864

8:45 A.M.

The pioneers had worked quickly and well to complete the log bridge over the high banks of Peachtree Creek. Once over, the last natural barrier to Atlanta would be behind them. The next barrier would be wherever the Rebels desired it to be.

Brigadier General John Geary sat on his big horse, which was perfect for his large frame. His dark hair was thinning, and his widow's peak was now more obvious than when the war started. Though he was much larger than Sherman, some said that above his facial hair and from a certain angle, he looked a bit like Sherman. He assumed the observation to be a compliment. He was vain enough to know that with his intelligent, nearly handsome face, straight nose, sharp eyes, and full beard, he presented an impressive martial figure. Geary thought that perhaps when he was dead and gone, people might erect a statue of him someplace, mounted and looking bold just as he did now. But he had been shot at and hit so many times and survived, he thought that maybe he would never die.

Geary, like so many of the volunteer generals, was a lawyer. He had been a lot of things including clerk, surveyor, land speculator, and teacher. Always interested in the military, he enlisted in the 2nd Pennsylvania and became its lieutenant colonel during the war with Mexico. He was wounded five times at Chapultepec, promoted to colonel, and viewed as a hero upon his return.

When the war broke out, Geary raised two regiments and became colonel of the 26th Pennsylvania Infantry Regiment, which he equipped at his expense. Since then, Geary had been injured numerous times, but what hurt the most was the death of his son. During the Battle of Wauhatchie, Geary's eighteen-year-old son Edward, a lieutenant in Battery E of the Pennsylvania Light Artillery and in command of a section of guns, was mortally wounded and died in Geary's arms.

Geary's 2nd Division of Joe Hooker's Twentieth Army Corps shares credit for the victory that opened up the Union supply line. After the battles around Chattanooga, members of the 2nd Division reenlisted and were rewarded with a furlough, after which the Atlanta Campaign began. And now, nearly one hundred days later, they were close—oh so close—to the object of so much blood, death, and grief. Atlanta lay no more than three or four miles from where Geary's horse stood.

Geary was personally studying the rear area of the 2nd Division just south of the creek. Under the orders and guidance of Hooker, all three divisions of the Twentieth Army Corps would take their place generally in the middle of the Federal battle line. On the far left near Peachtree Road was John Newton's division from the Fourth Army Corps. Next were Ward's three brigades, which made up the 3rd Division of Hooker's corps. Although separated by a small creek, Ward's division was to Geary's immediate left, and to Geary's right was Williams' division, the last of the three to cross the creek.

To the right of Williams were the men of John Palmer's Fourteenth Army Corps, which had pushed the Southern troops across the creek and now were entrenched on the south bank. Palmer lacked enthusiasm for advancing first, as he believed he had been doing a substantial amount of that and someone else could get the glory from the next opportunity. He would move forward when his left was protected, but until then, he hung onto the creek bank. Palmer was sure the Rebels would not wait long since they were far from whipped if the last several days were any indication. Meanwhile, he kept his men digging.

Geary had orders to move up to the little road with his division to determine what, if any, enemy was ahead of them. From Thomas down to and including Geary, there was doubt that any gray soldiers were anywhere near the powerful Union front. Geary, having moved forward to be closer to his men, was aware that both divisions to his right and left had advanced skirmishers to the road.

Upon arrival at the road, he held Ireland's brigade in reserve and deployed Charles Candy to the left and Patrick Jones to the right. They began to erect fieldworks as they waited for their brother divisions to move up. Though almost impossible to see much ahead given the undergrowth and trees, Geary planned to send the 33rd New Jersey forward to a hill 250 or so yards to their front as an outpost, which he hoped would provide an early warning if the enemy appeared.

Geary retrieved his pocket watch. Significant time had passed, as he had spent longer looking and thinking than he had realized. The black hands indicated 12:45 in the hot Georgia afternoon sun. Maybe the Union would gain the road and encamp there for the night and go after the Rebels tomorrow, giving Palmer time to move forward to Collier Road. He needed to find Colonels Candy and Jones and discuss what he had in mind for the outpost. Maybe, he thought, he could get something to eat while one of his staff could go find the two colonels.

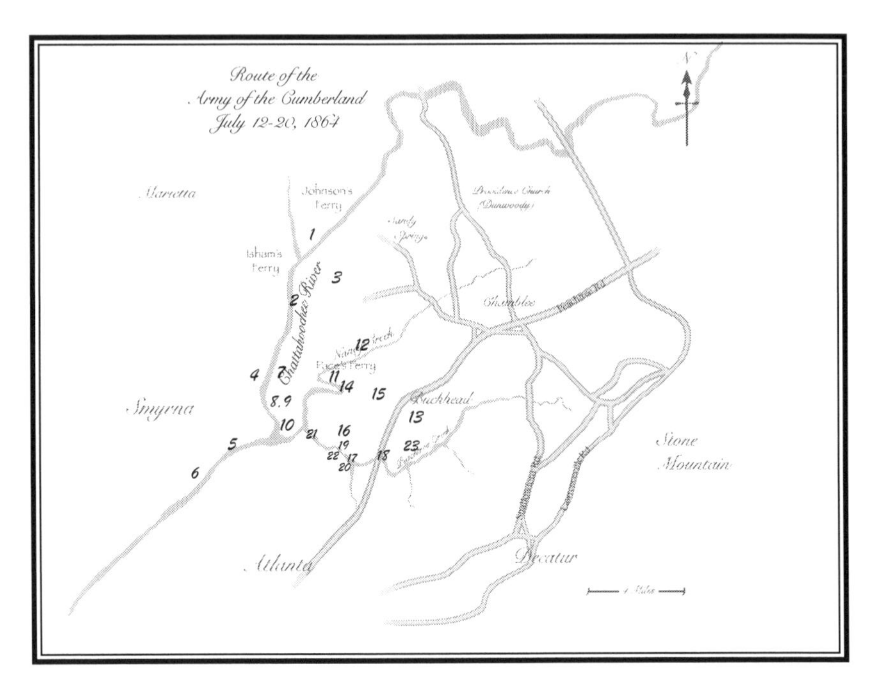

The Movement of the Army of the Cumberland, July 12-20, 1864

1. The Army of the Cumberland was commanded by Major General George Thomas. It was the largest of the three Federal armies and was composed of three corps: the Fourth Army Corps, commanded by Major General Otis Howard; the Fourteenth Army Corps, commanded by Major General John Palmer; and the Twentieth Army Corps, under Major General Joe Hooker. Each corps had three divisions. At 5:00 a.m. on July 12, 1864, Howard had his 1st Division under General Stanley across the Chattahoochee River, where Schofield's troops had placed a pontoon bridge.
2. Stanley's 1st Division of the Fourth Army Corps moved south along the river to Power's Ferry and covered the area where Thomas Wood's 3rd Division was floating their own pontoon bridge.
3. The 1st and 3rd Divisions of the Fourth Army Corps entrenched along the ridge with the 1st on the left and the 3rd on the right.
4. On July 12, the Fourteenth Army Corps remained across the river from Pace's Ferry.
5. On July 12, the Twentieth Army Corps extended the Federal line to Montgomery's Ferry.
6. Also on July 12, the Fifteenth and Seventeenth Army Corps, of the Army of the Tennessee, further extended the Federal line south beyond Proctor's Creek.
7. On July 17, the Fourteenth Army Corps crossed the river at Pace's Ferry.
8. With the 1st Brigade of the 2nd Division leading, the Fourteenth Army Corps moved to Nancy Creek where they camped on July 17. They skirmished with the Confederate forces of Adams' brigade of Loring's division.

9. To Davis' left was the 1st Division under Major General Johnson, whose 3rd Brigade encamped at Nancy Creek on the night of July 17. They also skirmished with the enemy.
10. On July 17, the Twentieth and Fourteenth Army Corps moved east on Paces Ferry Road. At the intersection with today's Ridgewood, the Twentieth Army Corps went to the left and camped about two miles northeast on Mount Paran Road while the Fourteenth Army Corps camped on Ridgewood. Both overlooked the valley at Nancy Creek.
11. Twentieth Army Corps camped here the night of July 17.
12. On July 18, Newton, Stanley, and Wood of the Fourth Army Corps moved toward Buckhead. They encountered Williams' Kentucky brigade of Wheeler's cavalry, who set the bridge over Nancy Creek on fire. Federal artillery drove Williams away with assistance of the 13th New Jersey and the 82nd Ohio.
13. On July 18, the Fourth Army Corps dug in on today's Grandview and East Paces Ferry Roads, facing east and southwest. Contact was made with Schofield at Solomon Goodwin's house and with the Twentieth Army Corps at West Paces Ferry Road. They camped here for the night.
14. Twentieth Army Corps were here on July 18.
15. Twentieth Army Corps camped here on July 18.
16. Fourteenth Army Corps marched to near Howell's Mills on July 18.
17. Twentieth Army Corps moved to Peachtree Creek on July 18.
18. Wood's division of the Fourth Army Corps crossed Peachtree Creek, pushed Hardee's troops south to higher ground, and were later relieved by Newton's division on July 19.
19. Major General Geary moved south down today's Arden, turned east, and crossed Peachtree Creek at today's Northside on July 19, following a firefight with artillery and muskets.
20. On July 19, Baird's division on the Fourteenth Army Corps crossed Peachtree Creek at Howell's Mills.
21. On July 19, Davis' division crossed Peachtree Creek at Moore's Mills.
22. On July 19, Dilworth's Third Brigade and Mitchell's Second Brigade of Davis' division crossed Peachtree Creek and established a bridgehead on the south bank.
23. The divisions of Wood and Stanley moved to fill the gap in the Federal line on July 20.

CHAPTER FORTY-TWO

Confederacy | BENJAMIN CHEATHAM

HEADQUARTERS OF CHEATHAM'S CORPS

JULY 20, 1864

10:15 A.M.

Cheatham was concerned. His red, long-sleeved undershirt stuck to his skin. It was hot, but he suspected the sweat came from his mental state, not the weather. His orders had seemed clear when Hood had explained them, but they were now less so. Somehow, the orders and the risk he was operating under did not seem consistent.

As he sweated, he took some liquor, sometimes for pleasure and sometimes because he damn well wanted to. While he had already enjoyed the first couple pulls, he realized that so far the clear, oily fluid had not slaked his thirst. Moreover, it had not provided any emotional relief or any particular insight. Cheatham still did not know how big the enemy force was and whose it was. Some called it a corps, and others said it was an army. Most agreed the force belonged to McPherson. McPherson's units, whatever their number, were coming from Decatur almost due east of him, moving steadily down the Decatur Road that ran along the railroad. More than that, he believed a separate Union force was moving toward him from the northeast.

Hood wanted a division front, but how far exactly was that supposed to be? Was it the same now as when regiments had contained 1,000 men, the number they had before the three hard years of war? Or was the front supposed to be shorter now that two combined regiments might only have 200 or 250 men? To him, it seemed to make a difference. He didn't know for sure, but the line of his responsibility might be five miles long with no one of worth beside him.

He currently had nothing to guard his exposed right flank except the civilian soldiers of the Georgia Militia under General Smith. Those men and boys dressed in their civilian clothing—which sometimes included stovepipe hats, suit coats, and city shoes—were on his right. However, the Georgia Militia also supported Wheeler, so Cheatham knew it was probably better not to count too heavily on the militia. They were brave and responsible to show up, but they were not combat-proven soldiers.

His new corps would not be behind heavy dirt fortifications either. The line would not be there to fight from as he moved toward the railroad. It just petered out. He would have to find some geography that held promise and could be defended. He knew from past experience that well-selected ground held the key to a battle. Cheatham had held good ground with his Tennessee boys at what he now heard called Cheatham's Hill. He and Cleburne had held off some well-led Union soldiers on June 27. They had killed lots of western boys and held on to win a defensive victory near Kennesaw Mountain. Good ground had ruled the day there specially at the dead angle. In this upcoming conflict, if he did not find some ground or geography to hold, he would have no fortification and no one on his right. No one, that is, except those enemy soldiers who for all he knew might be bearing down swiftly to confront his weak right flank and smash his thin-stretched line.

Cheatham continued to muse. At a minimum, he thought that he could push his rightmost brigade all the way to the tracks, as that brigade was a good one by reputation. A formidable South Carolinian, Brigadier General Manigault commanded it. Manigault would see to it that the railroad would be covered by artillery fire.

Cheatham could only hope that he could move his corps successfully and not encounter anything too bold that day. This was Cheatham's first coordinated tactical move since becoming the corps commander. Hardee and Stewart, who were over on his left and at an angle to his force, were supposed to engage and destroy the large host of the Union right. He was not certain, but he thought that wing of the Federals might be the same group they had whipped at Chickamauga. Somehow, he was supposed to keep those other massive columns to his front from joining with those to his far left.

He knew Wheeler and his dismounted soldiers on his right and out in front would fight for all they were worth to delay the Union force. A lot was expected from the arrogant young pup and his horse soldiers. Wheeler had fewer than 2,000 men—not very many—and Cheatham found it difficult to imagine it as a corps even though that was what they called it. He hoped the horsemen could stand and make a difference.

He took another pull of alcohol. He had been in scrapes before and done well, and he would do well this day. With sudden clarity, he knew that he could do all that was needed.

He hoped Hood's plan to attack while Sherman's forces were separated would work, and the entire Army of Tennessee could then turn and strike whatever remained. Yet he was pretty sure that what would remain was the same as what he now confronted essentially alone.

CHAPTER FORTY-THREE

Confederacy | JOSEPH WHEELER

HEADQUARTERS OF MAJOR GENERAL WHEELER'S
CAVALRY CORPS
WEST OF DECATUR
JULY 20, 1864

The past several days had been filled with hard work. Wheeler and his tireless troopers had ridden many miles, fought several defensive battles, and flown into the face of the enemy several times. All had generally been with excellent results. Two days ago, they had been north of Peachtree Creek and had held against many times their number until finally they pushed back to the creek. During that battle, they had taken thirty prisoners, and later, they had burned the bridges behind them as they passed to the south bank.

Wheeler thought about his force of hollow-eyed and nearly exhausted soldiers. If the corps had begun as a heavy fighting blade, the troops had now been ground down and sharpened so many times that it was only a rapier. They were sharp and thin, and he hoped they would not break. Though, even then, the jagged end could be shaped to a fine point to make a shorter blade.

This situation was not the ideal use of mounted soldiers, but it was a function he and his slender corps had become used to. He had become used to being alone with support only in the most general of senses. He knew that the entire Army of Tennessee lay six miles or so to the west of him, but six miles is a long way when you are acting as the covering force, attempting to delay and harass a Federal force that contained at least three full corps. Of course, the size could not really be brought to bear. The Union forcers were strung out over miles of choking clay roads. They were in long columns, not lines of battle.

Hence, Wheeler came into contact only with the leading edge of the enemy. Neither did it appear that they were intent on getting where they were going, or in any haste. Keeping them at bay was possible until the Union commander sorted out some of the realities on the ground. For now, Wheeler could do a good job.

The Federals had pushed into Decatur last night and were showing signs of stirring. Wheeler had become a pretty good infantry officer in addition to his pure cavalry responsibilities, so during the lull the darkness afforded, he had forced his worn and ragged troopers to prepare a series of strong points along the two major roads leaving Decatur and going west to Atlanta. Now they were positioned at the first of the strong points on both roads, awaiting the ponderous blue force, which surely would come.

Brisk firefights would burst into being, but the efforts were small, not heavy hammer blows. He had no illusions. He would be forced back. It was just a matter of time. He was already yielding ground slowly. He had again done the best he could and was sure in his heart and mind that no one could fault him or frankly have done more.

Only the Union commander would see what Wheeler's efforts produced. None of his Confederate comrades would be able to determine the level of his accomplishments, but any fair report would reflect considerable honor and praise on his small gallant force. These brave and resolute soldiers got by mostly on their own grit. They seemed to know what to do without much direction from him. He knew they must be one of the finest mounted organized fighting units the world had ever known. He hoped history would see it the same way.

Shooting was taking place up the road. The men had eaten their bacon, cornbread, and coffee, and now it was time to get back to the fight. A dusty messenger rode up. He halted his horse and saluted, "Message from General Hood, sir."

July 20, 1864—10:20 a.m.

Major-General Wheeler, commanding Cavalry

GENERAL: General Hood directs me to say that you must retard the enemy as much as possible; that General Jackson has been ordered to send 1,000 cavalry to your assistance. Should you finally be forced back, form and strengthen yourself upon the right of our infantry, which is now being extended to the railroad.

Very respectfully,

A.P. MASON,

Major and Assistant Adjutant-General

Wheeler read the message again and started to comment when a second messenger arrived. *"At a minimum they know where I am,"* he thought. The messenger saluted. Wheeler returned the greeting and reached for the paper.

Headquarters Army of Tennessee,

July 20, 1864. -11 a.m.

Major-General WHEELER

Commanding Cavalry corps:

General: General Hood desires you to form a portion of your cavalry on the right of the infantry, holding the remainder in readiness to strike the enemy in the flank in case they should attack General Cheatham. He sent you a note to this effect, and sends this to say that he does not wish your entire command formed on the right. He also desires you to keep them from General Cheatham's front as long as possible, and use every precaution to keep them from our flank. He wishes me to say that your own judgment will prompt you when it may be best and at what point to strike the enemy in case they should attack General Cheatham.

Very respectfully, general, your obedient servant,

E.B. WADE,

Aide-de-Camp

Wheeler hoped his own judgment would be enough when all was said and done.

CHAPTER FORTY-FOUR

Confederacy | ARTHUR MANIGAULT

MANIGAULT'S BRIGADE

NORTH OF THE RAILROAD, FACING EAST

JULY 20, 1864

NOON

On the night of July 18, Manigault's brigade and the rest of the Confederate division it was part of had moved northeasterly toward Peachtree Creek. The tired men had dug in, taken supper, and gone to sleep. During the next morning, some light brush firefighting took place north of them, but none of the division had taken part. It didn't pay to get too comfortable or used to a place, so that evening they slid off again to the right. That movement took them to the east and then, after a right angle turn, to the south. The division came to rest on this day, July 20, about two miles east of the Atlanta fortifications. They were holding the extreme right of the Confederate line for Cheatham and were tied into the wagon road and the rail line from Decatur. Manigault's brigade was made up of men from his home state of South Carolina and three regiments of Alabama boys. They were fine soldiers and ably led.

As they began to prepare their trenches, the brigade discovered that they would soon be joined by some of Wheeler's cavalrymen. For the rest of the day, the Carolinians and men from Alabama dug and shaped the trenches that they expected to fight from. These lines of new works were less imposing than those that lay about one quarter mile to the west of them. These were more workman-like, dug by the spare movements of regular infantry and not by the thousands of slaves the government hired from slave masters.

Their lines snaked around the unfinished two-story home of Troup Hurt near the road to Decatur, and the division artillery was positioned. As the sun moved to its highest point, they began to see the first of the Union skirmishers, who were widely spread and moved with caution.

Manigault felt secure in his newly created works, and he anticipated defending this well-placed line that occupied a slight ridgeline. When it came to killing the enemy, defense was the best way to have it. Some might argue with him, but it seemed no less manly to stand and defend then to advance and attack. Experience taught him what he preferred. Let ‘em come. He was ready.

CHAPTER FORTY-FIVE

Union | JAMES MCPHERSON

DECATUR ROAD

JULY 20, 1864

1:00 P.M.

Dirty, dusty, sweaty men uniformed in the dark blue jackets and pale blue trousers of the Union army confronted ragged, dirty Confederate soldiers, who always stayed just beyond them. Both forces moved cautiously down the wagon road. Near the road, the railroad ran through three sets of deep red clay cuts where engineers had carved away the centers of finger-like hills that riled the ground, which the tracks ran over. These cuts were fifteen to twenty feet deep and could hide a locomotive. The purpose was to lessen the grade a train would have to climb and to make the road as flat as possible. The location of these cuts coincided with the point of intersection with a road that ran north and south.

The junction of the Decatur Road, the railway, and the north-south road lay almost exactly two miles from the angry earthen and wood fortification that lay counter to the dirt and steel links as they entered Atlanta. This professional-looking fortification was the work of Captain Lemuel P. Grant who had been creating the interior ring around Atlanta since the preceding August. Captain Grant had purposed and built a perimeter wall consisting of rifle pits and forts for artillery, which was ten linear miles in circumference. The works lay about a mile from the city center at all points. The first seventeen letters of the alphabet designated the redoubts for the artillery. The ground was cleared and the position made more secure by the addition of walls of slanted stakes, fraises, logs with thick spikes driven through them, chevaux-de-frise, and cut trees with their trimmed and sharpened branches facing outwards, known as abatis. Colonel Moses Hannibal Wright, the Commander of the Atlanta Arsenal, estimated it would take 55,000 troops to merely man the line.

Where the roads entered the city walls, the fortification ran generally north and south and represented the eastern interior line. The works ran along the top of one of the hogbacked hills, the high ground, which seemed to roll in like a series of waves rising and falling from the east to the west. There was high ground and a shallow valley followed by a gradual rise of earth followed by yet another undulating valley. The intersecting north-south road lay on one such gentle ridge separated by an intervening hogback and its adjoining valleys.

Out beyond the big earthworks at the railway cuts, the clay wagon road became undecided and ran on the south side of the tracks for about a mile and occasionally tied in with roads that crossed the tracks and that then ran on shoulder to shoulder into the city with the railroad. Between Atlanta and Decatur, there were six deep cuts for the train tracks. At this first cut east of the impressive works was the imposing-yet-incomplete, two-story home of Troup Hurt. East of the house and running north of the wagon road were the soldiers of Manigault's brigade as they dug in at the far right of Cheatham's corps.

Wheeler's cavalry were still being pushed back firmly, if slowly, as they fought their way back down the road toward Atlanta. Union skirmishers and sometimes larger units thrust and were parried over the course of the fight until Southern troops dropped dead dog tired into the works of their countrymen.

Wheeler's forces were thin and far too sparse to resist any determined effort, but the three- or four-mile march had worn down the lead elements of the Union Army of the Tennessee to a considerable degree. It now looked to be a far bigger job to assault those Confederate lines than anyone had the stomach for or a plan for in this hot, miserable afternoon. Here, the two forces ground to a halt.

They stopped for different reasons. Wheeler's exhausted men stopped because they could back up no more. The long column of Union soldiers, who were strung out on the Decatur Road, ran out of momentum because McPherson was hesitant.

McPherson sat easily on his horse. Sometimes, his intuition ran headlong into his other core system of belief: his ingrained respect, even love, for the United States Army. The institution of military service placed emphasis on leadership from the top down and the importance of seeking and receiving permission to modify or deviate from an order, even with the nearly always slow order response to even the hardest attack. Most of the time, McPherson's innate caution worked in harmonious tandem with the army way. But occasionally, his intuition ran at odds with the expectations of those above him. This could make him question himself, his fitness. He would, at the appropriate time, seek permission. Sometimes, civilian political generals, such as Logan, Dodge, and Blair, acted and then explained or begged forgiveness. Most often, they just plowed ahead without remorse or understanding how this behavior upset the ordered army's expectation and institution.

Outwardly calm, McPherson sat astride his horse, surrounded by anxious staff. An anxious staff most often reflects an anxious commander, and McPherson was certain he had pressed too far, too fast.

"Hood is entirely unpredictable, and this army is spread out from here back to Decatur. We are too deep down this road. The Rebels seem to be stiffening and now look to be entrenched ahead of us. Let's get into a line of battle here and see what results," he said. Members of the staff nodded their heads in affirmation. What McPherson said made the best kind of sense. They were strung out.

McPherson trusted his intuition. It was generally an intuition that didn't push its way up into his active, order producing brain. It was not something he could order up as he could a corps or division. Rather, it rose unbidden into the hard light of day when it deemed best. With it came an understanding or knowledge that he trusted on instinct.

Among the lead elements of the 2nd Division of the Fifteenth Army Corps was the 1st Illinois Artillery Battery H's six-gun battery of huge 20-pound Parrott rifles. The big guns and caissons had moved up, unlimbered, and then went into battery on the right side of the road. Each of the artillerymen and their eager young commander Captain Francis DeGress anticipated an opportunity to fire the first shots into the Southern gate city. It had been days since the big guns had fired, as there had been no real opportunity to shoot them since leaving the river line along the Chattahoochee.

Young, eager, and capable, DeGress got the ear of Brigadier General Morgan Smith, his divisional commander who was riding up with General McPherson.

"General, the boys think it is time to heat up Atlanta, if that's possible on a day as hot as this," said DeGress.

"Well, a little light practice should encourage everyone," McPherson replied. "What do think, General Smith?'

"My boys are good, and I believe it will be productive," said Smith.

"Captain DeGress, you have my permission to fire when you are ready."

"Yes, sir." DeGress wheeled his horse around and galloped over to assume personal command of his four heavy pieces.

Moments later, the first shells soared into the superheated afternoon sky and raced into downtown Atlanta. In a case of unintended consequences, the 20-pound shell burst, killing a young girl who was walking with her parents on the corner of Ivy and Ellis Streets about two and a half miles and a few seconds from the smoking maw of one of the four black guns.

A cheer went up from the men in the 2nd Division as they began to file off to the north of the road, regiment by regiment. They were looking forward to letting the cannoneers do the work the infantry had been at all day.

As they rode along, McPherson and the commander of the Fifteenth Army Corps, "Blackjack" Logan, conferred on horseback. Logan attempted to convince McPherson that they should press forward instead of stopping since Logan thought the enemy would be as worn as the Union troops. McPherson had expected exactly this from Logan and explained what he had planned. McPherson was at his best when he had determined to abandon the unpredictable risk taking of offensive action for the predictable comfort of the defense. He quickly outlined the placement of the Fifteenth Army Corps.

"Put General Woods and his 1st Division north of the road as our right flank. Have him search for and tie into Schofield's Army of the Ohio. The 2nd Division should be here on both the north and south sides of the road. Then put Harrow's 4th on down that way as our left flank. I will deploy the Seventeenth Army Corps when they come up on our right."

CHAPTER FORTY-SIX

Confederacy | WILLIAM LORING

HEADQUARTERS OF LORING'S DIVISION, STEWART'S CORPS

MIDWAY BETWEEN THE BUCKHEAD-ATLANTA ROAD AND HOWELL'S MILL ROAD

JULY 20, 1864

3:00 P.M.

The entrenchment Loring's two brigades occupied ran nearly east-west and, at this point, lay along a hillside. Scott's brigade of Alabama and Louisiana foot soldiers lay on his left, and the Mississippi Brigade led by Featherston made up his right. As Loring understood things, the new outer defense line, a part of which his force occupied, was nearly six miles long before it turned and ran south. The area in which the long-anticipated Confederate attack would soon take place lay essentially in the middle of the fortification's red trenches and covered what he estimated was about a mile and a half between Howell's Mill Road and the nearly parallel road that ran between Buckhead in the north and Atlanta, which lay behind him.

Early this morning, he and his two brigade commanders had ridden toward Peachtree Creek, some two miles to the north, to reconnoiter the area his division planned to attack at. That effort was now mostly a waste since at about 1:00 p.m., the entire two-corps force was ordered to move to the east. Now, more than two hours had passed, and the order to initiate the attack was still not issued. By this point, the line had shifted more than a mile to the right, and he was about where Cheatham's former division had been.

The terrain north of him was seemingly nothing but thick forest. He was smart enough to know that could easily not be the case, as an enterprising farmer may have cleared hundreds of acres for farming, and that reality was just hidden and unknown to him. Knowing what was beyond the line of trees would have been good information, and it could have come from those skirmishers who had occupied positions along the creek and south of the creek at one time.

One could not be critical about the manner that Loring's boss, Alex Stewart, had explained the mission. Stewart was merely a conduit and not to be blamed for the message. Stewart had told him that Loring's division was to move forward as soon as the division to his right had gained a distance of 200 yards. Loring was to advance in a single line of battle, without reserves. He was not to stop for obstacles and should then charge enemy breastworks with the bayonet. Finally, he and his soldiers were to incline gradually to the left and press the Yankees down Peachtree Creek.

The first part of the plan was fine, but the idea he could push Thomas' strong, veteran, 40,000-man force down the creek to the river seemed like fool's talk. First, his men would be so tired following their attack that they would be in poor condition to push. Oh, he might get a few individuals to bolt and run initially—a couple of companies, a regiment might even break—but for God's sake, these were the same Federals who had been pushing, maneuvering, and beating this same Southern force since May. They were unlikely candidates to run like rabbits.

The type of topography here also favored the defense. First, the area was dense with briars, undergrowth, and old forest growth that made for dark, shadowed areas where one could see for only short, limited distances. Finding the enemy was akin to a blind man searching for a black cat in a dark room—a matter of happenstance, not skill. Then, the land itself was cut by ravines or gulches along with hills and ridges and the valleys between them. Beyond that were, no doubt, creeks and streams with their steep banks or low, swampy borders. On top of this, it was a hellishly hot afternoon, and the simple exhaustion of the exercise of getting to the fight would leave men scattered all along the route so that he would be fortunate to have two thirds of his 2,700 infantry available at the time the jarring, smashing confrontation of the actual combat took place.

The sheer distance to the river, the nearly impassable terrain, the north-south axis of the land elements all made the ambitious rout to the river seem unrealistic, poorly planned, unworkable, and uninformed. That was Hood's fault, not Stewart's. In Loring's mind, Hood was a danger to others.

Loring, better than most, had the background and experience to make these judgments. He was forty-five years old, and for a substantial part of his life, he had been a soldier. At age fourteen, he had volunteered to serve in the Florida Militia and had been a soldier since. Loring was tough. When he was wounded soon after his troops breached the gate at Mexico City, he was carried from the field. With adrenaline as a natural painkiller, Loring sat in a chair as his left arm was removed. He smoked a cigar and never made a sound.

Loring also carried himself as though he were someone in command, and he often had been. He was intelligent, ambitious, well educated, and somewhat vain. He had a dark complexion, very black hair and eyes, a strong nose, and a soldierly posture. He was five foot, nine inches and had a strong, stout body. He believed he possessed an innate military presence.

He didn't think he held others in contempt so much, but rather he recognized their true abilities, which were so often invisible to others. This honest evaluation centered most often on those who were appointed over him. These men, often with a military academy background, generally seemed to benefit from being politicians in uniform rather than to finding their way by virtue of merit or proven command ability. Their true abilities were almost always far less lofty than they themselves believed and had somehow convinced others of. On the other hand, he felt that his accomplishments were substantial, real, and bold.

This belief often led to conflict between him and his superiors. At one point, his command became subordinate to Stonewall Jackson. This did not go well. Loring, going outside of military channels, appealed to the government in Richmond. In a superb display of power politics, Jackson offered to resign, a move that was rejected. Loring, somewhat mollified, was promoted to major general and given a command away from Jackson. Again, he found conflict. He did not get along well with John Pemberton, the department commander, and following the Battle of Champion Hill, either by design or happenstance, his division was separated from the Confederate main force. Loring then joined Joe Johnston's makeshift force. Thereafter, he served in Polk's corps and finally in the Army of Tennessee.

On this day, Loring settled himself and waited to hear from one of his own staff or corps that it was time to march again.

"Sir, the unit on our right has moved forward. This division should be next." With that, Loring was up and alert, giving what few orders remained. The men had already grounded their knapsacks and other paraphernalia and carried only the essentials needed for killing: rifles, ammunition, and water. Soon, he knew he would lose control over the men moving forward except to send and receive information using messengers and staff. He liked it better when he personally led from the front.

CHAPTER FORTY-SEVEN

Confederacy | THOMAS SCOTT | *Union,* CHARLES CANDY

SCOTT'S BRIGADE, LORING'S DIVISION, STEWART'S CORPS

JULY 20, 1864

4:00 P.M.

CONFEDERACY, THOMAS SCOTT

General Scott had a good idea of what lay before him and his brigade. It would be a hard assault through the woods and then a violent confrontation with a solid Union foe. As Scott stood behind his command, he was very much aware of how worn, short, and thin the brigade line of battle was. The line was made up of the consolidated regiment of the 35th, 27th, and the 49th Alabama on his left and then the 5th and the 55th Alabama regiments in the middle and 12th Louisiana on the right. They were all veterans, and they had done this before. These were the men who had survived. They were still here, and they knew how to do this. But they were also so few. Their depleted ranks told the story. Now, there were no more than 1,400 men. In a line of battle, spread out as they were, they created a brigade front of just a bit more than 1,000 yards. Earlier in the conflict, a single regiment in a double line occupied the same front.

The forest was thick and little, but green could be seen. They had moved half a mile in the sweltering heat with briars and thorns fighting them nearly every step. They collided with a few of the blue skirmishers but had killed them or pushed them out of the way as only well-trained, experienced infantry can do.

Suddenly, the three regiments on Scott's left broke through the thick trees into an open field. Scott knew it would be nice to be able to see and move over the flat terrain, but the openness held its own dangers. They could be seen and would be unprotected. With no cover and no concealment, they'd be good targets. Some 600 to 700 yards away was the main line of the Federals.

Given their different line of attack, the consolidated regiment remained within the forest for a moment, but as they proceeded, they found their own difficult situation. As they prepared to struggle up a hill, they discovered a Union regiment had arrived at the same high point. It was quietly reported that there were fewer than 200 Federal troops on the hill. They halted and adjusted their line, and Colonel Ives discussed the matter with Scott. The leadership determined to hit this obstacle fast and hard, just as their orders had directed. They would hit them from the front and both sides with the Rebel yell on their lips as they struck. They had surprise and mass. It shouldn't take long.

UNION, CHARLES CANDY

As Confederate soldiers were marching in the briars and thorns, Colonels Jones and Candy were in discussion with their commander, Geary. The Union army had not made much use of the good defensive spots that ran along the road. The road, like so many in the area, ran along a ridgeline, so it was high ground and a good defensive area. Since May, mostly it was the Confederate army who lay between them and Atlanta, as they had a good eye for such places. It seemed to Jones and Geary that they were the spear point of this advance, and Candy agreed with them about being out ahead of everyone. He also knew Geary well enough to know Geary enjoyed being in front, especially if he believed an opportunity existed to add glory to his record. Geary was ambitious and was looking for the main chance of glory.

The skirmishers for Geary's division were about 300 yards to the south of where the three officers stood. It had just been confirmed that the hill they believed was out in front and over to the right would be a good forward position. Geary was wise enough to listen to his subordinates. He knew they often had good ideas, sometimes ones that were better than his own. All the officers concurred that it would be a good idea to send a regiment now and, when a pathway could be managed, put a battery or at least a section of guns there. It was agreed to send a couple more regiments once the first one got established.

"Send the largest regiment you have, Patrick, and who would that be now, my boy?" Geary said in a mock Irish brogue with a smile on his face. Jones and Candy grinned at each other. The order was wrapped in a question so smoothly it seemed no order at all, more like neighbors discussing prize cattle—important but pleasant. It had the effect of making the officers feel more at ease and believe they were special to the big man. Geary's humor made this brutish, ruinous, devastating business of war a bit more palatable.

"I think I will send the 33rd New Jersey. They have been chewed on but are still solid," said Jones.

"Good choice," Geary said.

"I will go tell Fourat to stand his boys up and get out there."

Colonel Jones and General Geary decided to go see first-hand what had been reported, and so both went out to the hill with the 33rd New Jersey. Southern skirmishers were on the hill, and it took some time to drive them back. But, a light skirmish line is no match for an entire regiment, especially a regiment made up primarily of veterans who had volunteered and been together for a while.

As their own skirmishers were posted and men began to clear underbrush, Geary, Jones, and Lieutenant Colonel Enos Fourat listened to the answers given by a couple of Rebel prisoners. The hard, lean, and dirty men freely volunteered that there were no large units of Southern infantry within two miles. Out here, there were only the annoying skirmishers who never stood and fought.

The afternoon was very hot and very still, and it was easy to agree the place was safe and quiet. This was a mistake. Around them, the men of the 33rd dug ditches to fire from and clear fields of fire following the instructions of the division commander. Fifteen minutes later, hell erupted on a small, tight hillside.

From the front, right, and left, murderous fire was directed at the 33rd New Jersey from the six Alabama infantry regiments who swept toward and over the outmatched Federals. Union soldiers, after firing once or twice, realized they would die or be captured if they remained, and many began to retreat. The Confederate soldiers were attacking the 33rd's right flank, so Colonel Fourat moved two companies over to bolster it. With Rebel yells ringing in the fetid heat, it seemed demons from hell had descended on the boys from New Jersey and Pennsylvania. They were being overwhelmed, and they knew it.

Gunfire was nearly solid. The color bearer and two members of the color guard were hit and killed, and John Abernathy of the 27th Alabama almost immediately picked up the colors. Union resistance was adequate only to allow the fast and agile to crash their way back to the main body of infantry on Collier Road. The wounded and dead remained, as did many who could not escape.

CHAPTER FORTY-EIGHT

Confederacy | Union

BATTLE FROM CLEAR CREEK TO BEYOND

HOWELL MILL ROAD

JULY 20, 1864

4:30 P.M.

CONFEDERACY

Unobserved by the Union soldiers, their Confederate adversaries had spent a good part of the day shifting to their right and forming a long line of battle, which now formed the outer line of defense for the city. Until yesterday, the outer line was Peachtree Creek. Even now a substantial number of Southern pickets were in place no more than a mile south of the creek.

Two ridges south of Collier's Road stood the main line of Confederate soldiers. A first, quick look would convince few that they were looking at some of the world's best, veteran light infantry, the experienced soldiers of Hardee's and Stewart's corps.

There were about 30,000 men, who were organized into 7 divisions, 24 brigades, and 117 infantry regiments. They were dirty and smelled bad. The mishmash of gray- and butternut-colored clothing was filthy but still had an appearance of rough uniformity. It appeared, to the casual observer, to be a large, tough, hard, determined group without much discipline. A closer inspection revealed bulging ammunition pouches and lightly oiled, well-maintained, large caliber killing rifles. If the plan were well executed, this line of hard men would reverse the roles they had been playing for the last eighty or so days. They would attack instead of defend, and they would march into glory with a Rebel yell and victory, rather than defeat and retreat.

On the left half of the dirty gray line, the troops had been exposed to the corps' commander, who had personally explained the mission, the orders, and the importance of what they were going to do—in great detail. To most, it seemed that it would have been better if they had jumped off then rather than shifting and waiting for hours in the hot sun, but by now, they all knew the army was many things, but efficient, it was not.

If earthworks were encountered, they were to run through them with bayonets and rifle butts. They should then drive the blue-coated bastards back to the pocket formed by creek and river and pen 'em up. Up and down the line, the men understood they were to turn a little to their left as their assault hit home in an effort to drive the Union to their right toward the river. They would step off when ordered, but that would be initiated by the unit to their right having moved forward. Like a huge rippling snake, they were to attack en echelon, just like Hood wanted. The attack would start with the division led by Bate, part of Hardee's corps, which represented the extreme right of the attacking force, and the troops would then move down the line in what was hoped to be an efficient, coordinated assault.

UNION

Across the way, parts of three Union corps were engaged in lots of tasks that were deemed important based on the lack of information about the engagement that was about to envelope them in a storm of artillery, rifle fire, and well-honed bayonets—all being delivered in the most personal manner. Some of the Union troops were digging on the ridgeline, some were lounging, some building small fires and boiling coffee, some were writing letters, and some were cleaning weapons, but all were working with the studied indifference common to soldiers who believe that there would be no fighting that day.

The Union troops, all members of Sherman's Military Division of the Mississippi, were also among the most able of infantry and had a record of success, especially since May of this year. That record caused them to be sloppy about their profession and somewhat lax and undisciplined.

CONFEDERACY

Hood had caused the shifting of the line to the right to give Smith's militia and Wheeler's horsemen some relief from the Army of the

Tennessee, which was still moving slowly from Decatur to the nearly unprotected east side of Atlanta. As a result of the poorly explained order to shift and even more poorly performed movement itself, Bate's division of Hardee's corps—the extreme Confederate right—was placed, quite by accident, in a manner allowing them to overlap the three brigades and ten artillery pieces that formed the Federal left.

Bate's men stepped forward at almost exactly 4:00 in the afternoon, about three and a half hours after the fight was planned to start. The first division into the conflict mostly fought the vines, thorns, thickets, brambles, undergrowth, trees, and mud. The noise of battle could be heard to their left but they could not find it and generally thrashed about in the briars and the muck. Being confused, isolated, and hemmed in by the demon briars was exacerbated by the shelling from the artillery at the bridge and light skirmishing with the two regiments of Union pickets positioned on the Federal left. The torments of this place and action caused Bate to finally withdraw without contributing much of anything to the attack. On Bate's left, General Walker's division moved forward with a three-brigade front right up the Atlanta-Buckhead road.

"Hey diddle diddle, right up the middle," mouthed a private from the 29th Georgia as he advanced up the inclining road. To his left, he saw, heard, and tasted the four unrifled guns of the Howell's Georgia Battery as they spewed forth steel, flame, and smoke. The smoke was heavy and blinding to his eyes, the noise deafening, and the taste was foul to his tongue. Unlike most of the men present, Captain Evan Howell had the substantial advantage of knowing with considerable certainty where his 12-pound rounds were landing. The battlefield was the land belonging to his father and the same he had played and hunted over since the age of nine when he and his father moved to Atlanta.

Walker's three brigades started moving forward after the division to their right should have been in contact with the enemy or nearly so. In reality, Bate had nearly a third farther to travel, about a half a mile, to even reach the location of the Federal line. In addition, the ground was swampy and much harder to traverse. On the other hand, Walker's soldiers moved up a route that was easier and included a good road. Walker's competitive nature caused him to push his troops so they moved quicker. The result was that Walker made contact with the best prepared of the Union forces before Bate and his men had time to arrive, even if they hadn't eventually withdrawn.

When things develop properly from an echelon attack, the first success is aided by the arrival on a flank by the next assaulting unit. This lends weight to the initial attach and is, in turn, helped by the next arriving unit. Unfortunately, it works in the opposite fashion when the initial foray is unsuccessful. The next arriving unit is unprotected on its flank and cannot achieve its specific goal. The next attacking unit runs into an even greater problem, and the entire action comes undone.

This mistake gave the Union time to position itself. John Newton's division had two Union brigades on the high ground on either side of Peachtree Road. As a forty-one-year-old West Point graduate, Newton was an intelligent, combat savvy engineer, and it showed. His two forward brigades both bent backwards to protect their ends and were joined in the middle by the six Napoleons of the 1st Ohio Light Battery A. Major General Newton positioned a brigade on the right front and the another brigade on the left front. Without much planning, both brigades fell back on throwing up defenses as a matter of well-disciplined routine.

The Union 3rd Brigade under the command of self-taught, able, and personally brave Colonel Luther Bradley was placed perpendicular to the two in front and protected the left and rear of the Union forces. In the rear, just north of the creek, two batteries belonging to General Ward's 3rd Division, consisting of twelve tubes of light artillery, were unlimbered and prepared under the personal direction of Major General Thomas. Thomas loved laying artillery pieces and was an expert in the use of artillery. He had proved it at the Battle of Buena Vista in Mexico in 1847 when he did so much to avert disaster. These batteries from Ohio and Michigan provided visions of unvarnished hell to the three brigades of Bate's troops as they fired canister and solid shots into the soft ground between the creeks.[3]

Walker's division had more men, maybe 4,700, compared to Newton's Union 2nd Division of about 3,200, but the defense is always favored over the offense, especially when the defense has some cover, is on an elevated site, and is not exhausted after a hard march through bad terrain in the heat of the day. It was not an even fight, regardless of the numbers.

Briefly, the Confederate brigade under Hugh Mercer and the Georgia Brigade smashed into the head of the Union entrenchments and then flowed to the sides and corners of the breastworks. There, they were punished severely and then began to lose momentum. They backed away, rallied, and attacked again, but soon began to remove themselves from the killing ground they had entered.

Confederate Brigadier States Rights Gist's brigade of 1,200 men, which had come forward on the left, then crossed to the right and discovered a cut leading down the hill on Newton's left. Gist's men poured down the depression toward the Union rear and the Collier Bridge, but before they could exploit this depression, they were met with canister fire and galling rifle fire from Bradley's brigade. Under violent pressure, they withdrew, and Walker's effort began to recede.

Among those retreating were the six regiments from Georgia led by Brigadier General Clement Stevens. As he turned in his saddle, as though to be certain his order had been heard and to see he had no stragglers, he jerked a little. His head pitched, and he fell from the horse, mortally wounded, with a hole in his head. Stevens was forty-two years old. He had served at First Manassas as an aide to his brother-in-law, General Barnard Bee, and had heard Bee provide the sobriquet "Stonewall" to Jackson. Stevens had never been sure the name had been issued as a positive or negative view, as Jackson had posted his regiments behind a hill and was preparing to defend rather than attack. Stevens had been wounded that day. He survived and was promoted to colonel of a South Carolina regiment. He fought at Vicksburg and at Chickamauga, where he was wounded again. In 1864, he was promoted to brigadier general and had commanded the Georgia Brigade under Walker since January. As he lay on the ground, he was bleeding only a little from the head wound. Men gathered around him, tried to make him comfortable, placed him on a stretcher, and removed him from the battlefield. He would not survive.

Cleburne's division, one of the best in the Southern army, had been held in reserve by Hardee in the hope they might be used to take advantage of any break through. No such event took place, and Cleburne's brigades waited in place. When they were called, it was to backup Wheeler's cavalry, the Georgia Militia, and the stretched Cheatham's corps in an effort to hold back the plodding Federal Army of the Tennessee. Cleburne's division moved out immediately upon receipt of the order from Hood.

Newly appointed divisional commander Brigadier General George Maney of the Confederate army stacked his brigades, with troops led by Colonel Michael Magevney on the left and Colonel Carter's brigade on the right. Otho Strahl's Tennessee Brigade was behind Magevney's, and the brigade now led by Colonel Walker was placed behind Carter and to the right of Strahl's. With the Federal line holding strong on Maney's right and concern about what exactly awaited them at the top of the ridge, Maney called a halt and sent a light force of skirmishers to investigate. With this, their momentum was broken, and they took up a defensive position and waited.

Across Tanyard Creek to the west, behind them to the left, stood two brigades from Loring's division. As part of his preparation, Confederate General Featherston had placed his 1st Mississippi Battalion Sharpshooters and a couple of additional companies in front of the main force to act as skirmishers. After waiting for Maney's division to advance 200 yards ahead of him, Featherston determined to move forward without any confirmation on what was going on to his right.

Without good intelligence, the commanders at all levels in Loring's division did not know exactly who was in the valley behind the ridge that rose out of the low marshy ground, which was cut by the run of a sluggish creek. They did not know how many men there were, what their combat record was, by whom they were led, what their attitude was, how they were armed, or any of a number of things that would be interesting or useful to know. Had they been told the answers to these questions and had a vote been called, the 1,500 or so Rebel veterans now advancing in a long, single line of battle—all boys from Mississippi and members of Major General Winfield Featherston's brigade—would have voted to remain in the defensive trenches they had earlier vacated. Yet no matter how democratic a society, battles are not fought on the basis of votes taken by the soldiers themselves. Rather, there is a framework of "justice" that essentially forces and trains men to do as ordered or face consequences so dire that combat is judged acceptable.

At the edge of a field, Featherston's column caught up to the skirmishers and deployed in a line of battle. Three hundred yards to the front was a meandering creek and then woods, followed by open ground that rose to a ridgeline, on which Federal skirmishers were arranged. The blue-clad soldiers could see those wearing gray, and those in gray can see those in blue. Maney's division moved in line with Featherston, not ahead as they should be. Featherston thought that waiting a few minutes would give Maney time to advance, but even after waiting, that desired result went unmet. Maney's troops roused themselves, moved off to the right, and were no longer visible to Featherson's force on Maney's left.

At this point, Featherston's infantrymen had crossed an old farm field and clamored down, up, and out of a ravine, where they halted to redress their line and make it appear more organized and disciplined. Somehow, they crossed what seemed to be the same ravine and then crossed a big open field. During the movement through the field, they were hammered by artillery fire from the high ground to their left. The so-called "light" artillery was deadly since the anti-personnel rounds of grape and canister exploded one after the other, over and over along the ragged butternut-clad men in the assault line. No less deadly were the shots from the skirmishers along the ridge, only they were hard to hear among the detonations of the cannon fire. A soldier might see a puff of smoke as the spinning round left the rifled barrel and then feel the hammer blow as a .58 caliber chunk of lead smashed his back. Were the two events connected? He would never know as he lay bleeding his life away or as he lay dead.

Exhaustion was nearly universal. It was hot as hell, and it was difficult to get a drink of water from a canteen when they were supposed to be firing and loading and firing and loading. The Yankee field works could be clearly seen, looking like fence rails along a road, behind which death or maiming continuously seemed to pour. The regiments still maintained their cohesion, and they still were lined up as they had been when they left. The 1st Sharpshooters were in front as skirmishers. Following them, from left to right, were the 40th, 31st, 22nd, 3rd and 33rd Mississippi.

Featherston looked at the various flags of the several regiments. With no breeze, they hung limply from their staffs. The white flag with the Beauregard battle flag in the upper corner was beautiful when extended in a breeze or when carried rapidly forward. Near the flag bearer, on Featherston's right, stood Colonel Jabez Drake, the 33rd Mississippi's commander. Featherston had confidence in Drake and his boys—that they would be okay. After all, Drake had been with the regiment since it was formed. Drake would certainly put up a fight.

It was time to go forward into the battle. The order rippled down the line as "Brigade" was rapidly followed by "Regiment" and "Company" and thereafter by "Forward," which was followed by "Harch!" The line moved forward in a practiced manner, and despite the undergrowth, the brigade maintained its cohesion. The right of the line struck the blue line first, and despite the existence of incomplete earthworks, the 33rd Mississippi pushed the Federals off the ridge and down the reverse side.

UNION

On the receiving end of this wild Rebel charge was the 3rd Division of the Twentieth Army Corps, under Brigadier General Ward. His unit had crossed Peachtree Creek where Newton's division had been and who now were to Ward's left and some distance ahead. Ward had moved his three brigades across Collier Bridge and halted them in a small valley. He had pushed skirmishers out to the second ridge where the county road ran east and west, and the rest of his men had started doing those military domestic activities soldiers do when no action is anticipated.

Colonel John Coburn, in command of the 2nd Brigade, was the first senior officer to become aware of the attack now developing and threatening to engulf his command and the rest of Ward's troops. With no warning, he had been confronted by the rapid retreat of his skirmishers followed by hundreds of yelling, shooting, killing Rebels. The veteran troops began to defend themselves, and Coburn encouraged the division to move forward as one. Colonel Coburn sensed reluctance to this idea because Colonel James Wood, the brigade commander on his left, said his orders were to stay where they were. However, Colonel Harrison, the brigade commander on his right, was quick to respond appropriately—with fire. Despite Colonel Wood's lack of enthusiasm, Coburn convinced Lieutenant Colonel Fred Winkler, the commander of the immediate neighboring 26th Wisconsin on Coburn's right, to join them. Together, the two brigades of Harrison and Coburn plus the 26th Wisconsin began to fight back. Through the weight of numbers and determination, they forced the Southerners back and beyond the second ridge that the little lane ran on. It was this enfilade fire that broke the back of Drake's attack.

By that time, Wood's regiment had collected itself, deciding that the order to stay was no longer relevant, and the division arrived on the ridge more or less at the same time. The Southern force, led by Colonel Drake, smashed into Wood's 3rd Brigade. Fire was coming from both the front and the right as Drake's 33rd Mississippi closed with the six regiments of the Union 3rd Brigade, primarily the 26th Wisconsin and other units who pushed to the left to participate directly in the fight. No support had come to the Southern right, and soon the defensive response from the Union force was simply too much for the right of Featherston's brigade.

Compounding the Confederate difficulty was the loss of Colonel Drake, who was quite close to the front rank of the Union 33rd Indiana of Coburn's brigade and whose death was nearly immediate. Drake's 33rd Mississippi lost their colors at nearly the same time Drake was killed as he waved his sword above his head, exhorting his men to follow him into the teeth of the Federal fire. The color bearer died in front of the 33rd Indiana as he waved the banner back and forth in an effort to hurry his fellows onward. He was hit and went down, the flag finding its way into the waiting arms of young Bill Conner of the 33rd Indiana. Near them died fifty of Drake's faithful soldiers.

The fire from the now fully engaged Union force rose in volume as the men of both the 2nd and 3rd Brigades fought to save themselves from death, wounding, or capture. With heavy fire coming from the front and right, a lack of cover, and what clearly must be a vastly superior force, the Confederate Mississippi regiments were in peril of being wiped out as a fighting force. Confederate troops sensed these life and death facts and began to turn away from the fight. An order to retreat was called, and those who had not already anticipated such a reasoned decision began to move up the hill that was to their rear. Regimental command in the 33rd Mississippi transferred to Captain Moses Jackson, who ordered a retreat and led his men to the relative safety that distance from the fighting brings. The entire brigade managed to maintain its cohesion, and upon seeing the Confederate troops from Maney's unit, they halted and established a line.

Captain Jackson and the rest of the 33rd Mississippi formed a line and dug in, preparing for whatever was coming as best they could. To Jackson's right were the men of Maney's division, who had remained in their position and failed to provide the expected support required on Featherston's right.

Jackson swore quietly to himself. "The cowards. Those bastards failed us. Cost us men and the fight." He shook his head. *"Pickets must be sent out. The wounded and dead must be retrieved. The line must be improved."* All these thoughts ran through Captain Jackson's head as he grappled with the problems and business his senior officers had always taken care of. The brigade remained at this area until about 9 p.m., when they withdrew.

It became clear to all of the infantrymen from Mississippi that they had received no support on their right from Hardee's men as they had attacked. The lack of support had exactly the results any soldier could have predicted. The attacker got the hell shot out of them from two directions, one more direction than what usually made for a fair fight, let alone one you could win. Relations on the 33rd Mississippi's right flank were tense, where they came near the nearly fresh men from Tennessee in Magevney's brigade, under Maney.

The terrible work of removing the wounded and dead began as night fell. Even the hard veterans were appalled and sick as they discovered the toll that had been extracted.

On the road running along the top of the ridge, blue-clad Union soldiers strengthened their lines, told their comrades their personal stories about the battle, and were excited and exhausted at the same time. Fighting was going on to their right, but they were finished for the day unless some Rebel general decided they weren't.

CHAPTER FORTY-NINE

Union | JOSEPH HOOKER

Defensive Line of the 2nd Division of the Twentieth Army Corps

July 20, 1864

Late Afternoon

A little before the beginning of the battle from Clear Creek to beyond Howell Mill Road, Hooker sat on his horse, thinking. Hooker had been at his best over the past several days. He had been close at hand and immediately available to his division commanders. He lent his superior knowledge and authority in an easy and helpful way so the accomplishment of the mission was made easier and learning took place.

When Geary had arrived at Howell's Mill and found his way blocked by the troops of the Fourteenth Army Corps, Hooker had worked with Geary to move to the left down Peachtree Creek to a good place for crossing. He and Geary had set the guns from Geary's two batteries appropriately to command the south bank, and he had encouraged Geary in his placement of the three bridges with their supporting cut roads. Geary had good instincts, but Hooker knew that one can always help someone improve and provide encouragement at the same time. Hooker understood leadership was personal. He knew staff officers could deliver messages and give direction, but no one could replace him or make the singular impact he could.

Hooker was also on hand to help General Williams halt his advance in the face of an enemy strong point at Embry's plantation house off the Howell Mill Road and had directed the alignment of Williams' three brigades. Without Hooker, Williams might have felt obligated to play the rooster by flinging several regiments at the Rebel force in an effort to win favor. Hooker, by being there, relieved Williams from any need to be the rooster on top of the dung heap and enhanced Hooker's own knowledge of troop and unit locations along what, more and more, gave the appearance and odor of a battlefield.

Hooker sat impressively on his handsome horse. His future depended on these generals and especially on their infantrymen. Victory here, especially if it were obvious he had personally had a hand in it, could only help in his pursuit of recognition and advancement back to the role of being at least an army commander. He had commanded the Army of the Potomac following Burnside's debacle at Fredericksburg. Hooker had gone after Lee as soon as he could hammer out a plan that was consistent with the President's requirements to keep an army between the Rebels and Washington, D.C. It was viewed as a good plan, and all it needed was competent, military execution.

History would see General Lee's reaction and General Jackson's enthusiastic acceptance of tremendous risk—dividing a small army not once, but twice, in near contact with the Federal army—as one of the most awesome pieces of military genius ever performed. It would likewise make Hooker the goat. Not helped at all by a nearby explosion of an artillery shell, which stunned him, Hooker simply lost his nerve, and Lee scored a major victory. Hooker had always had detractors, but as a poker-playing army comrade had said, "Hooker was an excellent poker player until it came time to go a thousand dollars bet. Then he would fail."

That failure at Chancellorsville led to Hooker's removal from command of the army just prior to the huge fight at Gettysburg. Hooker was certain he would have fought the Army of the Potomac more successfully than George Meade who, after all, looked more like a snapping turtle than an army general. He would have gone after Bobby Lee rather than let him escape again back into Virginia.

It is easy to point out the obvious—to snipe at the actions of your superiors—when you are safely away, hidden in the weeds. Hooker had done that several times over, but he now understood, far better, the responsibility of independent, high, senior command. The guy he must hold responsible was the person looking back at him in the mirror.

Hooker smiled to himself. From what he knew from the back channels of the "West Point Protective Society," which carried gossip not only within the Federal army but with certain members of the senior Southern military hierarchy as well, Hood had mounted a campaign against his boss, Joe Johnston. The move was an article of faith. It was far easier to always be right as a subordinate than as a superior, whose results were revealed for all the world to see. Hooker knew that Hood would soon find this out, just as Hooker had.

Despite all of his victories since, Hooker knew he was not welcomed by either Sherman or Grant. He tended to be spit and polish, and they were mostly just spit. He was paper collars and unit badges while they were slouch hats. They were on top, and he was trying to claw back up. He was an intrusion into their status quo. He sought an independent combat command, and they wanted him to obey orders. Nonetheless, both Grant and Sherman valued achievement. Who knew how long the war would last and what opportunities would be unveiled. Lincoln had given others a second chance. Maybe Hooker would get the same opportunity if he worked hard.

So here he was astride his horse, waiting for something to happen. Hood was no fool, but from what Hooker thought he knew about the young Confederate general, Hood was bound to come out of his defensive works and attack. Where? When? Who knew? Maybe a night attack. Maybe some flanking attack. Time would tell, and he would be ready.

A sound like thunder came over from the left, where Newton's division occupied the Buckhead-Atlanta road. He knew George Thomas was just north of Peachtree Creek with twelve pieces of artillery covering that road.

Hooker had three divisions spread across his front: Williams to his right, Geary in the middle, and Ward on the left. If Newton were under attack, it might roll in his direction into Ward's area of responsibility. He hoped Ward was flexible enough to react to this unforeseen combat. On one hand, Hooker could ride over there and see, but on the other, his presence was well known here. He thought that maybe he should stay here in the middle so he could be found, if needed, and could relocate easily to other areas of the field if he were needed there.

Men around him were beginning to look to their weapons and adjust their uniforms—all the little habits done out of nerves or simply to prepare for what now was no longer unforeseen. From the sounds, the fight was spreading, becoming more general. Where was General Geary and, maybe more importantly, where was Colonel Jones, the second brigade commander? Under ordinary circumstances, they would be near him, if for no other reason than to provide what they knew, to learn what he knew, and to tell him where they planned to go.

Soon, on the north side of Collier Road to Hooker's left, the Union soldiers pushed the Confederate men back up the hill, across the road, and beyond. As Hooker waited for his own military conflict, the noise on his left rolled over to his immediate front, and he could hear the noise caused by firing: trees, bushes, dirt, men, and horses being pelted by steel and lead. Firing erupted 200 yards or so to his front, and without much warning, men in blue garb ran toward the perceived safety of the Union main line. Hooker saw General Geary and Colonel Jones on horseback moving along with the disorderly retreat. They would be here soon and begin to correct the unfolding disaster.

Hooker knew without saying it that Hood had launched an echelon attack. It should, depending on the length of the Confederate front, hit the men to his left, collide into his front, and then roll to his right. The initial attack would be over, but the hard aftermath would remain. A close fight would ensue and run its course.

The 2nd Division's front erupted into a storm of gunfire, yelling, explosions, blinding smoke, and bright yellow, orange, and red flashes. Men to Hooker's right—what Hooker thought must be Jones' 2nd Brigade—were being overrun and pushed around in a very disorderly manner.

Hooker instinctively knew he could stem this surge of defeated men and rally them to make a stand. They needed to swing back with their left as the pivot—swing back nearly ninety degrees. Their line should then extend north down the hill, across the ravine, up the next elevation, and tie in with Williams' left. This could create a killing pocket the Rebels might be lured into. He explained the matter to Geary and Jones, and they issued orders to make it so.

The pocket formed, the nearly 3,000 Confederate men of Scott's and O'Neal's brigades entered it, the killing crossfire ensued, and the high tide of Hood's first foray was achieved.

CHAPTER FIFTY

Union | ANSON MCCOOK & DOUGLAS HAPEMAN

1ST BRIGADE, 1ST DIVISION, FOURTEENTH ARMY CORPS

FAR RIGHT OF UNION LINE

SOUTH OF PEACHTREE CREEK AND HOWELL MILL ROAD

JULY 20, 1864

ABOUT 5:00 P.M.

UNION, ANSON McCOOK

Colonel Anson McCook was a member in good standing of the "Fighting McCooks." He was of the tribe of John, who was his father. Between the three sons and numerous grandsons, the family provided nineteen or more men who fought for the Union or served in other ways. For example, two were contract surgeons. Six of them attained the rank of brigadier general or higher. As a family, the McCooks prospered and achieved success in their business affairs.

Anson McCook was twenty-nine years old. He was at the battles of Bull Run, Perryville, Stones River, Lookout Mountain, and Missionary Ridge. Since the second of the month, some eighteen days ago, McCook had command of a brigade, the 1st. Under his command were nine regiments with men from Illinois, Indiana, Kentucky, Ohio, and Wisconsin.

The division and the 1st Brigade had been busy and in contact with the enemy for several days. They had left camp and crossed the Chattahoochee on July 17. On July 18, they skirmished as they crossed Nancy Creek. On the July 19, they camped on the north side of Peachtree Creek at which time, the Southerners destroyed the bridge at Howell's Mills. The creek was crossed on that morning, and they had traveled about a mile south by this point.

McCook arranged the regiments with the first being the 104th Illinois under Lieutenant Colonel Douglas Hapeman on the outermost right. Then came the 15th Kentucky, the 42nd Indiana, and then the 88th Indiana on the outermost left, all making up the front line. The 104th Illinois was about 125 yards in front of and to the left of the 15th Kentucky because a ravine ran between the two regiments. The 104th was close to the right of General Hooker's Twentieth Army Corps. Orders were given to start digging earthworks, and that work got underway.

Sounds of battle were heard to the left, and soon, combat had begun among the troops of 1st Division of the Twentieth Army Corps on the left. From the sounds of things, it seemed an even contest. Not long thereafter and with no real warning, two lines of an enemy force struck Hapeman's 104th. The Union force returned fire but was overwhelmed by the mass and momentum of the Confederate regiments confronting them. The Federal line bent, and for a while, it seemed it might break. Confederates were into the rear of the 104th, but Hapeman rallied his troops. Soon, the butternut tide receded into a ravine

UNION, DOUGLAS HAPEMAN

Hapeman was no hero, and he was sure the Confederates had not danced their last waltz. He knew he needed help, and he was sure it was available.

He turned to a courier, "Go, hurry. Tell Colonel McCook that it is imperative I have some help. Get him to send at least one regiment to us. We need them now." McCook, having been watching the beleaguered regiment from his position, had already made a decision to send the 21st Wisconsin to aid their sister regiment. The order was given just as Hapeman's request arrived. McCook debated and decided to send a second relief regiment once the 21st was on the way.

Moments later, the same attacking force or its twin plowed hard into the right flank of Hapeman's beleaguered 104th. The shock of the attack caused the unit to recoil. Breaking and running seemed to be a likelihood.

But Hapeman was with his men on the front line, and he was cool and deliberate in his directions. When events seemed their darkest, the welcome noise of a regiment coming at a full run could be heard over the clash of the blue and gray men locked in combat. The 21st Wisconsin arrived. They were loaded and ready, and their arrival was most welcome by the exhausted men of the 104th. The remaining troops with the bulk of the brigade began to provide an enfilading fire into the formerly confident attackers, who then retreated from a hard fought near-win.

The retreating Confederate regiments, which had exhausted themselves, moved south away from the bloody field and back toward the defensive line protecting Atlanta. One of those regiments was the veterans of Reynolds's Arkansas Brigade, one of the two brigades from Edward Walthall's division participating in the attack. The other was led by Colonel Edward O'Neal, whose soldiers were from Alabama and Mississippi.

The left part of Reynolds' brigade had come close to breaking the 104th. Only the obvious cool leadership of Hapeman and the timely arrival of the additional regiment had saved the Federal position. Earlier in the battle, Reynolds' right had fallen on the rightmost of Hooker's Twentieth Army Corps and had no support on either their left or right. They were easy targets as they twice entered the deep ravine that ran along the Federal front. The terrain, the advantages of earthworks, and a stout defense resulted in defeat for those soldiers from Arkansas.

They had been whipped and worn out with a two-mile retreat before them. All were aware of the possibility they might be pursued, and that caused them to move faster. Pursuit of a defeated enemy was something discussed all the time, especially by those who were not in the fight, but it was seldom seen on the battlefield. Men were too glad to have survived and generally were too worn out to follow. Still, there was no reason not to move along as quickly as possible.

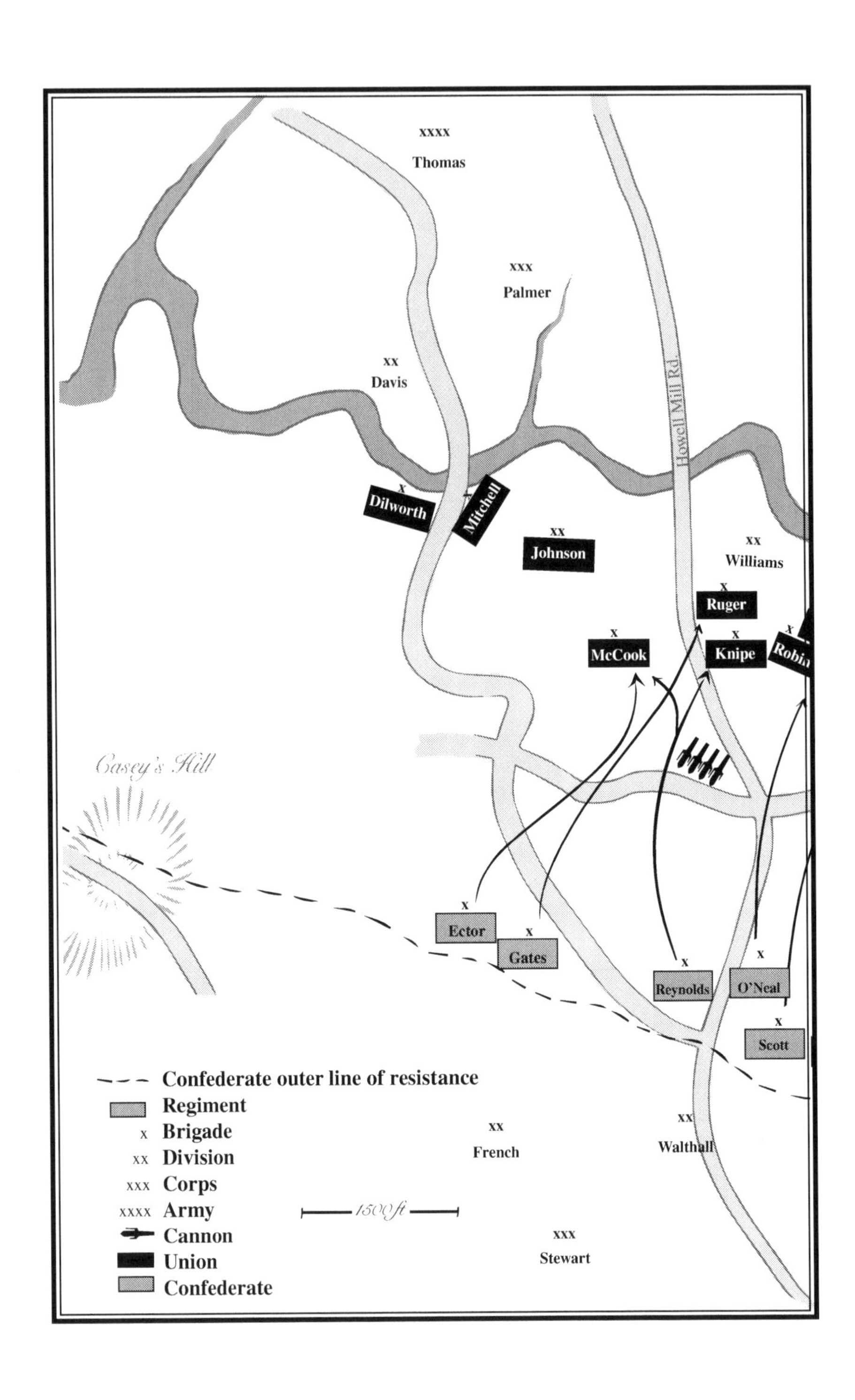

xxxx
Thomas
xxx
Palmer
xx
Davis
Howell Mill Rd.
x
Dilworth
Mitchell
xx
Johnson
xx
Williams
x
Ruger
x
McCook
x
Knipe
Casey's Hill
x
Ector
x
Gates
x
Reynolds
x
O'Neal
x
Scott
Confederate outer line of resistance
Regiment
x Brigade
xx Division
xxx Corps
xxxx Army
Cannon
Union
Confederate
xx
French
xx
Walthall
1500 ft
xxx
Stewart

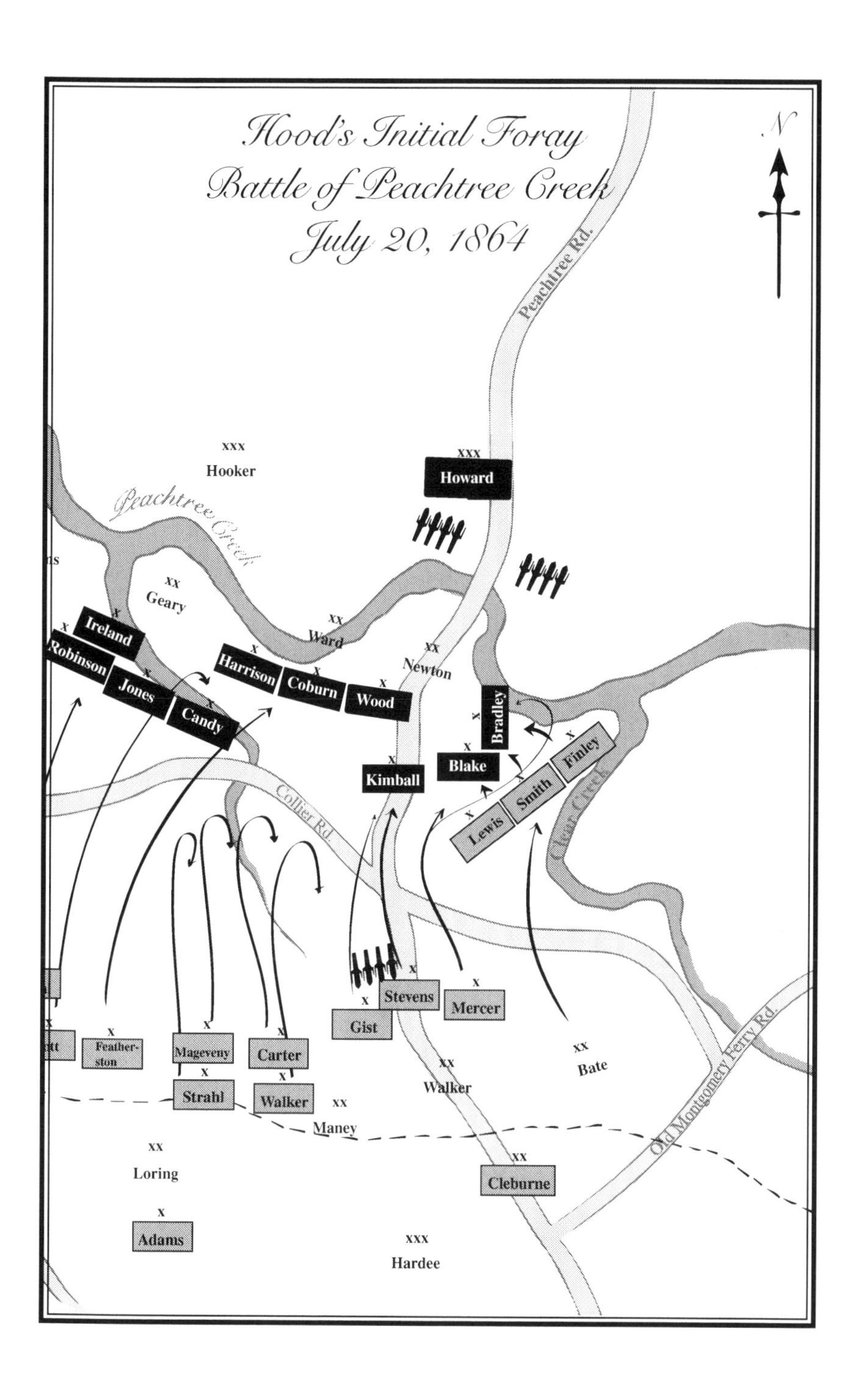
Hood's Initial Foray
Battle of Peachtree Creek
July 20, 1864
N
Peachtree Rd.
Peachtree Creek
Collier Rd.
Clear Creek
Old Montgomery Ferry Rd.
XXX
Hooker
XXX
Howard
XX
Geary
XX
Ward
XX
Newton
Ireland
Robinson
Jones
Candy
Harrison
Coburn
Wood
Kimball
Blake
Bradley
Lewis
Smith
Finley
Stevens
Gist
Mercer
Feather-
ston
Mageveny
Carter
Strahl
Walker
XX
Maney
XX
Walker
XX
Bate
XX
Loring
Adams
XX
Cleburne
XXX
Hardee

CHAPTER FIFTY-ONE

Union | FRANK BLAIR & WALTER GRESHAM

BALD HILL

JULY 20, 1864

AFTERNOON

UNION, FRANK BLAIR

As the Fifteenth Army Corps and the Sixteenth Army Corps, under Major General Dodge, moved hesitantly toward Atlanta on the Decatur-Atlanta road, Major General Frank Blair was also on the move, unencumbered by the close physical proximity of General McPherson. The Seventeenth Army Corps, with its two divisions, was driving forward on the Fayetteville Road. This road ran southwest out of Decatur toward Widow Terry's Mill and a large rancid millpond and then on to Cobb's Mill. It was not the plan to go as far as Cobb's Mill but rather to turn to the right and run a parallel course with the rest of McPherson's Army of the Tennessee. That road would be found about two and a half land lots away and provided a less direct, more roundabout path to Atlanta.

Blair's face was lean and hard. A quick look revealed prominent cheekbones visible over a full dark beard. His head was covered with thick, well-combed hair. He was a hard man of ideas and action and a political sophisticate. As a lawyer and congressman, he was a powerful speaker.

He had used his oratorical skills on Lincoln's behalf during and after the Chicago convention. His father had served as an advisor to President Andrew Jackson and published *The Globe*, an influential Washington, D.C. newspaper. Blair had graduated from Princeton and practiced law with his brother Montgomery in St. Louis in 1842.

Blair was a complex man. He had owned slaves but had become an ardent "free soil" man. In Congress, he had advocated an all-out war effort to bring the Confederate states back into the Union. He had organized the "Wide Awakes" and Home Guards in his successful efforts to keep Missouri in the Union even if force was required. He declined a brigadier general commission in 1862, but accepted the commission after having raised seven regiments for the Union. Some three months later, in November 1862, he received his second star. He led a brigade during the Yazoo expedition and at Vicksburg. Blair was ambitious and, like others, saw the White House in his future. He was forty-three years old in 1864 and now commanded the Seventeenth Army Corps. He was not yet a proven corps' commander, but he had an easy confidence about him and most of his soldiers felt confident of him. Leadership was innate, and he possessed what many jokingly referred to as the qualification for high Union command: he was a lawyer.

Frank Blair was also the quintessential political general, perhaps even more so than his friend and fellow corps commander John Logan. For a while, he was both a congressman in contention for the speakership of the House and a major general. At Lincoln's personal direction, he pushed forward his army career, but this happened only after he played a major role in removing Secretary Salmon Chase as a cabinet member and potential presidential contender in the upcoming election of 1864. Some believed the Blair family to be the most influential political family in America. Curiously, Frank Blair was the most successful army officer of the family even though it had been his brother who had graduated from West Point.

Blair was a man of conviction and was willing to take personal action pursuant to his beliefs. Quick minded and a gifted speaker, he was also quick to do what he saw as required. Notwithstanding their personal disdain for political generals, both Grant and Sherman had openly praised Blair's military skills and ability.

UNION, WALTER GRESHAM

About two miles down the Fayetteville Road, the roundabout route to Atlanta turned off to the right. The 4th Division of the Seventeenth

Army Corps, led by Brigadier General Walter Gresham, was the vanguard.

Walter Gresham, as a result of Brigadier General M.M. Croker losing his command, became a newly minted divisional commander. Gresham, at age thirty-two, had been leading the division since the Atlanta Campaign had begun.

As the afternoon of July 20 moved along, the 4th Division's two brigades pushed down the wandering crooked little road toward Atlanta. They were following their skirmishers, who were constantly trading rifle fire with the hatched-faced men of Wheeler's dismounted cavalrymen. Wheeler's troopers, who had stretched but not yet broken, stiffened about three miles along the road, and Gresham decided it was time to deploy in appropriate lines of battle.

Gresham had two brigades: the 1st and 3rd. Deployed, the 1st Brigade formed on the right under command of Colonel Benjamin F. Potts. As soon as the Confederate skirmisher response became more vigorous, Potts deployed his own heavy skirmish line. After a brisk exchange, the Southern solders were forced to fall back. Behind Gresham's skirmishers, his brigade deployed along the clay road. The brigade was composed of the 53rd Illinois, 23rd Indiana, the 53rd Indiana, the 3rd Iowa, and Pott's own 32nd Ohio.

The Rebel line was posted atop a ridge of high ground in a strip of timber about three quarters of a mile west of the deploying Federals. From this same ridgeline came the first ranging shots of at least two sections of Wheeler's artillery.

Potts quickly summoned Lieutenant James Burdick. He wanted Burdick's 15th Ohio Light Battery with its four 12-pound Napoleons to provide some counter battery fire and to support his pending assault. The Ohio horse-drawn guns moved up and through the mass of Federal infantry and commenced firing. The Napoleons were terrific infantry support weapons. Each one in turn provided plenty of smoke, fire, and noise as well as deadly antipersonnel canister and shot.

Potts soon had his veteran regiments in a typical double line of battle and moved them forward. They progressed until they were about 300 yards from the concealed line of Southern soldiers. The Federal troops found themselves in one of the ravines made by the waters of Sugar Creek as it runs from near the railroad toward the South River. These ridges and the steep gullies at their bases provide natural cover to advancing troops and almost always provide an opportunity for advancing lines to halt. Here, the assaulting lines rested, drank water, checked weapons, and collected themselves.

General Gresham rode up to the ravine where he found Colonel Potts. Potts said, "General, you need to dismount. I doubt your horse will be much use in getting down into this ravine. Perhaps of more interest to you is that the Rebs are just up ahead. They have a cannon and all that good high ground to the west of us. You will be less of a target on foot from here forward."

Dismounting, Gresham replied, "Potts, what can we do to push your brigade out of this damn hole and up that ridge?"

Without waiting for a reply, Gresham plunged into the natural trench and began moving toward the opposite bank. "Come with me, Colonel. Let's get out of here and get a bit closer to the skirmish line. We can both have a good look at what is holding us up."

The two men moved out of the depression and dog trotted forward. As they neared the halted skirmish line, Gresham uttered a yell and fell to the ground. His left leg had been ripped hard by a .58 caliber round from a concealed Rebel sharpshooter. He went down, moaning softly to himself. It hurt like hell. Three inches of bone was shattered. Gresham remained conscious, but his time as a division commander had ended.

Several strong western soldiers removed Gresham from the immediate danger of the battle line, back to the road a half-mile back from where the advance had jumped off. As he laid awaiting transportation to the rear and the bloody surgeons, Blair rode up.

In an effort at humor, Blair spoke. "It is just too bad, Gresham. I'm racing John Logan to get into Atlanta first, and you go and get shot. I was counting on you. Don't you know this might set me back?"

Gresham now, in and out of his senses, was removed to the nearby home of Green Clay, where his leg was amputated with dispatch. He was soon in an ambulance on his way back through Decatur and Roswell and then to Marietta. From Marietta, trains were moving toward the North with their mangled human cargo.

Blair realized the assault force on his right was confronted with a well-positioned Rebel foe. His immediate problem was to replace Gresham, who he believed would not return to his command. He had seen men with similar wounds, and he was doubtful as to Gresham's chances of survival. He would look for Colonel Bill Hall, who was the senior colonel in the 4th Division.

General Blair and some of his staff moved back down the road, searching for Hall and the leadership of the 3rd Division. Upon finding Hall, he ordered him to assume command of the division and then admonished him to keep pressing the enemy.

"Keep after them," Blair commanded. "Don't let up. If you can't finish him, keep him firmly in place. I'll get you some help on your right."

Hall agreed, saluted, and moved off toward his new responsibility.

Blair felt confident that he had resolved the immediate command problem and that the pressure from the Federal force would be maintained. He continued down the road in search of his 3rd Division. He soon found Mortimer Leggett with his brigade commanders. The 3rd Division had been trailing the lead division and was to the rear and left of the engaged portion of the Seventeenth Army Corps.

Blair and Leggett moved off to the south in an effort to understand the terrain and the disposition of the enemy. The ground confronting him was different though from the terrain the fight was currently being fought in. Specifically, on the right, the troops were in woods. Here, a huge open field presented itself, which piqued Blair's interest. There would be no cover for the advancing infantry—a nearly perfect killing ground.

Across the field rose the most commanding piece of terrain on the battlefield: a bald hill. It was covered with grass and low bushes. It was highest at its southmost end, which lay directly in his path. Looking north along the hill, he saw that it was really three hilltops, which fell off toward the north.

Along the base of the high end was a dense, wooded area. Those trees could have well-concealed Southern infantry, and on the hill proper, Confederate field artillery was positioned. A frontal assault across the field and into those trees could be horribly expensive in terms of Union lives, but Blair needed to figure out a way to capture that hill. He and Legget knew Bald Hill was the key to this area and maybe to the city itself.

Blair and Leggett were in earnest conversation when McPherson rode up. The two subordinate generals saluted, and McPherson explained that the Fifteenth and Sixteenth Army Corps had halted their attack, as the opposing force was now entrenched.

All three officers then looked at the hill in front of them. The hill represented excellent ground and an advantage to the force that had it.

General McPherson spoke, "General Blair, do you think this bald hill represents the extreme right of the forces before us, or do they extend farther to the south?"

"Sir, I really don't know. My best guess is that they are stretched mighty thin, and the hill seems an obvious point to end their line."

Leggett then turned to a nearby officer. "Major Munson, go forward and find our pickets. I want you to press our skirmishers up toward the hill and to our left there where the big hill tails away. See if they can turn up any of the Johnny Rebs south of the hill."

The three generals continued to glass the hill and the near terrain. They spoke the occasional word and reexamined the hill with their unaided eyes.

The staff talked quietly among themselves. Firing continued from the Union right, and the smoke from the Rebel reply fire could be seen. It was bright white against the green and blue of the vegetation and sky.

Major Munson returned after the passage of some time. He reported to Leggett but was overheard by the other two generals. Munson informed Leggett that the Confederate line extended down the south end of the hill and a bit beyond, but that for all practicable purposes, the line ended at the base of the hill.

All eyes turned to McPherson. He, in turn, looked at the sun and then removed his watch and looked back at the sun. Finally, he said, "Considering the lateness of the hour and the time it will take to get a divisional assault formed up and underway, let's postpone the attack until morning. What say you?"

There was little disagreement with the cautious and thoughtful suggestion, but they soon settled the matter.

"General Blair, I will leave the matter to you to arrange as you see fit. We must have that hill. It is the key. Get your folks ready to go first thing in the morning unless you hear from me to the contrary. Be in position early. Let's hit them first thing," McPherson said as he left.

Soon thereafter, as Leggett conferred with his brigade commander, Leggett instructed Force, "Move as soon as it is light enough to see. I will support your left with the 2nd Brigade or at least part of it. I'll have the 3rd in reserve, close behind you. The 4th Division will demonstrate on your right to keep the attention of the enemy in their front."

Tomorrow, the Union would strike.

CHAPTER FIFTY-TWO

Confederacy | JOSEPH WHEELER

On the hill, east side of Atlanta, about a mile forward of the Confederate line

July 20, 1864

4:15 p.m.

His troopers, dismounted and deployed as infantry, were hard pressed and had been for most of the day. This was not unusual. His horsemen were often called on because of their mobility and enthusiasm as fighters. This day was no exception.

To the east were the thousands of hard blue men under McPherson, coming down two roads. Back behind him to the west were the red clay earthworks manned by nearly 5,000 men of the Georgia Militia under Gustavus Smith.

Wheeler had about 2,400 men at this moment and two sections of field artillery. He was responsible for a front of about a half-mile wide. With him were three brigades: William Allen's Alabama brigade, Alfred Iverson's boys from Georgia, and Samuel Ferguson's three regiments from Alabama and Mississippi.

As was his fashion, he appeared in a simple gray frock coat—no insignia, no mess of gold frogging. The only adornment was also functional and consisted of twin rows of seven gold buttons. These buttons reflected his prior U.S. service in the mounted rifles and the cavalry. The plain coat and trousers constituted practical and serious garb, which was at odds with the public's view of flamboyant cavalry commanders. Oh, he had a fancy uniform, and if the activity demanded, he would wear it. But this was work, important work, honorable and hard and dirty work, and his entire being was engaged.

Wheeler was complex. He could not understand the emphasis others, generally older men, put on their personal feelings. He subordinated his feeling to the task at hand and the overall struggle for liberty. He felt that the cause was an honorable thing, and no individual disappointments should color one's wholehearted response.

In part, because he knew he looked like a boy—and in fact, he was at best a young man—Wheeler responded well to the authority of older, more seasoned officers. He respected his elders and saw them early on as wise and worthy of his respect and obedience. He believed in those placed above him by the legitimate government of the South, and as a result, he had functioned well under angry, sour, old Braxton Bragg as well as precise Joe Johnston. In his mind, these older and wiser officers embodied and personified the cause itself to a degree, and he was their willing subordinate. Since he could not equal his superiors in age or position, he instead acted in a serious, pleasing, goal-oriented manner.

Senior commanders could not help being flattered by the pleasing enthusiasm of the boyish Wheeler. This was especially true when it was combined with his fierce personal courage and can-do approach. He had demonstrated his was a courage that rose to face the challenge presented, one which allowed for an individual display of focused bravery or which was compelling enough to form part of the basis for his leadership. He seemed fearless.

Wheeler worked hard every day with his command to end the war. His life was nearly singular in his devotion to it, to its strategy, and, most importantly, to its tactical necessities. The military goal of each day was largely his life, and any effort motivated by less than a total commitment was inappropriate and unworthy. He would give his all every day. He had thought only a little about what his circumstances would be after the war. The here and now was what was important.

So focused, he could hardly allow himself to think of the woman he believed he would one day wed. She was a widow—Daniella Jones Sherrod. He met her on her father's plantation on October 9 of the last year.

He knew Ella, as he thought of her, would make a good and wonderful wife. He was certain she would be a true partner in whatever the future had in store. Joe Wheeler thought of Ella often before he slept, but in truth, he knew he held her memory in a small box in his mind. He had the ability to open up the box as he lay down to rest, and he could close the box up tight when he needed to plan the next operation or fight his way out of whatever adventure had befallen him. At this time, Wheeler kept that box closed.

Wheeler had been receiving messages from different people all afternoon. In the order he had received them, they were:

July 20, 1:10 p.m.

Are you driven back, or have you only fallen back to find a good position? What is your estimate of the enemy? Hold at all hazards. General Smith, with all the reserve artillery, occupies the works behind you.
Respectfully,
W.W. Mackall,
Brigadier-General

To Major-Gen. Wheeler
Commanding Cavalry Corps.
General Brown has been ordered to extend to the railroad. You will please keep in communication with him, and support him. I am now on the left of my line, which is along one. If you should find the enemy moving to my left, will you please inform me.
B,F. Cheatham
Major-General
My skirmishers on my left are now heavily engaged.

Ga. R.R. Fortifications, Atlanta,
July 20, 1864—4:35 p.m.

General:
I have seven hundred men here in the trenches, upon the right and left of the railroad, supporting the reserve artillery. There is nothing to my right. Where is your right and left, and how far are the enemy from this position? Please notify me of anything of moment regard to your position, that of the enemy, etc., and oblige.
Very truly yours,
G.W. Smith
Major-Gen. Wheeler,
Major-General
Commanding Cavalry Corps

July 20, 5:30 p.m.

General Wheeler
Commanding Cavalry:
I have one thousand men in my center, with troops deployed in a single line, and have been compelled to take a brigade from my left, which is now not protected. I need 2,000 men to fill my line. General G.W. Smith is near you. Call on him.
B. F. Cheatham
Major-General

Hold until tonight, if possible, and keep me posted.
B.F. Cheatham
Major-General

July 20, 1864, 6:30 p.m.

General Wheeler:
General Cheatham has been ordered to send you a brigade. Hold on as long as you can, but if forced back you must go into the fortifications with General Smith, who is now behind you, and hold them, says General Hood.
Respectfully,
W.W. Mackall
Brigadier-General

July 20, 6:15 p.m.

General Wheeler,
Commanding Cavalry Corps:
The enemy are pressing my center, which is only a single line for one mile. I am afraid it will not sustain itself. I have weakened my entire line to fill up the gap of one mile. I have sent word to General Brown to assist you if he can. You will communicate with him.
B.F. Cheatham
Major-General

Headquarters
July 20, 1864, 7:15 p.m.

General:
Your dispatch of 5:45 is received. General Hood directs me to say that Cleburne's division is moving to your support, so communicate this to the men and urge them to hold on.
General Hood desires to see you as soon as you can safely leave your command.
Yours,
A.P. Mason
Major-Gen. Wheeler
Major and A.A.G.

Joe Wheeler had hit the approaching Union columns all day long and now had his brigades drawn up on some high ground a little less than a mile from the slopes of Bald Hill. This was the last of the prepared positions, which had provided the next place to go as he fell back from the three corps confronting him. He grinned to himself. He had been around General Johnston too long.

This had been a hard ten days. He had probably lost nearly 300 men, more than ten percent of his force, in killed and wounded since he crossed the Chattahoochee River. He had been in at least sixteen small engagements, more than one a day. It was all damn hot work.

He was pleased with his men's performance, and he hoped to be able to keep the lid on the famous insubordination of Ferguson. He didn't need any distractions, and it was important to know his commanders would do as he ordered. Right now, he needed all the discipline he could pull from his exhausted troopers. His war sense left little doubt that this now quiet section of line would not remain quiet indefinitely. The Yankees were still out there, as they had been all day. Wheeler gazed through his field glasses down the forward slope of the hill he was positioned on. He looked down to the stream-filled valley and up the next hogback that rose east of him at least half a mile away. The Union soldiers were there—at least a division just over the brow of that hill.

He turned to one of his aides. "Let's get some artillery fire on that big group of Yankees just on that hill. Let's make it hot for them."

The aide was off, and soon, Wheeler could hear the sound and see the results of the shellfire that shook the hill. Wheeler was satisfied for the moment but knew it would be only a short time before the Yankees brought up a battery to fling some death and destruction back at the hill and at him.

All afternoon he had been asking for help, and nothing had been forthcoming. He knew about the plan to attack the Federals after they crossed Peachtree Creek, but it seemed odd that his calls for reinforcements had gone unheeded until now. Nonetheless, he was gratified that Cleburne was on his way. Cleburne might just be the best divisional commander left, and his unit would be most welcome. Cleburne's division was unique and had the colors to prove it. Johnston had allowed Cleburne's division to retain their Hardee pattern flags with the distinctive blue field and white center circle. All the rest of Hardee's old corps marched under the Saint Andrew's cross. It would take a while for any division to move three miles, even one as well led and as disciplined as Cleburne's. Maybe when they arrived, he could go meet with Hood.

Here the blue bellies would come. His boys would give them unshirted hell for a time. In a way, it was wonderful to be on elevated ground with all the time to load, aim, and fire at the boys in blue as they came down the hill across the creek and through the briars and then slowly up the 60-foot hill. The ground before him was cut by streams, and around them grew thick grapevines and blackberry briars. These were probably better defensive works than he could create. *"There must be five regiments in a double line of battle,"* Wheeler thought. Wheeler and the rest of the men would do their best and then retreat back to the line being held by the militia.

The Union could have this hill. Given the time of day and the nature of the Confederate leadership, the South should be able to pull back, eat, rest, and get ready for tomorrow. Thus, late in the afternoon, with some daylight left, the cautious Army of the Tennessee halted.

Wheeler wouldn't know it yet, but he had been successful. His underfed, overworked, outnumbered, and underappreciated cavalry had worked untiringly in the face of a huge force and had kept them out of the city. A large part of Wheeler's success lay in the mind of his opponent. McPherson, cautious as ever, was satisfied with his advance and had found a tactical reason to halt. He was always worried about what the enemy had in store for him and seldom imagined it would be pleasant. With a huge advantage in numbers, an assault by two or three Federal divisions in all probability would have swept aside the slender and largely isolated force before him, but that reality was obscured by the fog of war, a lack of confidence, and an inbred caution.

Accordingly, the outlines of what would take place tomorrow began to take shape as the opposing forces went to ground. On the Union left wing, General Force's 1st Brigade of the 3rd Division tied into the two brigades of the 4th Division, under its new commander Colonel William Hall. To the left was the remainder of the troops of General Scott's 2nd Brigade, which consisted of only three regiments. Beyond him was the 3rd Brigade, under Colonel Adam Malloy. Malloy's force was just one regiment and a battalion. This small group was refused so that they faced nearly south. The line was bent back on itself in the shape of a "7" or a reversed "J." Either shape would provide width at the end of the line. Done properly, a "refused line" allowed soldiers to defend the end of a line and the back of the line by giving numerous men room to fire.

As the summer sky darkened, the Union skirmishers were gently pushed out in front of the two-division force of Frank Blair's Seventeenth Army Corps. This light infantry had been pushed forward through the dense trees at the base of Bald Hill and to the western most edge of the tree line. Surprisingly, they met no Southern skirmishers. As the Union troops began their long night, the commander of the 3rd Division saw that Force's brigade was directly before the bastion Bald Hill represents.

On the Southern side of the field, delay on the part of the Union was having its rewards for the defending force. Cleburne's division of Hardee's corps was on the move, and even now advance elements of the lead regiment were arriving at the railroad. Men from the 17th and 18th Texas, led by General Smith, were the first to start filing into the almost nonexistent trenches held by the worn out men of Wheeler's command. The cavalrymen began to move to their right, toward the highest part of Bald Hill as they were displaced first by the Texans and then by Daniel Govan's brigade.

Cheatham and his corps were to his left, spread out north from the railroad for at least two miles. Wheeler's own dismounted troopers lay in shallow trenches from the railroad to the hill. For what it counted, he believed the Georgia Militia lay behind him, protected by the fortifications of Atlanta. Later, near dawn, all of Cleburne's division would be moving toward his line and augment the forces defending the eastern approaches to Atlanta. Wheeler thought, *"If I have to use my cavalry as infantry, it will be good to keep the high ground and be responsible for a little less length of trench line."*

Along the hilltop, the troopers would soon try to get a few hours of sleep. It would not be easy to do so with the knowledge that at least two Federal divisions were facing them about 600 yards to the east and that the sun would soon peek over the horizon.

For the Union, it would be a vastly different task to root out the newly augmented defensive Confederate force that lay spread out before the Federal Seventeenth Army Corps.

CHAPTER FIFTY-THREE

Confederacy | JOHN HOOD

STEWART'S HEADQUARTERS

WEST PACES FERRY ROAD, NORTH SIDE OF ATLANTA

JULY 20, 1864

EVENING

The attempt to smash into the advancing Union force and roll it up right into the river had not gone as well in the execution as it had in the planning, and Hood was already well on his way to explaining the situation to himself.

Hood wasn't sure what more he could have done. He had gathered his senior commanders together and explained the entire operation. They had all seemed to understand what was expected of them before they went back to their commands. But in the end, they had wasted too much time. Cheatham had bungled his first simple corps move, and Hardee had made it worst. It seemed to Hood that Hardee's corps had stalled before it started. Lee never had these kinds of problems.

Here, though, good judgment seemed in short supply. Perhaps it was that the army had been retreating too long. Troops hadn't fought up to their potential, and tremendous opportunity was thus lost along the creek and the high ground above it.

Reports continued to float into the headquarters. Some reports were couched in terms to make both the sender and receiver feel good. Others explained the situation plainly. Then, there were those continuing reports from Wheeler. All day, Wheeler had sought aid as he resisted some kind of Federal force moving west from Decatur toward Atlanta's eastern wall of fortification. Hood wondered if Wheeler understood the fact that most of the Union army was right here in front of Stewart's and Hardee's corps.

Either way, late in the afternoon, Hood had finally been able to shake Cleburne's division free and send it to help Wheeler. As he understood it, Cleburne had not even gotten into the fight raging to his north. In effect, he had been just standing there. The presence of Cleburne's veterans should stiffen the resolve of both Cheatham and Wheeler. It was probably impossible to expect much of Smith and his Georgia Militia.

Hood sat, thought, and checked his map. Where was the next opportunity to come from? How could Sherman's blue tide be checked and destroyed? The decision to hit the Federals' right while the army was divided was clearly the right thing to have done. Maybe he should try the Yankee center or maybe the far left. If the Union soldiers were really past the railroad, the forces must be spread thin. It was an enormous distance from the Chattahoochee River to where Wheeler's troops were holding Bald Hill. Hell, Hood figured it must be twelve or thirteen miles. There must be a weakness somewhere in a line so long.

It seemed obvious to Hood as he sat staring at the map that Sherman was moving toward the rail lines to the south of the city. Hood thought that Sherman must intend to push his left down and around the city's southern defenses and cut that valuable line of supply and communication. At the same time, Sherman would keep pressure on the north side of Atlanta with the force that had moved so quickly across Peachtree Creek. The railroad between Atlanta and Macon, some ninety miles to the south, was critical to holding the city. It was likewise critical to the survival of the Army of Tennessee. That railway must not be cut or destroyed.

Hood didn't know that at the beginning of the campaign, Grant and Sherman had discussed the importance of keeping the Confederate's western army from reinforcing Lee in Virginia. By keeping pressure on both Lee in Virginia and Johnston in Georgia, neither could come to the aid of the other. In other words, the Chickamauga option, in which Lee had dispatched Longstreet's entire corps by rail to Braxton Bragg, would be closed.

Now, here in Atlanta, on a smaller scale, Hood could see the same tactic was being executed. As General Thomas and his huge Army of the Cumberland advanced from the north across Peachtree Creek, Sherman could maneuver with McPherson's force coming in from the east. Hood had the advantage of interior lines, but he recognized that though they may be interior, they were too long for his army.

As he had planned earlier, that first line of defense would have to be abandoned. He needed to bring the Army of Tennessee back into the main defensive works, where the distance would not be so great. It would give them more flexibility.

CHAPTER FIFTY-FOUR

Union | JAMES MCPHERSON

HEADQUARTERS OF THE ARMY OF THE TENNESSEE

SOUTH OF THE DECATUR ROAD, TWO MILES EAST OF THE OUTER CONFEDERATE LINE

JULY 20, 1864

8:00 P.M.

At the end of the day on July 20, the Army of the Tennessee had halted on its western trek towards the city. The Confederate line lay about a mile ahead and the inner ring of Rebel fortification another mile beyond.

McPherson sat at his field desk thinking about the disposition of his three corps and how the day had gone. Out ahead of him were the soldiers who fought for John Logan, the men of the Fifteenth Army Corps. They had moved out of Decatur and now were entrenching along a line that ran north and south and crossed the Atlanta-Decatur road. Their position lay about two miles west of him, and he judged it to be about three miles from the center of downtown Atlanta. The Fifteenth Army Corps covered about a mile of front. They would remain in place, essentially holding the enemy troops before it and preventing them from supporting those on the hill. In addition to the infantry force, the three divisions had thirty-four tubes of artillery. Twelve of these pieces were rifled guns of one sort or another, and the other twenty-four were 12-pound Napoleons and howitzers.

To the north of the road were the men of the 1st Division, under Brigadier General Charles Woods. On the far right was its 1st Brigade, under Colonel Milo Smith. His troops were stretched to the north in an effort to tie into the Twenty-Third Army Corps, under Major General Schofield. Its 2nd Division, under Brigadier General Morgan Smith, was composed of two brigades. He was tucked into the left of Wood's

1st Division. His soldiers crossed the road and over the tracks and the wide, deep railroad cut. This division had some twelve regiments made up of men who hailed mostly from the states of Illinois and Ohio.

The 4th Division, under Brigadier General Harrow, lay to the south of the road. The 4th Division was operating in concert with the Seventeenth Army Corps and as a result were back a bit from the line established by the 1st and 2nd Divisions.

It would be tomorrow before Blair's corps moved forward in effort to take Bald Hill, whose summit lay about a mile south of the Decatur Road. Meanwhile, the 4th Divisions of the Fifteenth and Seventeenth Army Corps were in communication with each other and were prepared to actively support each other. Logan and Blair were both easy about these ad hoc arrangements and trusted their subordinates to do the right thing. Crossing corps chains of command concerned McPherson, but the system seemed to work.

Further to the south, about three quarters of a mile from the railroad and not quite as far forward, were the two divisions of the Seventeenth Army Corps. On the left, preparing for the morning assault, was the 3rd Division. On the right and next to it was the 4th Division, which had been operating under Brigadier General Gresham. McPherson reflected on who should replace the felled division commander. Although it would be disruptive, the best he could do was order Brigadier General Giles Smith from his position as commander of the 1st Brigade in his brother's 2nd Division of the Fifteenth Army Corps. That needed to be done right now.

The 4th Division, to which Giles Smith would be sent, would be held in reserve, but it would push forward, if needed, into the space north of Bald Hill. Once the attack on the hill was successful, the Union line would be anchored by troops on that commanding height. From that point, the line would extend north to the railroad, a distance of more than one mile. From the railroad, the line would continue until contact could be made with the leftmost units of Schofield's Army of the Ohio. That was where he would move all, or part, of Dodge's Sixteenth Army Corps the next day. For now, they could remain in reserve back along the road to Decatur.

Dodge's boys had led the way from Marietta to Roswell and across the Chattahoochee River. They had been the last to leave Decatur. In fact, one of his brigades, under John Sprague, was to remain in

Decatur to guard the wagon trains. Dodge's Sixteenth Army Corps sounded larger than it was. In fact, its fighting force was only three brigades, a total of eleven regiments plus four batteries of twenty-two artillery pieces.

The terrain along the Union line undulated from north to south, generally falling in elevation from the north to the south. South of the railway, the elevation began to climb up toward the two high mounds that together made up Bald Hill. The men in the 2nd and 4th Divisions could see Bald Hill, but as of yet, they did not occupy it.

McPherson thought everything was in good order. He felt confident that he understood the ground and the way his army occupied it. Moreover, he had a plan to capture the big hill in the morning. He needed to publish his field orders to his subordinates and get a report off to Sherman. He was ready to begin.

Special Field Orders No 73
HDQRS. DEPT. AND ARMY OF THE TENN.
In the Field, three and a half miles from Atlanta.
July 20, 1864.

I. In accordance with directions of Major-General Sherman, Brigadier-General Garrard, commanding cavalry division, will destroy McAfee's Bridge across Chattahoochee River. General Garrard will cover Roswell depot and protect the trains of this army.

II. Corps commanders will cause their several positions to be entrenched to-night, and will have their commands in line of battle at 3:30 to-morrow morning, ready to repel any attacks of the enemy.

III. Brig. Gen. G. A. Smith, U.S. Volunteers, is hereby relieved from command of the First Brigade, Second Division, Fifteenth Army Corps, and will forthwith report to Maj. Gen. F.P. Blair for assignment to command of the Fourth Division, Seventeenth Army Corps.

By order of Maj. Gen. James B. McPherson:

WM. T. Clark,
Assistant Adjutant-General.

HDQRS. DEPARTMENT AND ARMY OF THE TENNESSEE
In Field, July 20, 1864—8:45 p.m.

Major-General SHERMAN, Comdg. Military Div. Of the Mississippi:

GENERAL:

Enclosed I send you a sketch of our position to-night. We have had some pretty lively skirmishing and have driven the enemy from several pretty strong positions, though I do not think there has been much of anything but cavalry in front of us on the left. But they have had four pieces of artillery and are armed with short Enfield rifles, making it difficult at times to dislodge them. Brigadier-General Gresham, commanding Fourth Division, Seventeenth Army Corps, was wounded in the leg below the knee by a minie-ball, which shattered the bone, and I am afraid he will lose his leg. I have assigned Brig. Gen. Giles A. Smith to the command of the division. You will see from the sketch that my left (Blair's command) is in lot 207, and the line runs nearly north, the right breaking to the rear slightly to connect with General Schofield. General Garrard's headquarters are in Decatur and his command is so disposed as to cover our rear and lines of communications back to Roswell. Our losses have been comparatively light.

Very respectfully, your obedient servant,

JAS. B. MCPHERSON,
Major-General.

CHAPTER FIFTY-FIVE

Confederacy | JOHN HOOD

SOUTH ON HOWELL MILL ROAD

JULY 20, 1864

LATE EVENING

It was evening, and the field of red clay was slowly releasing the heat from the afternoon sun. This piece of dirt lay south of the outer fortifications that Hardee's and Stewart's corps had charged from earlier in a vain attempt to dislodge Thomas' Union forces from the high ground south of Peachtree Creek.

Although he rode with a small escort, Hood was alone with his thoughts. Hood thought that it would get cooler, which would be a blessing, as it would provide some relief to those wounded boys on both sides. His long beard seemed to pull his face earthward, as if it were the force of gravity itself, and the hair of his moustache was turning white and seemed to make his face glow.

Hood rode well for a man with only one good leg. This current ride was an effort to clear his head from all that was going on at the headquarters. He knew he would soon be back to the house owned by Ira Foster, which stood a little less than halfway between the outer line of trenches and the heavy inner line that lay closer to Atlanta. Once he arrived, he would be in the middle of the busy, well-intentioned staff officers who worked for both himself and General Stewart.

It had been a long, hard, frustrating day. Nothing had gone as he had planned. His ability to guide and control his mount stirred his anger at being unable to do the same with the troops he had put into motion earlier in the afternoon. They had been retreating too long. They had lost their edge.

He also worried that Cleburne's division would not get in place to relieve Wheeler's force in time. Patrick Cleburne might not really be a Southerner or a professional soldier, but he was as reliable and stalwart a general as Hood had available.

As he rode, men were being moved toward the tents and houses to be worked on by the dirty-handed, aproned, and blood-splattered surgeons. Men who had been vital to the cause would come out from these places without an arm or leg—or more. It was a crude assembly line full of anguish and pain. There were plenty of sharp edges, knives, and saws, but damn little hope or relief, and none of it with a guarantee.

Hood knew it all too well. After all, he was the product of the surgeon's knife, probe, and saw. He knew the hell that each of those who embarked on this trail would endure. It was different for these men, many of them only boys. They were there because of his orders for the assault up the hill and into Thomas' Army of the Cumberland. The future for a one-legged or one-armed man was not good, but first they would have to survive the hospitals. The hospitals were often more deadly than the battlefield.

In a sense, these men were wounded three times: once by the ball or shrapnel from their blue-clad former countrymen, next by the physical movement to the rear, and finally at the hands of a dirty, knife-wielding, sometimes drunken surgeon. Which wound was worse?

There was something pure and glorious in the charge and defense, but the dying and the aftermath was a horror all men who clamored for the war should visit, view, and if possible live with. It would be worse tomorrow when, as he envisioned, Sherman's Yankee soldiers would be dying in their own trenches.

Later, he tried to find a comfortable position he could compose a report to Richmond in. Hood refused to be disheartened by the lack of success the assault on Thomas achieved. After all, the fault did not lie with him. Seeking the best possible face on the matter, Hood composed the following to the Richmond command authority:

Atlanta, July 20, 1864—11p.m.

Hon. J. A. Seddon:
At 3 o'clock to-day a portion of Hardee's and Stewart's corps drove the enemy into his breast-works, but did not gain possession of them. Our loss was slight, Brigadier-General Stevens severely wounded. On our extreme right the enemy attacked Wheeler's cavalry with infantry, and was handsomely repulsed.

J.B. Hood
General

Hood was worn out and pretty well used up for the day. He would just close his eyes for a brief instant. He needed to make plans, but he needed to shut his eyes for a little while. It was clear from what he had seen and the reports he had received that his first sally against the Yankees had achieved mixed results at best. It was obvious that Hardee was at fault. Hardee had waited too long. He was supposed to begin the attack at 1:00 p.m. and had delayed for reasons of his own until almost 4:00. Hardee was what was wrong with this army: too old, too slow, and now too accustomed to hiding behind earthworks.

Tired as he was, Hood knew that before retiring, he had to study the situation on the ground as he understood it to exist. The main point was that he was in command of a two-deep defense: the two lines of trenches outside Atlanta.

The first line ran from Casey's Hill, not far from the river, for about 5.5 miles, and then south along the high ground down to the railroad. He was certain a good horseman with a good local guide and a good map could ride from one end to the other in three or four hours. He knew, too, that he was not going to make that ride but rather would have to rely on the never-ending stream of reports and returns from various commanders who found themselves on this outer line of trenches.

Hood looked at his map. This long east-west line protected the northern approaches to the city. The easternmost point was about four and a half miles northeast of the city center. From this point, the Confederate line ran down the ridgeline south for two and a half miles, where it then struck the road connecting Decatur to Atlanta.

Most importantly, Hood needed to know with greater certainty where Billy Sherman's army was and what he planned to do with it. Thomas, with his army or corps, was now firmly established south of Peachtree Creek. He was digging in along the high ground of Collier's Road and would probably continue to dig. From Wheeler, Hood believed that McPherson, with another large group, was on the move from Decatur to Atlanta.

It was likely that McPherson intended to move south in order to tear up the rail link to Macon. The attack today reminded Hood that the two large groups of Union soldiers were separated and probably could not support one another. The day before, Wheeler's horsemen had delayed Yankees in at least division strength as they tried to cross at Cheshire Bridge. Those Federals could easily be moving to fill in the gap that had promised so much. McPherson posed a real and gathering problem.

In addition, there was a third and smaller group that had crossed the Chattahoochee first, days ago. They, too, had been reported moving toward Decatur. Hood figured that they were likely the troops skirmishing along Cheatham's front to the east. If so, they lay between the two larger Federal forces.

From this point on, he was less certain about the current circumstances on the ground. He hoped Cleburne's division from Hardee's corps was moving into the trenches south of the railroad and pushing Wheeler's dismounted horsemen off to the south, thus extending the line an additional mile. Hood knew that Cleburne should brace up Cheatham's right, bolster Wheeler, and answer the prayers of General Smith and his militia. Given the number of soldiers Wheeler had and the length of the line, Wheeler's forces were stretched very thin. It was less than perfect, but it would have to do until he could get back on the offensive.

Hood knew that complete knowledge of his own army's situation was not possible, but he thought he had enough information to serve as a beginning point to plan for the situation that confronted him, his personal and professional hopes, and the hopes of the Richmond government and this fledgling Southern nation.

What could the next strike be? Where should it fall? He knew he could not hope for assistance from the army fighting in Virginia. That had worked once last year in north Georgia, but it seemed impossible now.

Hood began to use the process of elimination. A frontal assault against Thomas was to be avoided. Likewise, it would be difficult to mount a flank attack on either of those increasingly well-entrenched wings. Thomas had his right up against Peachtree Creek, and his left would be no easier tomorrow than it had already proved to be. On the other hand, he anticipated that today's contest would prevent any immediate attack from Thomas.

The Yankee force that lay northeast of the city was less understood by Hood. The ground he thought they occupied was rough and hilly. The size of this force eluded him, and the location of the left and right flanks were simply matters of speculation. An assault on either of these poorly understood locations would probably result in a call on Thomas on the right or McPherson on the left. Hood's intuition told him that while both those Union commanders might be cautious, both would ultimately respond to an opportunity to surprise and smash any such attacking force. This did not seem to be the avenue to approach.

Since neither of these first two Union forces seemed to present a winning opportunity, he knew he must examine the third component of Sherman's army: McPherson. McPherson often acted as the maneuver element for the Union force, and this was exactly what he was now. Could he be hit before he struck the city or before he was entrenched to such a degree that it would make success difficult? Or was McPherson sliding off to the south toward East Point and the south-side railroad? Without Wheeler prowling about, Hood was blind to those hidden movements.

These queries seemed to demand that McPherson's left be hit and hit soon. Hood wondered if he could get a strong enough force behind the Union left to smash it with resolution. Could the rest of Sherman's army be fixed and held while he turned the Yankees' left? Moreover, could his attacking force get some help if the initial action was successful?

Hood thought to himself, *"What would Robert E. Lee do?"* His idea about the Union left was on the right track, Hood knew, but what *exactly* would Lee do?

"Well, Lee would make something happen," Hood said aloud. Lee wouldn't wait for something to go wrong with the enemy side. He would instigate the action. He would strike.

Reflection on the moving pieces he had available left him troubled. Wheeler's cavalry was not heavy enough for an attack of the sort he envisioned. What he needed was hard-hitting infantry. But who exactly should strike the Union left? Stewart wasn't much of an option. He was a long way from the critical objective, and he was largely untried. Cheatham was a bold fighter, damned hard to whip in the defense. It was a big step to move from a division to a corps though, and it took a very special professional to handle such a move in such a short period. Cheatham's move earlier that day did not instill confidence. Once again, Hood was pushed to the conclusion that he must rely on the tried and proven four divisions of Hardee's corps.

They had done next to nothing in the past several days and should be the freshest he had. He would have to move everyone back from the outer ring of trenches to the main inner line. This would be a smaller ring and could allow him to remove Hardee's men and still cover the line.

Hardee probably resented him and the fact that he was now the army commander. He was also slow and old. But Hood recognized that Hardee was the best hammer for the nail he had in mind. Great commanders had to be great with the assets available. He would call the four corps commanders together, listen to them, and get this plan in front of them. Maybe he could get them on the road tomorrow. Would it be possible to get a division or two back to Decatur and hit McPherson's entire force from the rear? Hood would find out.

In the field, near Atlanta, July 21, 1864—1a.m.

General Mcpherson,
Army of the Tennessee:

General: I have yours of 8:45 last evening, and regret much the wound which will deprive us of the services of General Gresham. I was in hopes you could have made a closer approach to Atlanta yesterday, as I was satisfied you had a less force and more inferior works than will be revealed by daylight, if, as I than will be revealed by daylight, if, as I suppose, Hood proposes to hold Atlanta to the death. All afternoon heavy and desperate sallies were made against Thomas, all along his lines from left to right, particularly heavy against Newton and Geary, but in every instance he was roughly handled; considerable firing has been going on all night along Howard's lines, and still continues. Tomorrow I propose to press along the whole line, and try to advance Thomas, so that we will command the Chattahoochee's east bank, and contract our lines by diminishing the circle. I think to-morrow Hood will draw from his left and re-enforce his right. Nevertheless, I deem it necessary that you should gain ground so that your artillery can reach the town easily, say within 1,000 yards of the inner or main lines. I have ordered Garrard to send to Roswell his wagons and impediments and push rapidly and boldly on the bridges across the Yellow River and Ulcofauhachee, near Covington, to be gone two days. Give orders that in the mean time no trains come up to you from Roswell. He will substantially cover the road back because all the cavalry in that direction will be driven away, still some squads might be left about Stone Mountain, as he will take the direct road from Decatur to Covington, passing considerably south of Stone Mountain. Order your ordinance wagons and those that you may have left about Decatur up to your immediate rear. I will ride over to see Thomas to-morrow morning and would like to hear from you before starting. If at any time you see signs of retreat on the part of the enemy follow up with all possible vigor, keeping to the left or south of Atlanta and following roads that will keep you on the flank. If Hood was as roughly handled by Thomas this afternoon as reported, and in addition the little artillery he has displayed to-day, I would not be astonished to find him off in the morning, but I see no signs looking that way yet. In case he retreats it will be toward Macon, whither all the advance stores have been sent, and most of the provisions. I want him pursued vigorously for a couple of days.

Yours, truly,
W.T. Sherman
Major-General Commanding.

July 21, 1864

CHAPTER FIFTY-SIX

Confederacy | PATRICK CLEBURNE | *Union* | JAMES MCPHERSON

CLEBURNE'S LINE

JULY 21, 1864

DAWN

CONFEDERACY, PATRICK CLEBURNE

Patrick Cleburne knew he had already lived two lives completely. By the same reckoning, he knew that he was well advanced into his third. In his first life, he was Irish, born in 1828. His family was Protestant, and his father was a well-to-do physician. He had many advantages then, such as attending private schools. When his father died, the family experienced hard times. Cleburne's failing the examination to enter the apothecary trade compounded this.

In humiliation, at age eighteen, Cleburne joined Her Majesty's 41st Regiment of Foot. He served three years and was posted near Dublin, where he rose to the rank of corporal. Between 1845 and 1849, Ireland suffered through the period known as the Potato Famine. Millions of poor Irish suffered and died. The involvement of the army in evictions and law enforcement was a difficult and unpleasant role for a young Irishman. Cleburne worked hard, and after his promotion to corporal, promises were made of a commissioned future. Nonetheless after three years, Cleburne purchased his discharge. Soon thereafter, with his siblings and mother, he left for America.

Upon landing in New Orleans in 1849, his second life began. In Helena, Arkansas, he became a partner in a drugstore, and then seeking greater opportunity, he sold his interest in the drugstore and studied law. At age twenty-eight, in 1856, he began his legal practice. He became a vestryman at St. John's Episcopal Church and joined the

Sons of Temperance. His practice was successful, and he had harvested much of what America promised her new citizens.

His third life began in 1860 when he joined the local militia as a private. As larger units were formed and war clouds were rising, he gained a promotion: colonel and commander of the 15th Arkansas.

Cleburne never owned a slave, and it was an accident of geography that made him a Confederate. Location and loyalty played important roles. He believed that Southerners had been his friends and had stood with him, and now he was going to stand by his new friends in his adopted homeland.

Cleburne was almost six feet tall. He was slender, shy, and reserved. His face was lean with high cheekbones, and he carried a full head of black hair. He carried himself like a British officer with a stiff, straight back. This made quite a contrast with the men he commanded, who moved with the relaxed posture of the frontier. Cleburne was disciplined and seemed different from those around him. With all that said, Patrick Cleburne was a superb fighter and leader.

By 1862, Cleburne was promoted to brigadier general. In numerous instances on the field, he earned his wreath and star and the position of command that went with them. His brigade performed well at Shiloh, and his two brigades played an important role in the battle near Richmond, Kentucky, where Cleburne was wounded. Cleburne's handling of his troops is credited with saving the Army of Tennessee after the disaster at Missionary Ridge.

Throughout all this, Cleburne became personally close to General Hardee. He had met Hardee when the 15th Arkansas joined with Hardee's forces. Cleburne's view of Hardee grew into one of respect and admiration that Hardee reciprocated. It was with pleasure that Cleburne accepted the request to serve as Hardee's best man in his wedding to his twenty-six-year-old bride, Mary Foreman Lewis. This was Hardee's second marriage, and it created a great stir and great festivities. The wedding was held in the plantation known as Bleak House, which was near Demopolis, Alabama. There, in the dazzling merriment, Cleburne met and fell in love with Susan Tarleton of Mobile at thirty-six.

Cleburne had been on top of the world. He was buoyed by his view of the future with Susan. He also believed he knew how to win the war. He gave the topic serious thought and arrived at a serious answer. Thus, early in 1864, while the army was wintering in Dalton, Georgia, Cleburne made a revolutionary suggestion. All of the senior military leadership could tell that the South was experiencing great difficulty in replacing the men they were losing from battle, disease, and desertion. This strategic difficulty was exacerbated by the fact that the Federals seemed to be able to deliver ever-increasing numbers to their army.

Cleburne's suggestion, which he put into writing, was that slaves be armed and trained to fight on behalf of the South. The incentive was to be freedom. This idea was received as though a bomb had exploded. Certain generals who were at odds with the transplanted Irishman for one reason or another made certain Cleburne's document reached President Davis in Richmond. It is doubtful that Cleburne ever understood the political firestorm his idea would create. His idea died, in the sense that it would not be put into effect in the immediate future.

But it also cast a lingering shadow over Cleburne to such an extent that he would never see promotion beyond his divisional command even though Cleburne was arguably the finest general in the Army of Tennessee. His ability was restless, hard- driving, and compelling, but merit within the military hierarchy is not always rewarded or looked upon with institutional enthusiasm. Between January 2, 1864, and July 21, 1864, the South had three opportunities to promote Cleburne from divisional command to corps leadership within the Army of Tennessee. The departure of John Breckinridge, the death of Polk, and the promotion of Hood all created a chance to select Cleburne to greater things, but he remained a divisional commander. This position was nonetheless a considerable achievement for a former British corporal.

Cleburne's birth, the fact that he was not a West Point graduate, and his willingness to propound a doctrine that would undercut the basis of Southern slavery combined to deprive the South of one of the great soldiers. Cleburne had dealt a blow—a blow only Cleburne could launch and that would redound to the Union's advantage. Yet even if he was personally or professionally disappointed, Cleburne's leadership never faltered, and his division was seen as the one to use when results were required.

Depending on who was looking at him, Cleburne seemed to be two different men. To some, when he was off the battlefield and away from troops, he was quiet, shy, and phlegmatic. He evidenced some insecurity, perhaps caused by his experience as a general up from the ranks and his immigrant status. This same sense of lacking may have provided the motivation that demanded he excel. He pushed his troops hard in training. If desire, time, and effort could improve his soldiers, then they surely would be improved.

On the battlefield, whatever lack of emotion he might have in a social situation would disappear. In its place, a furious, demanding, commanding greatness would seize him. As the bugle sounded and the advance began, the cape of charisma would envelop Cleburne. The battle light would shine from his eyes so that to follow was easier than not to and so that little short of death would prevent success.

Generally, he was in the forefront of the battle. The Hardee banner was always near him, and it was often the center of the action. Cleburne's inability to do anything other than lead by personal example resulted in wounds in his face and ankle. It also resulted in the loss of more than one horse. His demonstration of personal courage, excellence, and sense of mission combined in expressive and obvious leadership. His troops always followed, but less extraordinary officers resented his success.

Just the afternoon before, Cleburne's troops had started their march through the city and out the Decatur-Atlanta road to bolster Wheeler's sparse line of horse soldiers. His unit marched through Atlanta at night, moved east along the railroad tracks, and, at about midnight, halted to allow for about two hours sleep. His force had been on the move for more than eighteen hours. Arising well before dawn, his division continued until they reached the line of entrenchments.

The right of Cheatham's corps still ran north from the railroad. This section consisted of Manigault's five regiments and Hindmen's division, now under the command of Brigadier General John C. Brown. Manigault's brigade rested on the north side of the tracks, and Wheeler's exhausted horsemen stretched south to Bald Hill. Wheeler's men were on Cleburne's right. First came Iverson's five regiments of Georgians. In the middle, on top of Bald Hill, were the five Alabama regiments of Allen. Extending south from the hill's crest and down the hill were three regiments, all under Ferguson.

Cleburne was responsible for about 1,300 yards of line and had about 4,500 men in fifteen regiments. His soldiers were on a slight rise that dipped in the middle and then rose as it began to climb up the flank of Bald Hill.

Cleburne, as always, came with a plan. He would dislodge as many of Wheeler's troops as possible and push them south to a manageable front. His three brigades under Lowrey, Govan, and Smith would align themselves in that order with Smith on the right and next to Wheeler.

As his three hundred men of Hiram Granbury's Texans began to move the willing cavalrymen to their right, Cleburne had a chance to talk with Wheeler. They agreed that the job at hand was to keep the blue tide from entering Atlanta. They both anticipated that this would be a rough day. Walker suspected the Federals would start soon after dawn and said he'd admonish his commanders to tell the worn-out men to be watchful as the sun was making its appearance.

As Cleburne's soldiers entered the ditches, they discovered their bias against cavalry troops was correct this time. The trenches were hardly more than scratching in the clay. Ditches dug by slaves and militia who did not have to occupy them were nearly useless. Those exhausted horse soldiers who were there before Cleburne's soldiers, and who had hoped they could ride out of there on horseback, had done little to improve them. They were certainly inadequate to use as a place to repulse veteran Federal troops from. The line had also been poorly laid out and exposed the troops stationed within it to enfilade or flank fire. Under artillery fire, the ditches would be completely useless. As skilled civil engineers, the nearly 5,000 men under Cleburne immediately turned their attention to building suitable earthworks.

The second part of Cleburne's plan was to halt the advance of McPherson with the help of the rest of the Confederate troops.

UNION, JAMES MCPHERSON

As the dawn broke, McPherson's Army of the Tennessee was in place. North of the rail line, the Fifteenth Army Corps were dug in, facing west, and holding a line of about half a mile in length. The rest of the line ran south to the northern approaches of Bald Hill, a distance of about another half-mile. The Seventeenth Army Corps lay due east of Bald Hill and were prepared to assault the commanding crest.

What had been a small, determined Confederate force confronting McPherson was now a considerably larger and no less determined force, manned in part by some of the best the South had left to offer.

Artillery fire from the Fifteenth Army Corps began to fire, for range and effect, at about 7:00 a.m. into the trench line manned by Cleburne's division. Men in those trenches could smell the cannon smoke mingled with smoke from wood fires and the fragrance of hot, boiling Yankee coffee.

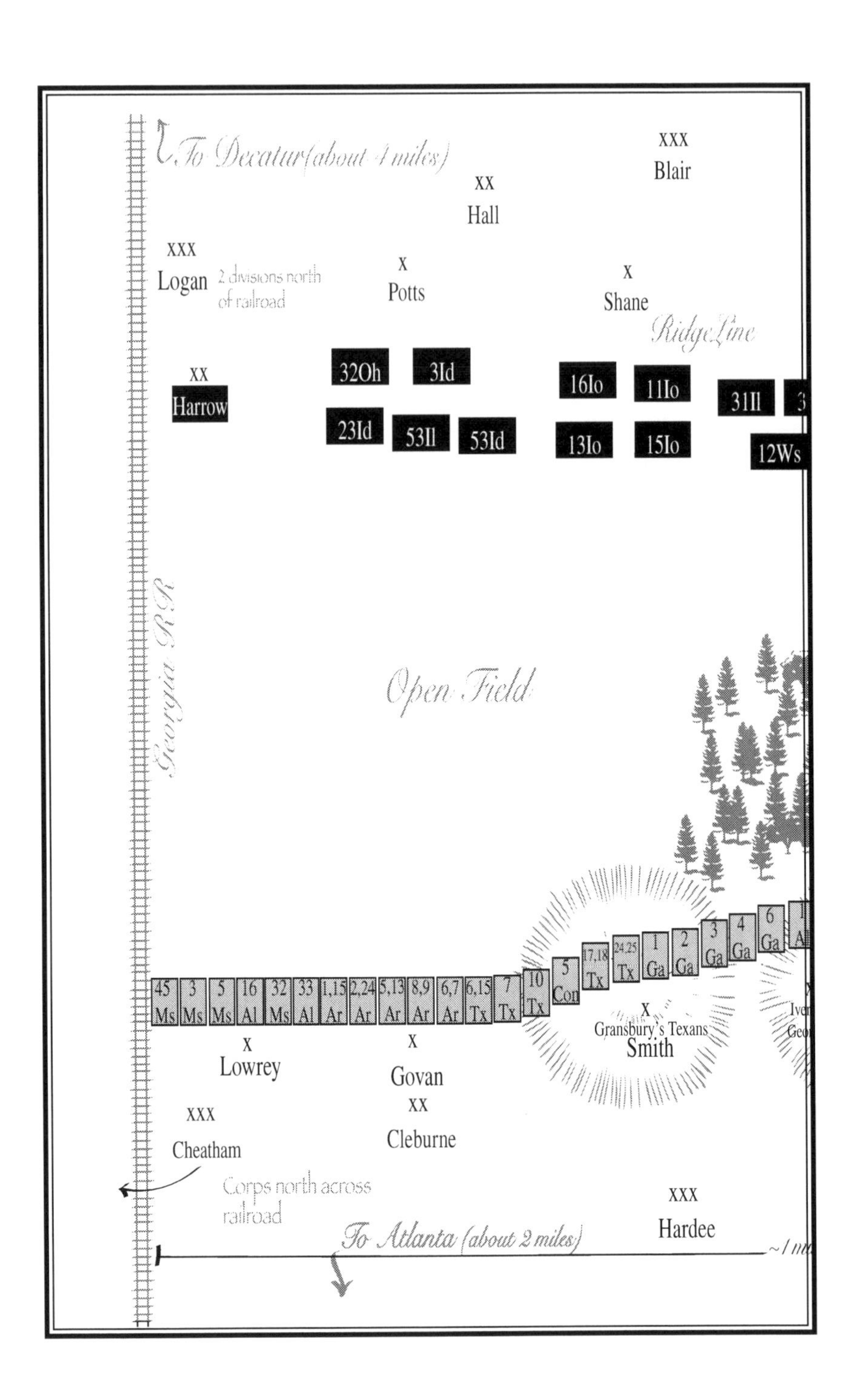
To Decatur (about 4 miles)
XXX
Blair
XX
Hall
XXX
Logan
2 divisions north of railroad
X
Potts
X
Shane
Ridge Line
XX
Harrow
32Oh
3Id
16Io
11Io
31Il
23Id
53Il
53Id
13Io
15Io
12Ws
Georgia RR
Open Field
45 Ms
3 Ms
5 Ms
16 Al
32 Ms
33 Al
1,15 Ar
2,24 Ar
5,13 Ar
8,9 Ar
6,7 Ar
6,15 Tx
7 Tx
10 Tx
5 Con
17,18 Tx
24,25 Tx
1 Ga
2 Ga
3 Ga
4 Ga
6 Ga
X
Gransbury's Texans
Smith
X
Lowrey
X
Govan
XX
Cleburne
XXX
Cheatham
Corps north across railroad
XXX
Hardee
To Atlanta (about 2 miles)

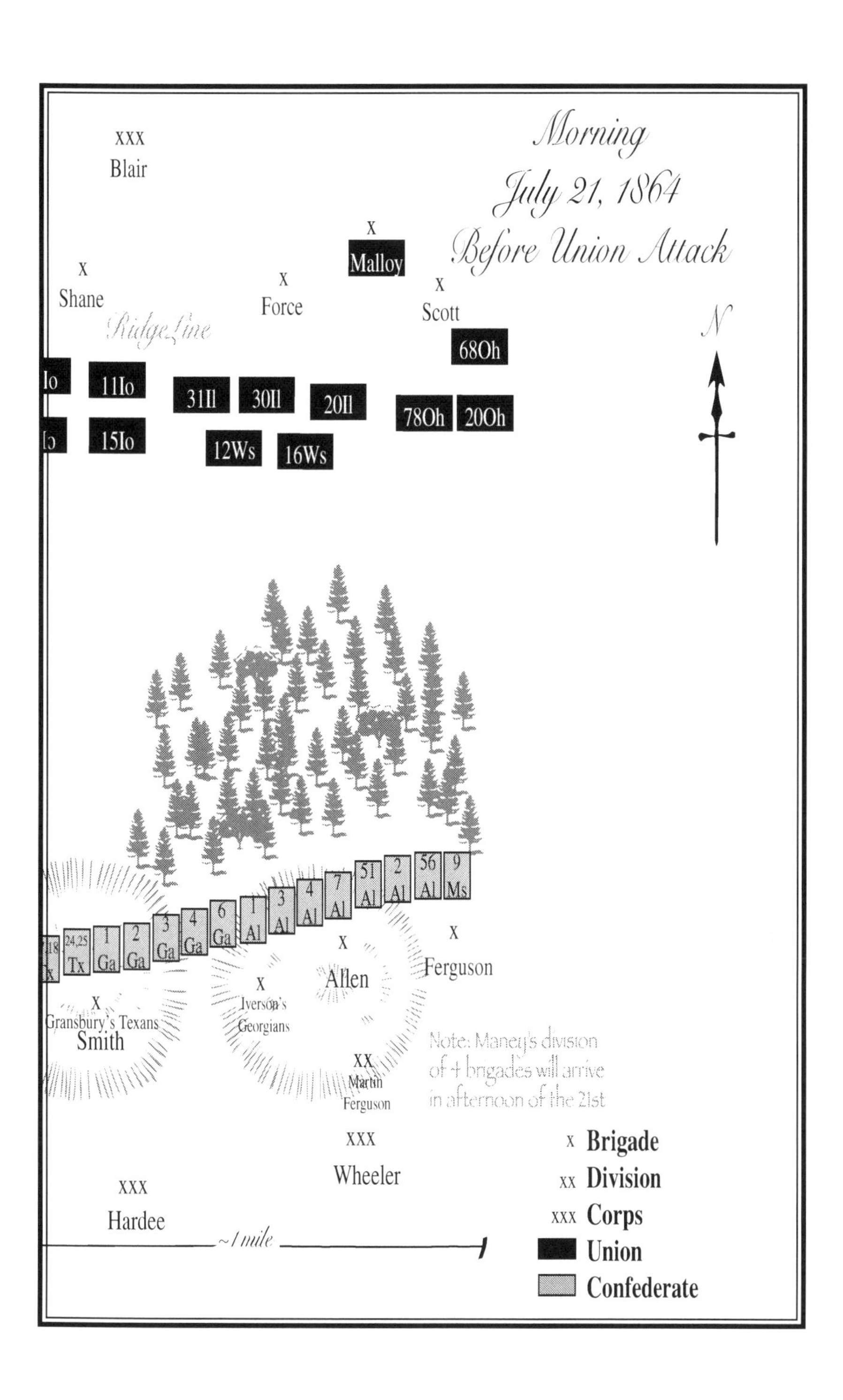

Morning
July 21, 1864
Before Union Attack
XXX
Blair
X
Shane
X
Force
X
Malloy
X
Scott
Ridge Line
N
68Oh
11Io
31Il
30Il
20Il
78Oh
20Oh
15Io
12Ws
16Ws
24,25 Tx
1 Ga
2 Ga
3 Ga
4 Ga
6 Ga
1 Al
3 Al
4 Al
7 Al
51 Al
2 Al
56 Al
9 Ms
X
Ferguson
X
Allen
X
Iverson's Georgians
X
Gransbury's Texans
Smith
Note: Maney's division of 4 brigades will arrive in afternoon of the 21st
XX
Martin Ferguson
XXX
Wheeler
XXX
Hardee
~1 mile
X Brigade
XX Division
XXX Corps
Union
Confederate

CHAPTER FIFTY-SEVEN

UNION

Battery F, 1st Illinois and 1st Iowa,

Fifteenth Army Corps

About 300 yards south of the railroad

July 21, 1864

7:00 a.m.

The movement from the small town of Decatur toward Atlanta had been a stop-and-go affair. The small force of Confederate cavalry under General Wheeler was contesting the advance whenever the opportunity presented itself. McPherson's Army of the Tennessee was strung out along the two roads leading to Atlanta. Like all armies, if the Army of the Tennessee bunched up, troops would spill out of the roadway, teams would collide, and then skirmishers would forge ahead until the army would right itself and move forward.

Soldiers would promise themselves to leave more room between the heels and backside of the man in front of them than they had before. It would not be the first or last time marching men had made such promises to themselves or to those around them. It also wasn't the first or last time they would break those promises.

In the afternoon of July 20, troops had stopped marching and started digging, as was their well-developed habit. Wheeler's butternut troops had entrenched themselves across the road, and the fortifications of the city had seemed to announce themselves even though they were not yet visible to the columns of marching men. The resistance of the Southerners was increasingly stiff as they neared the city. The Union line troops dug into the military crest of the ridgeline, very nearly mimicking the line that lay about a mile ahead and contained a growing number of Rebel soldiers. Between the two lines lay the deep ravines that sometimes held water flowing to the South River: the valley of Sugar Creek.

The two artillery batteries of the 4th Division of the Fifteenth Army Corps of McPherson's army had not gone into battery when the Union column had halted. Rather, they had waited, stretched out on the south side of the railroad. The men from the 1st Iowa and the 1st Illinois had heard the deep boom of the Union 20-pound Parrott rifles of Battery H as they fired into the city and occasionally into the ranks of the enemy stretched out on either side of the road and down to the strange-looking, treeless hill about a mile off to their left.

About 4:00 on July 20, the twelve guns of the two western batteries had been ordered forward. They were directed to the edge of the cornfield out in front of the slowly forming infantry trenches. The position was at the edge of the division's right flank, about 900 feet off the Decatur Road.

A Rebel battery had been at work from inside the tree line on the Rebel ridge to the west. It had fired at the troops from Blair's Seventeenth Army Corps as the Seventeenth made their way toward the area east of Bald Hill. The soldiers of the Seventeenth Army Corps moved with Gresham's 4th Division on the right and Leggett's 3rd Division on the left. Thus, the men of the 3rd Division had been in close contact with those Confederates on the ridge and were sharply engaged. The Rebel gun section was on the lower of the two peaks of Bald Hill and accordingly held a commanding position.

Around the same time, Lieutenants Gay and Burton with the Union artillery had objected when they saw the position they were being told to occupy. They had sought out Divisional Artillery Officer, Captain Griffiths, and Griffiths agreed that it was a most unlikely position. It was, in the minds of the three artillerymen, a miserable place that lacked any form of protection and would expose them to artillery fire from the front and rifle fire from the flanks. Major Maurice, the artillery officer, had come riding up and agreed with the opinion of the 4th Division men, but he was shortly overruled by a superior in rank and position, if not in military judgment. The two batteries soon formed in the open.

While awaiting permission to fire though, a well-hidden Rebel battery had opened fire against them, and in seconds it seemed, one man from Burton's guns had been dead. Soon, three Union men from the 1st Iowa battery had joined their companions on the ground before Atlanta. The fighting on the left slackened, and Gay's and Burton's men had begun erecting such protection as they could.

Now, on July 21, guns from Burton's and Gay's batteries were moved outside the protection created during the night. The target was too inviting. The guns went to work against Cleburne's line with the special intent of providing protection to the Union's 3rd Division of the Seventeenth Army Corps. Given the curved nature of the lines, the 4th Division guns were able to obtain nearly flank fire down the butternut line. This enfilading or galling fire, combined with the still shallow trenches, proved deadly to the Southern defenders.

The Federal cannon fire was quite effective. In the trench held by Confederate's 18th Texas, six men were beheaded and twelve were severely wounded by the passage of one shell. Within minutes, Smith's brigade had suffered forty killed and more than one hundred wounded. Cleburne was heard to have observed that it was the worst time of combat that he had seen.

Casualties among the men serving the twelve Union guns were slight.

CHAPTER FIFTY-EIGHT

Union | *Confederacy* | VARIOUS

EASTERN BASE OF BALD HILL

JULY 21, 1864

8:00 A.M.

UNION, MANNING FORCE

Manning F. Force sat easily on his horse. Force first became associated with military activities through his acceptance to the Club's Burnet Rifles. It was more social than military, but the members did learn the basics of drill and marching. Based in part on this experience, Force was commissioned as a major in the newly formed 20th Ohio Infantry Regiment after the war began. The regimental commander was a West Point graduate, Colonel Charles Whittlesey.

Whittlesey was called upon to design and build the fortifications for Cincinnati, and as a result, Force acquired the de facto command of the regiment. He was likewise responsible for its training. Through leadership and study, Force was able to train the men into a well-drilled organization. Because of his success, he was promoted to lieutenant colonel. He learned, or already knew, the art of delegation, but he would often appear where the training was taking place to offer suggestions and provide criticism. He was seen as a hard man by his troops, but they believed he tempered his discipline with fairness. The regiment saw its first combat as part of the Federal force that sought to take the Confederate bastion known as Fort Donelson. The command did well there.

The brigadier general was handsome and possessed a scholarly air, so much so that he might be confused for a staff officer. Closer inspection would reveal an intense penetrating gaze that seemed to capture everything it beheld and to file it for instant reuse. He had a patrician appearance with a high, intelligent forehead. The only hint that he was not a youth was the part on the left side of his head that began an inch or two farther back than one would expect. Force had a naturally curious cast to his face, and this was particularly apparent when he was thinking, which Force was doing now. He was concerned about the regimental alignment. The formation bothered him.

Force's brigade, under Leggett's 3rd Division of the Seventeenth Army Corps, was composed of four regiments from Illinois—the 20th, 30th, 31st, and 45th—as well as the 12th and 16th Wisconsin. All these were good veteran regiments whose combat worthiness had long been tested and proven time after time, with the exception of the 12th Wisconsin. The 12th Wisconsin, commanded by Colonel George Bryant, had not joined the division until July 10, and so it had been on board for only eleven days. Yet everyone believed the regiment was well manned and ably led.

Upon reporting to the 3rd Division, Colonel Bryant had come to a parade ground position of attention, locked his heels audibly, rendered a stiff and formal salute, and stated, "General Leggett, the 12th Wisconsin, Colonel George Bryant commanding, is reporting for duty as instructed."

Leggett replied, "Welcome to the 3rd Division. Glad to have you aboard."

Bryant had remained at attention and replied, "Glad to be here, sir. General, you should know, sir, that the 12th is a good regiment with good men."

"Never doubted it for an instant."

"As you may know, sir, they are veterans and have been in the service for three years. They have done much hard marching. Unfortunately, sir, we have never been under fire. Now, General, if you have any fighting to do, you must give us a chance."

Leggett smiled with understanding. "Colonel, you and your regiment will soon enough get all the chance you want."

Now, as a result of the order issued last night, the 12th Wisconsin was to be found in the front line of the formation. Force had been anxious about the matter and had a talk with Colonel Bryant after the troops had been bedded down for the night. Bryant had been convincing in his expressions of confidence about his soldiers. Force explained the assault was likely to be difficult, up a hill into entrenched positions against a skilled, resourceful enemy. The front line was always expected to do the most work, and the opportunity for death and danger were the greatest. Bryant remained adamant, and Force reluctantly conceded the point.

General Force wished he had ordered a new arrangement last night when there was time to change things without calling attention to what was happening or damaging the pride and morale of the 12th Wisconsin. Now it was too late to change anything. They had courage, and he would do nothing at this late time to diminish it. He would leave them in their place.

Nonetheless, both Leggett and Force viewed the coming assault with concern, especially with the 12th Wisconsin among the leading combat elements.

The organization for the assault was to have the 12th Wisconsin and the 16th Wisconsin in the front line, with the 12th on the left. Behind them in the second line of battle would be, from left to right, the 20th, 30th, and 31st Illinois. The 45th Illinois was already settled in the thick band of woods at the base of the hill as skirmishers. Colonel Robert Scott of the 3rd Division had his 2nd Brigade to the left of Force's 1st Brigade. Scott's 78th Ohio was next to the 20th Illinois with Scott's 20th Ohio to the left. In the rear, the small 3rd Brigade under Colonel Adam Malloy would act as the divisional reserve. This brigade consisted of only the 17th Wisconsin and the knocked-together Worden's Battalion.

General Force directed that all regimental commanders in his attacking brigade would advance on foot when the time came to attack. Ordinarily, they were mounted. The only exception to this directive was to be him and a few of the staff. In this way, Force believed his regimental commanders would not be so exposed to enemy fire, and he would have the height and mobility to enhance his ability to command. Beyond the composition of the line of battle, he ordered that all weapons be loaded but not fired until in the enemy works. The battle lines were to move forward with no halts or delays to reload along the way. The skirmishers, who had sneaked forward as close as possible to the enemy lines, would rush the enemy and fire as rapidly as possible with surprise on their side.

To these Union skirmishers hidden in the underbrush, the time for the initial assault seemed to have come and gone. Wheeler's Confederate troops from Ferguson's dismounted cavalry started their smoky breakfast campfires, and a few even came forward from their shallow trenches to stand or squat to relieve themselves. They were so close.

The Federal skirmishers remained still and quiet and, more importantly, undiscovered. The Confederate troopers were unaware of the Union presence and, for whatever reason, had no pickets of their own posted. The high ground, the earthworks, and the arrival of Cleburne's division had combined to inspire them to believe that the Union forces were still where they were the night before.

Back in the trees, consternation developed when it was realized that the 4th Division, now under Giles Smith as per McPherson's order the night before, had not been informed of their area of responsibility, the area immediately north of the 3rd Division. The attack by the Union 4th Division of the Seventeenth Army Corps would jump off about the same time as the main attack. Under Giles Smith's direction, his two brigades, under Potts and William Hall, would advance in support of the attack taking place to their left. An open field would lie ahead of Giles Smith's 4th Division, and behind the field were Cleburne's division in improved entrenchments, particularly the watchful soldiers of James Smith's Texas brigade.

The role to be played by the 4th Division was to assault the Confederate lines west of them. If they could get through and into them, all was well and good. If they could not get into them, then a strong show of force or a demonstration would at least encourage the thin brigades under Cleburne to stand their ground and not be useful as reserves or reinforcements to Wheeler's troops on Bald Hill, the hill that was the primary mission for the Seventeenth Army Corps, including Force.

Around 8:00 a.m., Force rose in his stirrups, drew his sword in his right hand, and from his position on the far right side of the brigade, he barked in his best, studied command voice, "Right shoulder, shift.... arms, forward, march!"

With an echo at each command level, the order rang out, guidons rose and fell, and the entire Union brigade struck out from their concealed positions. Color bearers removed the cases covering their regimental colors and unfurled their flags in the still morning air. The morning sun rising behind the Federals seemingly doubled their numbers from the effect of the shadows they cast. Long rifles, fixed bayonets, and the gasp of men at rapid movement all came together as the assault unleashed itself up the hill.

Ahead, the skirmishers had burst upon the Southerners, surprising them as they boiled coffee and fried bacon for their breakfast. The rapidly moving brigade came straight up the hill and soon merged with the advanced skirmishers, and together, they stormed the crest of the hill. The two regiments of Force's 2nd Brigade had moved forward on Force's command, climbing the hill from the southeast corner. The Union line on the hill overlapped the Rebel line by the width of the battlefront of these two regiments.

CONFEDERACY, SAMUEL FERGUSON

Now, cavalrymen don't generally make good infantry soldiers, at least not this early in the morning. Infantry, on both sides, often commented that despite all the dash and glory of the vaunted horsemen, something rarely seen on the battlefield was a dead cavalry trooper. Movement by foot or on horseback often kept horse soldiers alive. Today, some died, and many looked for a way of escape.

With the Union's movements and with the shift of the three brigades of Wheeler's horsemen to their right because of Cheatham's arrival, the three tired and worn regiments of Ferguson were put against Force's troops on the far right of the Confederate force. Insufficient time, inclination, or leadership had created a flank in the air, complete with typical shallow cavalry-style trenches.

Samuel Ferguson had been under Wheeler's direct command for only a short time. Ferguson knew that, in Wheeler's mind, almost any time was too long. Wheeler had resisted Ferguson's transfer from Jackson's command to Wheeler's own. But Wheeler got him anyway, and now Wheeler's dismounted troopers were poorly prepared for the charging, flanking, bayonet-bearing infantry from Scott's regiments as they rolled them up on the far right end of the Southern line.

Ferguson's men made some attempt at halting the aggressive Federals but then scampered away, creating a door for the Union. It was one thing to provide the enemy with a side door to the next brigade if that brigade was mounted and able to rearrange itself in a fluid, quick, coordinated cavalry maneuver. Yet the same open side door to a shallow trench when the neighboring brigade was merely posing as infantry presents quite another problem. The confused activities by Ferguson's three regiments helped dislocate Allen's brigade of six additional regiments of Alabama troopers, now with their right flank exposed.

The leftmost units of the Union battle line, which were in front of the Confederate's right, hit the right flank of Wheeler's corps. The Union line was longer than the enemy it was attacking, and that resulted in it overlapping Wheeler's corps. The overlapping units angled and wheeled to their right while the men in Force's brigade struck the enemy head on. Therefore, the Union attack came from two directions at once. This overlapping Union force consisted of the two units under Scott, the 20th and 78th Ohio. Next to them and immediately to their right were the untried veterans of Bryant's 12th Wisconsin and their sister regiment, the 16th Wisconsin.

Outnumbered, surprised, and now with their right flank exposed, Allen's Alabama troopers fell back, taking Iverson's Georgians with them. Movement, either in retreat or advance, tends to be contagious, and contagion began to create a rout—a particularly chaotic retreat.

CONFEDERACY, JAMES SMITH

When the blue tide of the 3rd Division pushed the three brigades of Wheeler's corps out and away from their original line, Yankee troops undid the very solid infantrymen of Cleburne's veteran division. These were the troops under General James Smith. They were known as Granbury's Texans, and they were a much more difficult nut to crack. They were at the right limits of their division and the next in line to Iverson's dismounted Georgia horsemen.

James Smith and his Texans had been assaulted by deadly artillery fire from Burton's and Gay's combined Iowa and Illinois batteries since early in the morning. These guns, pulled out in front of their supporting lines, had fired right down the Rebel trench line. It had been effective and costly to the defenders. Now, the other end of Smith's line was under infantry attack. As the Union infantry spilled into the trench from the east and south, they rolled up the Confederate defenders and tore them from their battle order. When Iverson's Georgia cavalry regiments were ripped apart and torn away, part of Smith's Texas infantry was torn away too. As the Federals of Force's brigade stormed up the hill, a wide-eyed Confederate cavalry lieutenant colonel came running along the line held by Smith's combined 24th and 25th Texas.

With panic in his eyes, the man yelled, "Leave here, or you will all be captured. The cavalry has given way, and the enemy is surrounding you!" The Union skirmishers under Potts and Hall—who had been tasked with preventing Cleburne's men from sending reinforcements to Wheeler and had succeeded—were about twenty paces from the Texans and about the same distance from the Georgia regiments. The Georgia cavalrymen fired a volley into the onrushing Union skirmishers. That volley killed some men and drove the Federals back, but the soldiers had seen enough of the determined infantry.

As the Union 12th and 16th Wisconsin combined with the advancing Union skirmishers, the Confederate troops first began to fall back and then to run in a disorganized manner. Smith watched in disbelief as the men in his rightmost unit, the combined 24th and 25th Texas, retreated as the dismounted Georgia cavalry to their right gave way and dispersed in front of the Union blue.

Smith's Texans were serious soldiers and damn good at their deadly work. Being pushed out, overwhelmed, and out-fought was well beyond their combat experience. The departure of 24th and 25th Texas and the fact that the first Union troops were also now in the rear of the 24th and 25th Texas caused the Texans to swing out of the trench. The outnumbered Southerners fought back and, for a while, regained nearly 200 yards of trenches vacated by Wheeler's troops. But the Federal tide was running at flood levels and was simply too much. William Neyland, in command of the 24th and 25th Texas, was hit in the thigh by rifle fire, but twice he gallantly rallied the regiment and led them into the charging Federals. Again, they took back significant amounts of trench line and held it until two relief regiments, one from Lowrey and one from Govan, were present.

Cleburne, in his usual masterful way, had picked up those two regiments from Lowrey's and Govan's forces to combine with the 24th and 25th Texas as well as those of Wheeler's men who Cleburne could find to form an ad hoc force.

CONFEDERACY, PATRICK CLEBURNE

Back at the beginning of the battle, Cleburne had felt, sensed, and saw the Federal attack on the top of Bald Hill and was ready for his own attacking Union force. Immediately, he had ordered up the Hotchkiss Artillery Battalion with its eight 12-pound Napoleons and four 12-pound howitzers. Without the benefit of earthworks, Key's Battery and Swett's men, under the command of Lieutenant Shannon, had been run up to the line. Here, on some high ground and in plain view, these guns had begun shelling the Federals. This direct and nearly horizontal enfilading artillery fire at close range was very effective. The blue-clad soldiers were struck by the antipersonnel rounds and fell in bunches.

Cleburne always liked to have his artillery right up among his infantry. Big massed batteries were favored by some, but not by Cleburne. To his way of thinking, massed guns firing at predetermined targets from a hill in the rear seemed better in planning than it turned out in practice. Battles often turned on force of will, determination, and hard-hitting individual effort. The plan was too often disrupted by events crashing in and rendering the plan an empty illusion.

Cleburne usually learned from his mistakes as well as successes, and he had learned this need for artillery among his infantry well. He remembered his lack of artillery at Shiloh and was glad to have it this fine summer morning. Having those wide-bore 12-pounders hurling sizzling steel and fire was like having another regiment. The enemy, especially when in the defense, had their artillery with them, and Cleburne wanted his. Close range doses of canister as well as the numbing, air-sucking boom, smoke, and fire encouraged his troops as much as it discouraged the enemy who the exploding rounds cut wide, bloody swaths into.

Of course, the two Confederate batteries didn't have it all their way. At the height of the fight, two Texas infantrymen were killed near the guns. For some reason, their fellow soldiers decided that the time to conduct a funeral was right then. Consequently, the two were wrapped in their blankets and then placed in a newly dug grave. A lesson was read from the Good Book, a hymn was sung, and a prayer was offered. The entire event was done amidst exploding shells and buzzing minie balls. The two Texans were buried within ten feet of the rapidly firing cannon.

When the 24th and 25th Texas and the dismounted Georgia cavalry retreated and the rest of the Texans were fighting to keep the trenches, Cleburne quickly got together reinforcements. With these troops—the 24th and 25th Texas, two regiments from Govan's and Lowrey's forces, and some of Wheeler's men—Cleburne mounted a counterattack.

The assault made by the brigades of Potts and Hall covered the entire front of James Smith's five small Texas regiments. They and the 5th Confederate held off an entire veteran division. Demonstration or not, the task presented to the Texans was formidable.

Then, Union General Giles Smith moved his 4th Division out and across a wide-open field toward the hard gray Rebel lines commanded by Cleburne. A distance of some 600 yards separated the two positions. As they grew closer, the right end of Cleburne's troops fell back from the combined onslaught from the front and flank. As this was taking place, the two Confederate batteries of Key and Swett began to work on the Union divisions under Giles Smith and Leggett.

The short-range effectiveness of the two batteries of Napoleons and howitzers brought the surprised Federals to a rapid halt, and that allowed James Smith's Texans to form a counterattack and reclaimed some of their lost trench.

The effort of the Federal division to move Cleburne's infantry was much different from the action required by the 3rd Division to rout the dismounted cavalry on the hill. Firstly, the Confederate batteries were effective and were able to deliver flat, accurate fire into the ranks of the 20th Illinois. The 20th Illinois, who had been in the second line of battle of Force's brigade, had ended up on the right flank of the brigade as the line had first converged and then spread out. Consequently, the 20th Illinois was receiving fire from Key's and Swett's splendidly managed guns. The 20th's colonel yelled out for the regiment to lie down in order to present less of a target and to gain some immediate relief from the intense artillery shelling. As good infantry, they were soon digging and had a hasty line of works completed quickly.

At the same time, the 13th Iowa, under Major William Walker, was brought up to Force's right and was placed there to re-fuse Force's right back to the left of Giles Smith's 4th Division, but it was a costly enterprise that resulted in the killing or wounding of ninety-eight Federal troops. As the two divisions were being melded together, the four 24-pound howitzers of the 1st Illinois Battery D were brought up to the top of the hill, and their fire and that of the dug-in 13th Iowa soon put an end to the fire from Cleburne's force, who were in the tree line northwest of the hill. By 9:00 a.m. or shortly thereabouts, the contest for Bald Hill, "the key to the line," was over, and the hill belonged to the soldiers in blue.

The entire attack was started and ended in a short period of time. As a result of the surprisingly swift attack by the Union forces on Bald Hill, the hill rapidly became home to a large number of Federal soldiers.

General Leggett was soon bringing up the remainder of his artillery. The trenches the Confederates had used were reversed and dug out more completely. In addition, the men of the 3rd Division began to dig traverses. In Force's 1st Brigade, these traversing trenches were perpendicular to the main line and ran to the Union rear in an east-west line. Five such trenches were dug for each of the regiments, which allowed for two companies per traversed trench. The 12th Wisconsin, now having had their experience with enemy fire, had seen the enemy and determined that they could best be viewed from a deep, strong trench. Accordingly, the main line facing west and the rearward traverse of the 12th were especially strong, deep, and well-constructed.

The results of the more stubborn Southern resistance in the face of the 4th Division attack resulted in a line that did not run in a smooth continuous arc but rather ran north and south on Bald Hill and then broke back for a distance of 150 to 200 yards to the rear of the hill line. At this point, it resumed its north-bound run.

As the morning wore on, the men of Giles Smith's 4th Division were moved from the right of Leggett's division to the left of it. Here, they extended the Union line down the south end of Bald Hill. The line was formed on both the east and west sides of Old McDonough Road, which here ran essentially north and south. Smith's soldiers bent the line back on itself, refusing the line into the shape of a fishhook. This fishhook lay across the Flat Shoals Road, which intersected with McDonough Road at a forty-five degree angle and then ran from that intersection off to the southeast.

From atop the hill, the movement of Confederate troops to the south through the city could be seen. This movement was reported up the Federal chain of command. The exact meaning of the troop movement was not fully understood. Some believed the Confederates were beginning to abandon the city.

CHAPTER FIFTY-NINE

Union | GRENVILLE DODGE

HEADQUARTERS OF THE SIXTEENTH ARMY CORPS

TENT OF GENERAL DODGE, EAST OF ATLANTA

JULY 21, 1864

Major General Dodge sat on his camp chair with a cup of coffee in his hand. Sometimes he thought he carried his willingness to cooperate with his fellow corps commander farther than he should.

For all intents and purposes, he had little left of his Sixteenth Army Corps to say grace over. The two brigades of his 2nd Division were effectively under Logan's command and were tucked into the line at the right of Logan's Fifteenth Army Corps. Their purpose was to extend the line to the right and to tie Logan's forces into Schofield's Army of the Ohio. At least this situation did have the benefit of Dodge not having to deal directly with Brigadier General Thomas Sweeny.

"Someday," Dodge thought to himself, *"I'm going to have to court-martial that profane drunk, but not today."* Dodge prided himself on being able to get the most out of a man, but he and Sweeny threw off more heat than light.

Sweeny had his 1st Brigade on the line where Logan was. The 2nd Brigade, under the command of Colonel August Mersey, was made up of three regiments. It formed the reserve and lay behind its sister brigade. This entire brigade was at the end of its enlistment and would be rotating out of the field soon, maybe today. The 3rd Brigade of this division was not present in Atlanta; it was miles to the north in Rome, Georgia.

The 4th Division, under the command of Brigadier General John Fuller, was really about all that was left for Dodge to command, and to say it was a division was far too grand. It had only two brigades here, with its third operating in Decatur, Alabama.

Dodge wanted to stay close to the 4th Division for two reasons: one was that it constituted most of his immediate command, and second was that its normal commander, General John Veatch, had become so sick he was unable to continue in his position. With Veatch on his way home to recover, Dodge had promoted John Fuller to the division's command on July 17, just days ago. Even a good man takes a while to learn to move a division instead of a brigade, and Dodge wanted to be around while Fuller learned.

Late yesterday, he had ordered Fuller to move over to the right and settle in behind Blair's command, becoming the reserve behind the Seventeenth Army Corps. That meant the distance between the two divisions of his Sixteenth Army Corps was at least two miles. His divisions were nearly as far apart as they could be and still be within the Army of the Tennessee's front.

Dodge hoped he would get his 2nd Division back soon from Logan. Dodge had confidence in the soldiers of the Sixteenth Army Corps but would feel better when he had them together. Although his corps was not directly involved, he knew that skirmishers were out all along the Union front. He could hear the artillery fire that was being shot at the enemy and into the city that lay before them, a little over two miles away. With this limited action taking place, no real fighting was occurring. The Union forces continued to extend its lines, and the Confederates were still moving to get themselves into their defensive fighting positions.

CHAPTER SIXTY

Confederacy | JOHN HOOD

HEADQUARTERS OF THE ARMY OF TENNESSEE

HOOD'S TENT ON PEACHTREE STREET

JULY 21, 1864

EARLY AFTERNOON

With the map spread before him on the table, and with a crowd made up of his staff and his corps commanders, Hood prepared to explain the plan that he believed was ripe for victory. To some extent, he knew he would need to convince his subordinates: Generals Stewart, Cheatham, and Hardee as well as Gustavus Smith, commander of the Georgia Militia. There was still firing coming from the lines east of the city where Cleburne's and Wheeler's soldiers had lost the prominence known as Bald Hill. This hill had been the strong right end of the Confederate line around the city. Now it was more or less in the hands of the blue soldiers of the Union.

Wheeler's scouts had reported that the extreme left of the Federal line was in the air. The scouts said the Union soldiers were loosely situated around the south side of Bald Hill, and some trenches were being prepared along Flat Shoals Road, which ran west and south of the hill. The map indicated the distance between Bald Hill and the all-important railroad that came in from Decatur was about a mile and a half.

Hood had racked his brain for a similar military situation. At Gettysburg, he had wanted to move around and flank the Union left instead of the uphill frontal attack that Lee had planned. That direct attack had cost Hood the use of his arm. Dash and surprise maneuvers often held the key to Lee's success but not that day in July in Pennsylvania a little over a year ago.

Hood remembered his argument with Pete Longstreet, his old corps commander. Hood had been a division commander when Lee's army had blundered into Meade's Army of the Potomac. Lee had been blind but for small glimmers of information from a spy. He was without the solid intelligence Jeb Stuart could have provided if not for Stuart's enthusiastic joy riding and complete failure to do his job. Lee's eyes and ears were effectively closed, and by the time they were open, the Union blue occupied all the high ground from Culp's Hill down Seminary Ridge.

Hood knew now that Longstreet had tenaciously sought permission from Lee to get between Meade's force and Washington, D.C. Such a strike would have forced Meade to come to him on ground of his own choosing. Longstreet believed this provided the best opportunity for an aggressive defense and a chance to provide a victory for the tattered but noble, proud, and lethal Army of Northern Virginia. But Lee, with the belief that the hard, barefoot, and ragged warriors could do anything, especially since the outcome was in the hands of God, had rejected Longstreet time after time. Longstreet was refused and rejected to the point that the old warhorse knew no choice existed regardless of the rightness of his appeal. Hood knew better than many the futility of frontal assault against a spirited and well-entrenched foe.

The situation he confronted now also had similarities with the opportunities he had realized on July 2, 1863. He recalled his scout rushing back to him with the report that no Union forces held the Round Top Hills, and that by sweeping behind them, he could be in the rear of the blue boys and then turn and eat up the surprised Union left.

He recalled vividly his three efforts to convince Longstreet and then finally Longstreet's direct order to attack. It had come about 4:00 p.m., and shortly thereafter, he was mounted and at the head of his division. The division spread out behind him in two long assault lines. The lines had not moved far when an exploding shell had sent hot, sharp fragments into his arm. It tore his arm open at the biceps, elbow, forearm, and hand. It had smashed him, in pain, from the back of his horse to the ground. Thereafter, his division under General Law had unsuccessfully marched across the boulder-strewn field to engage the Federal position.

The shell left Hood with a useless, flapping, irksome appendage. Had his courage bled away as the blood had pumped from his mangled arm? Was his boldness and audacity as crippled as his arm?

All these thoughts and more roared through his head as his eyes traveled over the map before him. Here was an opportunity much like Gettysburg. The Union left was in the air, and a tactical opportunity existed to attack the waiting army from the rear in surprise and to destroy it as it faced its enemy behind the walls of the citadel of Atlanta. Boldness, speed, surprise, and audacity could win the day.

The next idea that had come to mind and had found voice on his tongue was that of the wild wilderness fight at Chancellorsville. He had not been there, but when he was away on the Virginia peninsular with Pickett and Longstreet, he had listened with keen interest to the story of what occurred at the village of Chancellorsville, just down the road from Fredericksburg. He had learned how Lee and Jackson flanked Hooker and his vast army with its 70,000 or so troops of the Army of the Potomac. The huge tactical surprise was occasioned by dividing the slender Southern force and sending the preponderance of it slashing off for a flank attack on the hapless Howard, whose right was in the air.

Hood reflected on the certain similarities of Lee's situation with his own. With that, coupled with his belief that no greater teacher existed, he was determined to emulate his hero's example. After all, both Federal forces seemed tentative, if not timid. Hood had strong fortifications in his rear, which Lee had not had, thus making it far less dangerous to split his own less-substantial force while in contact with the enemy. He figured that the pounding at Peachtree Creek would encourage the enemy to move carefully on the north side of the city, if they dared to move at all.

To his staff and corps commanders, he explained he would withdraw Stewart's and Cheatham's infantry and the Georgia Militia closer to the city, just as he had determined before. This would provide the advantage of shorter interior lines that could be manned with fewer troops than a line formed on a longer radius.

He would back up Cheatham's divisions with a massing of artillery. Sherman's soldiers were still separated. Thomas, to the north of the city, was spread out along Collier's Road to the south of Peachtree Creek, and Schofield was to the northeast with McPherson joining him and extending the Union line to the south. Hood knew there was a space between Thomas and Schofield, and the distance could be as much as a mile and a half to two miles from one to the other. Whatever it was, it existed, and as it had yesterday, it was sufficient to keep Thomas from supporting the other two and them from helping him. In fact, it was distance enough to prevent the left from knowing the right was under attack or the other way around. Hood was willing to split his forces, and it appeared Sherman was willing to split his as well.

Now drawing on Jackson's successful, hidden flanking attack against Hooker, he would send General Hardee and his large veteran corps down through the city of Atlanta under cover of darkness. Hood traced the route with his finger on the map.

"General Hardee, sir, you will take your four divisions here to McDonough, south of the city. You will cross Intrenchment Creek here at Cobb's Mill and then come back up this road in a northeasterly direction to Decatur. At this point, you should be well to the rear of McPherson's large corps. No one will know that you are there. Sherman's left has been reported to be in the air and should be easily crushed.

"Starting here, you should be able to roll up that long blue line at least back up to the railroad. Wheeler also reported that a large Union wagon train is located somewhere in this immediate area. It should be rich pickings, but don't let your men stop to sample its contents."

Hood looked up and then continued, "Coordinating with General Hardee's assault will be my old corps. General Cheatham, on my order, you will attack due east out of the trench line into the Yankees north of the railroad. Between you and Hardee, we should maul the enemy rather badly." Hood then outlined that Wheeler, with his fast-moving cavalry, would precede Hardee and would go first into Decatur. There, he would take on the Union cavalry and destroy or capture the large Federal trains. Upon success in that regard, he would return to assist Hardee on the right.

As envisioned, the plan would be executed largely at night so that both darkness and distance would aid in screening the vast enterprise. The absence of McPherson's cavalry screen would leave no one on the Union side of the line to discover this calculated maneuver.

Though Decatur was only about six miles east of Atlanta, the distance Hardee's men would have to march to reach Decatur would be much longer. On narrow, dark, dusty roads in the heat of the evening, the Rebel troops would be required to march sixteen miles before they could attack.

The plan could work; Hood was sure. In his mind, Hardee's corps had hardly participated at Peachtree Creek. Hardee's comparatively fresh troops could be counted on to follow orders and bust up McPherson's army. This was a bold, compelling plan. If successfully executed with vigor and surprise, this maneuver would restore the luster to Hood's glory and shatter a large portion of Sherman's troops. It would be the talk of military historians for hundreds of years. Hood's star would shine as bright as Lee's, and his exploits would create a great victory and be studied by future generations of soldiers to come.

Hardee's soldiers began their initial movement in the early afternoon of July 21, not long after the meeting with the corps commanders. The movement was to be led by Bate's division. The plan was to be in position to attack early the next morning as dawn broke so they could surge forward with the rising sun at their backs. Sunset would come late in the summer evening around 8:00, and the big, bright furnace of a sun would slide away. It would reappear and begin its climb around 6:00 in the morning. That gave ten hours for the divisions commanded by Maney, Cleburne, Walker, and Bate to duplicate the feat of Jackson's foot cavalry under Raleigh Colston, A.P. Hill, and Robert Rodes as they had poured down the Orange Turnpike, past the Wilderness Church, and into the startled Union flank.

Hood would seize the initiative. He would do this so soon after the hard thrust of July 20 at the creek that the attack would surprise even the best prepared. He would be making the decisions that the enemy would have to respond to. His opponent would have to react, to guess as to an appropriate defense, and counterstrike. Pressure had been coming from the Union front, resistance had been steady, and now surprise and violence in the Union's rear could be devastatingly destructive.

Anytime one can meet a narrow front of troops—troops in the air—with a wide front, the wide front can bring more weapons to bear and generally can attack the narrower front from the left, right, and center. Even if one assumes that each soldier can fire as rapidly and as accurately as every other soldier, a wide front of a hundred men can deliver ten times more firepower than a ten-man front. The phenomenon is of even greater importance if the same ten-man front is five men deep and two men wide. Although the men in the column may be able to fire at an angle into the wide front, their ability to fire into the center is reduced because of the men in front of them within the column.

Another factor is also at work. Generally speaking, soldiers aim at a target, and the target will either be hit or missed. More often than not, a shooter will miss by firing high or low rather than missing as a result of shooting wide. This results in an oval-shaped "beaten zone" or "impact area." This is the area rounds fall into. Success comes most often when the oval shape of the "impact area" coincides most closely with the shape of the object of attack. A column would absorb all of an "impact area" while a line would intersect with only a portion of the "impact area" even if it is more than two men deep. Firing high or low against a line of troops only one or two men deep represents a good chance of missing entirely. Shots going wide have only two possible targets in a two-man deep line as contrasted with more opportunities presented by a column.

If a soldier were aiming at the middle of a column, even if he missed his target of choice, his round could strike ahead of his target with a low shot or behind his target with a high shot. In either event, the round could miss its intended target but nonetheless strike someone within the line of the column. If the target were missed by firing too wide, the round would still have a good chance of striking somewhere along the column's front or side.

Considering all this, the more a line faces another line—the more it's parallel—the less effective its firepower will be. But, as a line becomes more slanted, the more the oval-shaped "impact area" coincides with the shape of the target until the line is at ninety degrees to the area. At that position, the "impact area" lines up quite well with the line or axis of the target.

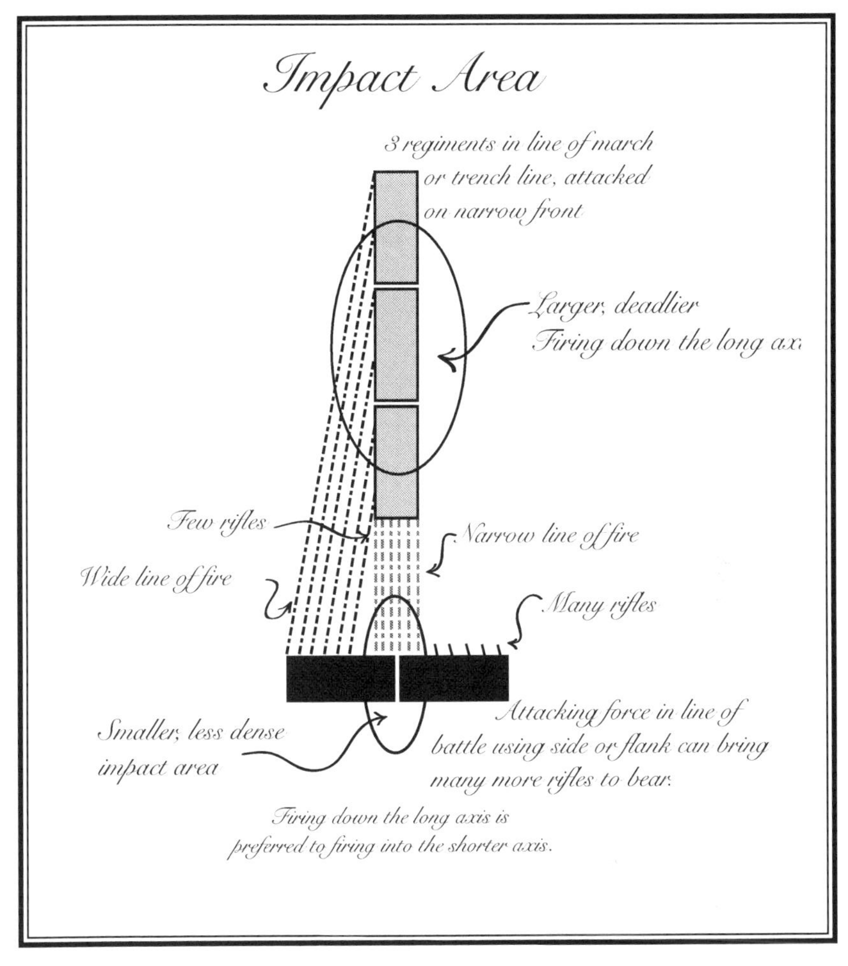

In the navy, "crossing the T" operates on the same concept. It is every admiral's dream to be able to cross ahead of or behind an enemy line of battle so that the line of ships doing the crossing can fire down the enemy line with the oval of the "impact area" to fully hit the base, or the "I" of the "T." The line of ships being crossed is at the same disadvantage the column has when confronted by the line. The ships doing the crossing get to fire gun after gun into the approaching line of ships, which in turn can offer little since their guns only fire to the left and right within a small arc, not to the front or rear. The oval of the "impact area" is in full play for the crossing ships and nearly nonexistent for the line of ships being crossed.

With this in mind, when Hood received intelligence from Wheeler's horsemen that McPherson's left flank was in the air, he was delighted. To him, it meant the Union line simply ended and faced west. No perpendicular line existed to give the end of the line width, so its width was only one or two men deep or wide. Generally a regiment or more might make up the refused end of a division force line, though even a refused line can be defeated if the attacking line overlaps enough to envelop the refused but too narrow front.

Hood assumed McPherson had stretched out to reach as far to the south as he could toward the Macon Railroad. He further assumed the south end of the Federal line ended in the air without the benefit of protecting the end.

With the benefit of the oval of the "impact area," a line of battle attacking a line that is in the air has the same benefit that the "T" crossing admiral has. When combined with surprise and mass, the line being attacked simply disappears as troops on the line die or are crushed or flee down the trench line, uncovering the next man, who is presented with the same fiery salutation. The line begins to disappear or be "rolled up" in front of the line of attackers.

Hence Hood believed that he could steal a march on Sherman and arrive in time to attack the end of the long, thin Union line. He was certain his attack would roll up the Union line toward the Decatur Road and, if very successful, on into Peachtree Creek. He saw it as a chance, and he grabbed at it with his largest, most experienced corps.

In The Field, July 21, 1864—3p.m.

Major-General Sherman,
Commanding:

General; Brigadier-General Leggett, commanding Third Division, Seventeenth Army Corps, advanced his lines and captured a hill, quite a commanding position, this forenoon, also some 60 prisoners, principally from Cleburne's division. General Leggett is on my extreme left. The Fourth Division (late Gresham's) made a demonstration at the same time in favor of Leggett, and the loss in the two divisions is between 260 and 300 killed and wounded. The hill is two and a quarter miles from Atlanta, and a portion of the enemy's works around town are in view. The enemy made one vigorous assault and two feeble attempts to recapture the hill, but were signally repulsed. Since that time he has been moving troops in the direction of our left. General Leggett reports having seen at least ten regiments of infantry passing in that direction. I have strengthened that portion of the line with all the available troops I have got, and I will simply remark in closing, that I have no cavalry as a body of observation on my flank, and that the whole rebel army, except Georgia militia, is not in front of the Army of the Cumberland.

Very respectfully, your obedient servant,

Jas. B. Mcpherson,
Major-General.

CHAPTER SIXTY-ONE

Confederacy | PATRICK CLEBURNE

WEST OF THE BALD HILL, EAST OF ATLANTA

JULY 21, 1864

LATE AFTERNOON

In the trees, across the way from where the Union line bent backward toward Decatur and down the Confederate line toward the railroad, Cleburne's men waited in exhausted silence. Some men worked at cleaning their fouled muskets, and some slept, but all were glad for the shade. From time to time, they would rise and fire as the artillery fire from the hill on their right and the battery from down on the left flayed the area. Always on the alert to detect another powerful assault, they worked unceasingly throughout the afternoon at strengthening their entrenchments.

The division had halted most of the Federal progress and had sustained more than 300 killed and wounded. If they had been tired the night before when they left the area near Collier's Ridge and marched to the relief of Wheeler, now twenty-four hours and a hot day under artillery fire and intense direct combat later, Cleburne's men were properly exhausted. They had, as always, made their presence felt. They had stayed and fought, counterattacked, and held on when others had scampered off to safety. Their effort had been substantial, even if their success had been slightly less so. The damned blue soldiers of the Union army were still outside the city, and while they had bent and stretched, they were still in place.

Cleburne had seen his share of hard, brutal action and reflected that it had been the bitterest day of fighting thus far in the war. He had watched in stunned silence as the rifled artillery from his left had cut down lines of men with shots that had simply roared straight down his trenches. Dismembered heads, torsos, arms, and legs and spurting blood had engulfed sections of the line. What had been men were now merely human wreckage and misery.

CHAPTER SIXTY-TWO

Confederacy | W.M. CUNNINGHAM

9TH TENNESSEE, WALKER'S BRIGADE,
MANEY'S DIVISION, HARDEE'S CORPS
SOUTH OF THE RAILROAD, WEST OF BALD HILL,
EAST OF ATLANTA
JULY 21, 1864
6:38 P.M.

War is a personal thing. History is written about the grand clash of corps and armies and the effect of terrain on high strategy. An individual private soldier sees none of that, except as it may be manifested in the dirty, dusty pair of trousers that walks in front of him and to his left and right. If a soldier looked up, he would see the sweat-stained backs of torn, filthy jackets crisscrossed by the few pieces of equipment that men were still willing to carry in their third year of war. Private soldiers knew what lay in their immediate vision and knew the men who stood on either side of them as they lined up time after time. In truth, they knew almost every man in the company that they were a part of. For many of these companies, the men had all grown toward young manhood in the same town and rural area. They felt comfortable among the troops of their regiment since those boys were from the same county or a nearby county. The same could be said for Cunningham.

Lieutenant W. M. "Bill" Cunningham had settled into his role as the commander of Company H. Cunningham had joined, like most of this outfit, from that most northwest county in Tennessee. Since joining the Southern army, he had been wounded in combat, taken prisoner, paroled, and promoted. He enjoyed the confidence of the men who had elected him to command after the failure at Missionary Ridge.

The men of Company H, most of whom were from Obion County, Tennessee, had joined what they all proudly knew as the Obion

Avalanche. It sounded better than Company H. Even now, years later, the boys still referred to the dwindling organization as the Avalanche. Every regiment, in both armies, had a Company H, but as far as the soldiers from Obion County knew, there was no other Avalanche. It pleased them and added to the pride they had as members of the proud 9th Tennessee, under the command of Lieutenant Colonel John W. Buford, who himself had served as captain and commander of the Avalanche following the Battle of Shiloh.

The 9th Tennessee Infantry Regiment was one of five regiments that made up Maney's brigade of Cheatham's division, except now the brigade was commanded by Colonel Walker. The division was now under the charge of the former brigade commander George Maney. Cunningham believed Maney was the right man for the job, especially because he knew Maney was Cheatham's best friend in the army. The two of them had been together as far back as the war with Mexico. Still, Cunningham thought that Walker's brigade and Maney's division would take some getting used to.

Following the attack at Peachtree Creek, Maney's division had been ordered back to the fortifications that guarded the north side of Atlanta. They had not really settled into any kind of routine yet when they were hustled quickly south, down to where the railroad tracks cut into the city. Maney's division arrived too late to prevent Blair's Seventeenth Army Corps from pushing Cleburne's exhausted division off the commanding terrain feature.

Now, the thin-faced Tennesseans filed into the trenches on Cleburne's left. Soon after finding their rightful place in the line, veterans began improving their defenses. Wheeler's horse soldiers had left shallow cuts in the hard, red ground. Cunningham looked to ascertain that the Avalanche was in its proper position in the regimental line. Company H should be the fourth company from the left, although the reasons for that were not clear in his mind.

He could remember when as a rifleman he had stood in a line of some forty others with an equal number in a second rank. Then, his front rank had covered about thirty yards, a company front. Now that line was much depleted. With no second rank, his company could still cover its required thirty yards, but each man was responsible for five or six feet rather than three.

"There are lots of good men gone," Cunningham thought. Somehow, his brothers John and Bob still survived as well as his cousin, "Lincoln Bob," who had recovered from his bad wound at Shiloh and later joined the cavalry.

It was late afternoon—hot and still. Others in the command were starting to get their bearings. Several of the men were in earnest conversation about the large downed hardwood tree that lay uprooted some forty to fifty feet to their front, including Sylvester McDonald.

Sylvester McDonald had joined the company from Troy in Obion County and had been with the unit since 1861. He was, in many regards, a typical Irishman—quick with a joke or a song. He enjoyed this great adventure that he was engaged in and had become a fine soldier. Cunningham abstained from all alcohol but knew that Vess, as McDonald was known, enjoyed whatever fiery drink he could find from time to time. Still, Vess was strong and well liked and always held up his end of whatever job was at hand.

For some reason, Vess was sure that if he went out beyond the line and climbed into the uprooted tree's inviting limbs, he could discover what the blue troops were doing. He thought he could obtain a better view of the ground that lay between them and Union sharpshooters. Vess was now motivated by the excitement his quest was creating as well as the implied dare. He could damn well get out to that tree and take a good long look and scamper back, regardless of all the advice he was getting. He removed his blanket roll, haversack, belt, and cartridge box and placed his rifle on the blanket.

"Take what you want if I don't come back," he joked. Cunningham stood silently near the small knot of men.

"I *should* order him not to go," mused the youthful, serious-faced Cunningham. But, quick as a cat, Vess took off.

"I'll be right back, Bill," Vess called back and sprinted to the tree. He quickly gained the protection of the tree and climbed into its limbs. The men watched, yelling encouragement and hoping the mission would end with success. Vess found a good knee in the tree, which afforded an unobstructed view of the low ground and the hillside beyond.

Although there was not a lot of firing coming from the line of Union troops on Bald Hill, there was a lot of activity as the 1st Brigade under Leggett consolidated its position. Skirmishers were forward of the defensive line, some distance down the hillside. There was little to do as the heat of the afternoon sucked the initiative from all but the most enthusiastic. Skirmishers dug into the hard hill ground in an effort to enhance their hasty fighting positions. Several saw the man dash into the fallen tree across the way. One man, less bored with the opportunity than the others, raised his rifle, guessed at the yardage, adjusted the sight, aimed, and squeezed the trigger. The smoke obscured his vision after he fired. It cleared, and his sight was rewarded by the man sprawled lifeless in the crook of the tree. A howl of rage could be heard from the Rebel line.

CHAPTER SIXTY-THREE

Union | KENNER GARRARD

ON THE ROAD FROM DECATUR TO BROWNING'S COURTHOUSE

JULY 21, 1864

7:00 P.M.

There was a light rain falling. The men riding in the lead elements of Garrard's 2nd Division were wet and getting wetter. They were moving slowly on the Lawrenceville Road toward Browning's Courthouse. They had left the comforts of the village of Decatur and were now miserably moving forward in the rain. Once at the crossroads near the one-room courthouse, they would turn south toward the peaceful town of Covington.

Brigadier General Kenner Garrard had pulled off into a cleared area with some of his staff to watch the 3rd and 4th Ohio Cavalry, part of Eli Long's brigade, pass by. The entire division was strung out along the road back to Decatur. It was as lean of a force as the Federals were willing to put on the march. Pursuant to Garrard's own special field order number 3, they were moving with only one two-gun section without caissons, the Chicago Board of Trade Battery. Each regiment and brigade had been limited to only one ambulance.

Until recently, the division had been used to ride the left flank of McPherson's Army of the Tennessee and to tear up the railroad track of the Georgia railroad. Now, protected from the elements in the division staff's ambulance, the piece of paper from Sherman gave new direction to this division, the largest of the four Federal cavalry divisions operating around Atlanta. The orders were clear. Garrard was to move quickly to destroy the railroad from Lithonia to Covington. The two bridges over the Yellow River were to be destroyed. He was to take all the horses and mules fit for service, but to use his judgment if the animals belonged to the poor and needy. Sherman even gave instructions on how to heat and twist the rails. Sherman wanted this all done in two days.

On receipt of the order, some thirteen and a half hours ago, Garrard had known it couldn't be done with the haste demanded, but he had begun the process of alerting and moving his many units anyway.

Kenner Garrard was more than a well-educated horseman. He had served with the elite 2nd U.S. Cavalry when it chased Indians in Texas. Early on, he had been captured and paroled at San Antonio. Upon being officially exchanged, he left his non-combatant role for the command of the 146th New York. He led that regiment at the Federal disaster at Fredericksburg and Chancellorsville. He was gallant at Gettysburg and took command of Stephen Weed's brigade. As a result, he was promoted to brigadier general on July 23, 1863.

Nonetheless, he knew Sherman believed he had no dash. He had been berated and belittled by Sherman, in fact. As a senior cavalryman, he knew all the various uses cavalry were generally given: gathering intelligence, screening the infantry flank, and harassing of the enemy rear. He and his three brigades had in the past two weeks some of all that, but now they were not being used properly.

Now, with the rain coming down around him, he thought back on his upbringing. Life, as the son of a respected attorney and then as the stepson of a man who sat on the Supreme Court of the United States, had been one of near aristocratic privilege. As a result, he was reserved, modest, and gentile.

Maybe Sherman was right. Garrard remembered his early cavalry training under careful George Thomas. Thomas had acquired the nickname "Slow Trot." The nickname arose as a result of the countless times Thomas admonished his youthful charges not to gallop but rather to slow trot the horses. Sometimes, as innocent as nicknames seem so many years before, they could have repercussions later.

Both Grant and Sherman were critical of Thomas and his deliberate ways. Whether Thomas exemplified the nickname or whether it colored his superior's view, Garrard was unsure, but he was certain that he and Thomas were bound together. Sherman had made it clear that he believed the early training under Thomas had rubbed off on Garrard. It seemed damned unfair to him, and he admitted to himself that he would prefer to serve under Thomas, who he admired as the "Rock of Chickamga." He supposed even that nickname could be twisted to imply that Thomas was not merely slow, but nearly immovable.

Garrard wondered if riding away from Atlanta was the correct thing to be doing given the closeness of the enemy. He had his orders though. McPherson, who he got on rather well with despite McPherson's affinity to Sherman, would have to be especially careful in the absence of Garrard and his troops. Appropriate caution in wartime was a characteristic Garrard truly admired in McPherson. He saw it as calculated prudence.

The lack of cavalry on the left flank of the slow moving Army of the Tennessee, caused by Garrard's new orders, was soon evident to the small detachments of Confederate horsemen, and that fact was duly reported up the chain of command.

CHAPTER SIXTY-FOUR

Confederacy | WILLIAM H.T. WALKER

HEADQUARTERS OF THE ARMY OF TENNESSEE

LEYDEN HOUSE ON PEACHTREE STREET

JULY 21, 1864

8:45 P.M.

"Major Cunningham, I want you to wait here for just a little while. I want to see General Hood for just a moment," said Major General William Walker. He halted his horse on Peachtree Street in front of the large house that Hood was using as his headquarters. The tired, dusty troops of his division continued to move south along the street with the divisions of Bate and Maney of Hardee's corps.

"Yes, sir," Major Cunningham replied.

Walker then expressed that he hoped Hood, who had gone up like a rocket, would not come down like a stick. Walker had gone on to say that he knew Hood was brave but wondered if he had the capacity to command an army. Cunningham hoped Walker would say nothing to Hood that could just as well be left unsaid. Walker had thin skin, and Cunningham knew it wouldn't take much to have him go off.

Walker looked about with some uncertainty, but upon seeing a cluster of officers on the wide veranda, he approached and asked for General Hood. As soon as he asked, Walker realized Hood was near and walked over to him. Walker turned so no one else could overhear the exchange.

"General Hood, sir. Pardon the interruption. I know you are busy tonight. I fully understand and appreciate the grave responsibility attached to your new position as commander of this proud Army of Tennessee. You and I both understand the condition of the army and how its morale has deteriorated after months of retreating and fighting from behind earthworks. I thought it was important, as my division undertakes this battle, that you know from me personally that I am with you both in heart and purpose. I will abide with you in all emergencies to come."

Hood knew Walker to be a fighter, and one of those generals who understood the debilitating nature of the days since they had left Dalton. Hood looked at Walker and said, "Thank you, friend. You must know that I value your counsel and leadership. I know your men will uphold our honor."

Walker, often formal, came to attention before the younger man and saluted before taking his leave. He walked slowly back to the street and to his badly worn marching columns of troops.

Both Walker and Cunningham had mounted their horses and began the movement south when Walker said, "General Hood says he believes tomorrow's battle is necessary to save Atlanta and that our efforts are critical to its success."

Cunningham looked over at Walker and saw that his eyes were aglow.

Then, Walker commented, "Someone told me Hood had his tent set up behind the house, and he did. Grand house like that might go to his head. Good that he kept the tent."

As the two rode together, Walker assured himself that he had handled the conversation correctly and that he had perhaps given some comfort to Hood. This night march and planned attack was bold. Whatever doubts Hood might have had about Walker's loyalty to Johnston should be behind them with the successful execution of this small amount of fence mending.

July 22, 1864

Last Day of
the Seven-Day Event

CHAPTER SIXTY-FIVE

Union | JAMES MCPHERSON

HEADQUARTERS OF ARMY OF THE TENNESSEE

JUST SOUTH OF THE RAILROAD, ABOUT A MILE AND A HALF FROM DECATUR COURTHOUSE

JULY 22, 1864

5:53 A.M.

The day before, it had rained just as evening had come over the thin lines of the opposing forces. The rain had been welcome then, and it seemed to McPherson that the cooling effects were still present that morning.

It was just getting light. As he sat in his camp chair, the cool of the morning and the peacefulness it contained helped his thoughts as he composed.

Hqrs. Department and Army of the Tennessee,
In the Field, July 22, 1864—6 a.m.
Maj. Gen. John A. Logan
Commanding Fifteenth Army corps:

General: The enemy having evacuated their works in front of our lines, the supposition of Major-General Sherman is that they have given up Atlanta and are retreating in the direction of East Point. You will immediately put your command in pursuit, passing to the south and east of Atlanta, without entering the town. You will keep a route to the left of that taken by the enemy, and try to cut off a portion of them while they are pressed in rear and on our right by Generals Schofield and Thomas. Major-General Sherman desires and expects a vigorous pursuit.

Very respectfully, your obedient servant,
Jas. B. McPherson,
Major-General.

As he finished signing the order to Logan, McPherson reached for his coffee cup and drank the strong, hot liquid. His orderly and honest mind reflected, not for the first time, that Logan with his fierce, animated, captivating face was in open contrast to McPherson himself. Logan, though slightly uncontrollable, seemed to be a wonderful weapon to have at his disposal.

If one stood toe to toe with Logan, one would determine that Logan was not a big man. Nonetheless, he always seemed larger than life, and something took place between Logan and the soldiers he commanded. There was an energy exchange. Logan was always ready to go, and his activities and energy boiled up and over like an untended coffeepot. He would give a short, hard, and rousing speech that would activate the men of the Fifteenth Army Corps to do good, to extend themselves, and to put their best into the action at hand. His energy seemed to jack up his troops, and the interaction fed back and forth between Logan and his soldiers. As a result, they became more certain they could prevail regardless of the challenge. Logan received something from men, and he then inspired them.

McPherson was more resolute himself once Logan got involved. Logan seemed without doubt. Even McPherson's caution would yield to the enthusiasm Logan could summon to deliver the solution he saw and begin to bend others to its result. After experiencing such moments, McPherson could see why men had joined the 31st Illinois, now part of Force's 1st Brigade. He understood why those men from southern Illinois thought Logan was a giant despite his physical characteristic to the contrary.

He reflected that this soft, pleasant, and almost cool morning would be perfect if the hot Georgia sun would stay below the horizon for the rest of the day. But he was sure that would not happen and that it would again be a hot, miserable day.

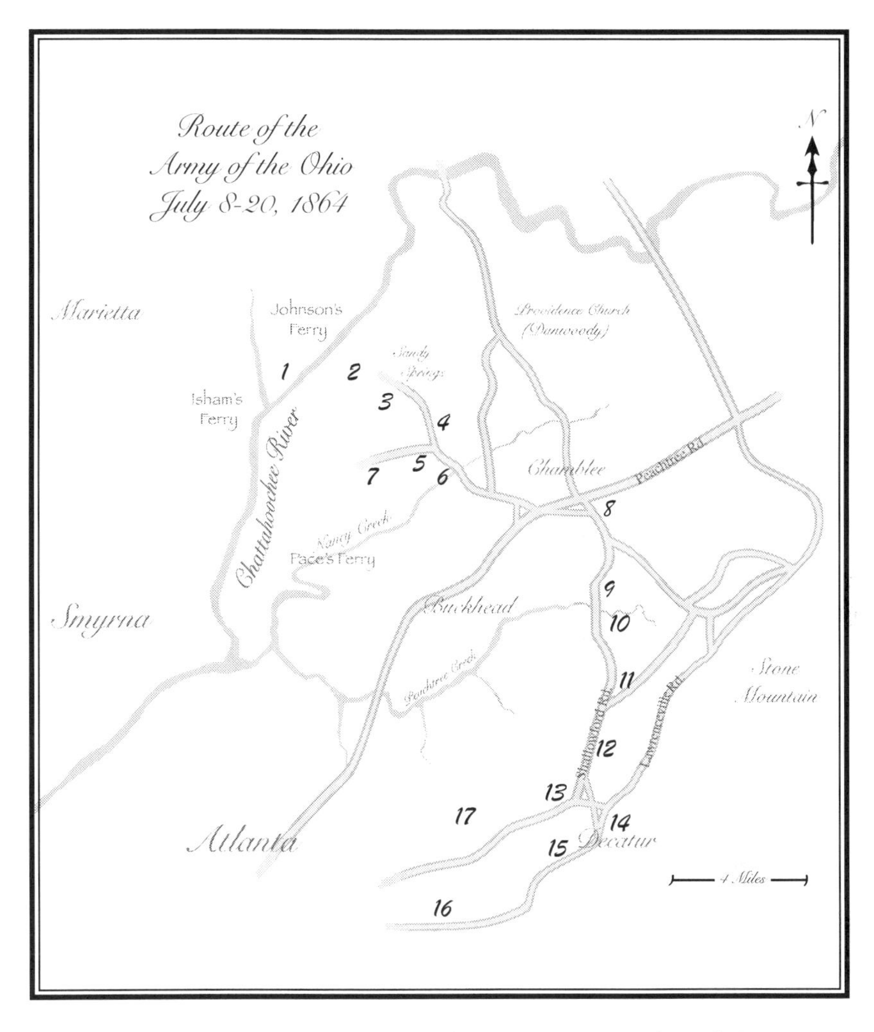

Route of the Army of the Ohio from the Crossing of the Chattahoochee River to the Arrival Near Decatur

1. The Army of the Ohio essentially consisted of one corps, the Twenty-Third. It, in turn, was composed of two divisions: one commanded by Jacob Cox and the other commanded by Milo Hascall. Led by Cox's division, the Twenty-Third crossed the Chattahoochee River at Isham's Ferry near the mouth of Sope Creek on July 8, 1864. Hascall's division crossed on July 11. After crossing the river, the corps entrenched on the ridge just south of and overlooking the river.
2. On July 14, the corps moved south to the Mount Vernon Road, where the troops formed a line along the road with their right tied into the left of Howard's corps.

3. On July 17, the Twenty-Third Army Corps moved northeasterly along Mount Vernon Road toward Sandy Springs. The destination was Decatur.
4. The corps left Sandy Springs on a rural path, today known as Johnson Ferry Road.
5. The corps marched to today's Glenridge and the road to Chamblee.
6. General Cox and his men continued on Johnson Ferry Road and, on the night of July 17, camped where Nancy Creek crossed the road.
7. General Hascall's division camped near a tributary of Nancy Creek at the Burnett Farm near the intersection of today's Long Island Drive and Mount Paran Road.
8. On July 18, Hascall's division retraced their path, marched to Peachtree Road, and spent the night camped just north of Solomon Goodwin's home at its intersection with today's North Druid Hills Road.
9. Cox's men camped that same night just north of Hascall's troops and south of the Samuel House Plantation. On July 19, both divisions turned left on today's North Druid Hills Road and marched until they reached today's Briarwood, where they turned left.
10. They crossed the north fork of Peachtree Creek near Johnson's Mill.
11. Both divisions proceeded to then Shallowford Road, now Clairmont Road, and then turned right and moved south.
12. They crossed the south fork of Peachtree Creek and passed by Sheriff Oliver Powell's home on the right.
13. Cox's division turned right, or west, on North Decatur Road and moved to Peavine Creek, where the men camped on the grounds of Peyton Plantation, now Emory University.
14. Hascall's division continued south on Shallowford Road to today's Ponce de Leon, where the division turned right, or west.
15. The corps passed through today's Druid Hills neighborhood during the afternoon of July 19.
16. The corps moved to the intersection of today's Briarcliff, where they turned left and connected with the extreme right of the Sixteenth Army Corps of the Army of the Tennessee.
17. On July 20, Cox moved to Williams Road, today's Briarcliff. He turned left and marched southwesterly to the intersection of today's Ponce de Leon. Here Cox's left tied into Hascall's right, and the two divisions were reunited facing Atlanta.

CHAPTER SIXTY-SIX

Confederacy | CARTER LITTLEPAGE STEVENSON

STEVENSON'S DIVISION, CHEATHAM'S CORPS,
ARMY OF TENNESSEE
JUST NORTH OF FAIRGROUND ROAD WITHIN ATLANTA'S
INNER DEFENSES, EAST SIDE OF ATLANTA
JULY 22, 1864
8:00 A.M.

With the late night move to Atlanta's inner defenses from the outer defenses behind them, the men of Stevenson's division worked slowly at improving the recently laid out ditches of the inner ring. Breakfast was underway, and the fires were adding to the heat from by the sun. Men made their way around their new divisional area and dug latrines or sinks.

Major General Carter Littlepage Stevenson was forty-six years old and had graduated from the United States Military Academy in 1838. He had ranked forty-two in a class of forty-five.

To some considerable degree, Stevenson's division's presence on the field represented a nightmare of sorts for the Union. A year ago, because of inadequate transport, Grant had agreed to parole the Confederate defenders of Vicksburg, which Stevenson's division was a part of, rather than imprison and send them north. Grant had rationalized that by allowing the defeated Rebels to go home, they would be grateful and as a result make less dangerous foes. Beyond that, he hoped they would return home and sow dissention among friends and neighbors. In spite of these wished-for results, the veterans were still fighting. Following their parole, Stevenson rejoined Bragg and the Army of Tennessee in time for the battle at Missionary Ridge and had been part of the eighty some odd days of maneuver from Dalton to Atlanta.

Stevenson was solid. He did not seek rank or position beyond the four brigades of his division, and no one thought his star shown so brightly that they reached down to elevate him to the command of a corps anyway. In this position, he was competent and steady. He possessed wide experience and felt comfortable and well positioned in his present command.

On this day, as he sat outside his divisional headquarters, he blew on the hot coffee in his cup and reflected on his position. His force had moved west out of their position and established communications with Major General Gustavus Smith, who commanded the three brigades of Georgia Militia over on his right.

Somehow in the movement back to this interior line, the space between his left and the right of Hindman's division, under Brigadier General John Brown, had expanded to a distance of more than 1,000 feet. Given the smaller size of units within the South's Army of Tennessee, this distance represented almost a division front. He assumed that in a pinch he could cover most of it with his reserve brigade, but it appeared that two Southern batteries were attempting to fill the otherwise empty space. Either way, it would probably be a while before the Yankees realized they had left the outer lines and longer still before they attacked these entrenchments. Littlepage thought that it would get sorted out.

On his left was Brown's old brigade, now under Colonel Joseph Palmer. On his right, next to the Atlanta Fairground Road, were the four regiments under his former classmate at West Point, Brigadier General Alexander Reynolds. Reynolds had two regiments from North Carolina and two from Virginia. When the anticipated assault jumped off, Reynold's brigade could keep the road to their right as a true guide into the action.

Between these two units, in the center, were the five Alabama regiments under lawyer and soldier Brigadier General Edmund Pettus. Pettus had helped raise the 20th Alabama, which formed part of his brigade. He was a hard fighter and, at forty-three years old, reckoned to be a mature and seasoned leader. If Pettus were half as good as a lawyer as he was a troop commander, then he was a damn fine lawyer. His Alabamians would lead from the center and spearhead the division's attack in a sense.

The 4th Brigade was commanded by Brigadier General Alfred Cumming, whose four regiments were stacked up behind the other forces. He, too, was a West Pointer and had spent considerable time fighting in Virginia. He had commanded his brigade under Stevenson since he had joined the division in the defense of Vicksburg. His regiments were all from Georgia, including the 2nd Georgia State Line, which had been with the brigade since June 15th. This unit was known to some as Governor Joe Brown's pets. Those boys, and many of them were little more than boys, had been formed to guard the railroads in Georgia. Now, they were soldiers. There were about 700 of them under Colonel James Wilson. They had all stayed together in their first offensive test at Kolb's farm a month earlier, had acquitted themselves well, and lost some eighty men. The men of the rest of the brigade were veterans of long standing.

"Without West Point and lawyers, there would be no field grade and general officers," thought Stevenson. *"Of course, without professional soldiers, lawyers, and politicians, maybe there would be no war at all."* Stevenson laughed. This seemed an amusing bit of irony.

With his four-piece brass telescope extended, he glassed the area to his front, eastward toward the line Cleburne's troops vacated during the preceding hours of darkness. Even now, it seemed he could see blue-jacketed Union soldiers cautiously moving into those trenches on the hill before him. Ahead of him was what had been a cornfield and beyond that rose the two humps of Bald Hill. The less imposing of the two humps lay directly before him with the higher one to his right. Despite its comparative lack of height, the smaller hump was a hill and would be covered with that potent Yankee field artillery and dug-in veteran troops.

This situation was a bit like the one he faced in Vicksburg. There, as he did here, he occupied the right of the defenses. There, too, he faced essentially the same western army. Of course, Sam Hood was no Pemberton, and they were not backed up to the Mississippi. He believed it was better to receive than give when it came to combat, and he would prefer the Yanks attacked him here as they had at Kennesaw. But he knew his commander and felt certain that unless the Yankees hurried, then it would be them, the Southern troops, moving out of their ditches to attack the boys in blue on the hill.

On Bald Hill, men from Blair's Seventeenth Army Corps were consolidating and reversing the trenches they had claimed. On the right of the Seventeenth Army Corps were troops from Harrow's 4th Division of the Fifteenth Army Corps, and they were moving forward to claim the empty trenches.

CHAPTER SIXTY-SEVEN

Union | WILLIAM SHERMAN

HEADQUARTERS OF THE MILITARY DIVISION OF THE MISSISSIPPI
TWO MILES NORTHEAST OF ATLANTA, ABOUT THREE QUARTERS OF A MILE NORTH OF DECATUR ROAD
JULY 22, 1864
10:00 A.M.

The group of Union officers approached the crest of the knoll, moving south and west toward Atlanta on horseback. Some time ago, they had ridden down Williams Mill Road to the point where they turned toward the house. They had turned off the road, moved up the hill, and moved across the ditches to the east of the large-frame house, which not so long before had been in the possession of the Confederate army. Department headquarters had been established at the house after they had encountered a disreputable man who called himself Howard. The fellow said the house was his, as unlikely as it may have seemed, and the headquarters was soon known as Howard's House. After having finished some administrative details, Sherman, Schofield, and others left the house to see what lay beyond.

General Sherman rode with a gaggle of staff officers, Schofield, and Schofield's senior divisional commander, General Jacob Cox. Sherman was mounted on his fine Kentucky thoroughbred named Lexington. Sherman's thoughts raced, as they often did. He indulged in the facts as he hoped they would be. That is, he hoped Hood and his Army of Tennessee were on their way out of Atlanta after their bold but foolish strike at Thomas over on the Collier Road ridge.

He had been receiving reports that the Southern soldiers had abandoned their trenches on the east side of the city, and he hoped this signaled Hood was leaving Atlanta. Today could be the day. Union troops were already moving out of their trenches and advancing into those left by the Rebels.

Reining in, the generals sat easily in their saddles, looking toward Atlanta from their excellent vantage point. Their looks were first directed at the downward slope of the hill where it ended in the sluggish creek that flowed north. Southern skirmishers lightly held the creek line. The generals could see the water wheel turning on the Lewis Mill a little further on and then Rebel soldiers up the next hillside, digging away on the fortifications that they had withdrawn to when they abandoned their eastern line. Other Confederate soldiers were busy shaping trees for an abatis.

The three senior officers and some of their eager staff pressed forward from the shade of the trees. This movement uncovered their position and made them visible to the sharp eyes of the enemy riflemen and those manning the dug-in artillery tubes. These grimy, sweaty Confederate soldiers began to warm up the area with resolute rifle fire.

That greeting, when combined with the visual message before him, immediately convinced Sherman that he was in error. His hopes were dashed on the hard red-clay facts before him.

He spoke to Schofield, "It now seems clear that the enemy is in Atlanta in force and means to stay there. I had believed those reports about substantial troop movement to the south and believed that Hood was moving out to East Point. But that can't be true."

As they moved back away from the ranging enemy fire, Sherman turned to his staff officers and prepared messages to McPherson, Thomas, and Howard confirming his new understanding of Confederate intentions. Sherman was confident that Hood would use the fortifications to his advantage. He was sure that Hood had learned something from his attack of yesterday and that a repeat of the offensive sally at the ridge and creek would not soon be forthcoming. Though he was wrong about Hood leaving, Sherman was certain that Hood would stay inside those thick walls of Atlanta.

The Union officers returned through the trees to the two-story house and the promise of cool shade. As they neared the house, McPherson could be seen moving resolutely toward them. *"He always looked like he has something important to do or say,"* thought Sherman.

McPherson dismounted and approached Sherman. Always correct from a military point of view, especially with his superiors, McPherson stopped and saluted his commander.

“Morning, General,” he called. I need to speak to you, sir.” He held a small sheet of paper in his left hand. It was from Sherman himself.

Hd. Qs. Mil Div of the Miss.
In the Field at Howard House
Near Atlanta—July 22, 1864
Genl. McPherson
Army of the Tenn
Genl.

Instead of sending Dodge to your left, I wish you would put his whole corps to work destroying absolutely the Railroad back to and including Decatur. I want that road absolutely and completely destroyed. Every tie and rail twisted. As soon as Garrard returns, if the Enemy still holds Atlanta I will again shift you round to the Extreme Right with Turner's Ferry as a Depot. Explore roads etc. with that view.

W.T. Sherman
Maj. Genl.

Sherman moved toward him and leaned down from his mount to shake his friend’s offered hand in a hearty fashion.

“Good to see you,” he greeted. “Tell me what’s going on down there on my left flank. Tell me you have old John Bell Hood on the run, and Logan is right behind him.” Sherman got down from his horse and led the way to the porch steps, where the two generals sat down.

UNION, JAMES MCPHERSON

McPherson was eager to tell Sherman all that had happened. As McPherson had attempted to convey in his written communication of 3:00 p.m. yesterday, Leggett’s 3rd Division of Blair’s Seventeenth Army Corps had taken the most commanding piece of terrain, Bald Hill, about a mile south of the railroad. It was from his position on that hill that Leggett had reported the movement of ten or more enemy regiments traveling to the southeast. McPherson was proud of the capture of the hill and excited about the troop movement.

"The enemy movement is part of something big. I think we are in for a huge battle at anytime. I need Dodge's Seventeenth Army Corps on my left and not out tearing up track," McPherson said. After more earnest exchange, Sherman was finally convinced of the immediate rightness of McPherson's call and reversed his previous orders.

"Go ahead. Move him as you want to. We can tear up track tomorrow. Firm up your left to support Blair. You are right when you say Blair is in the air. Let's hold what we have, especially that hill of Leggett's. Fortify the positions your force holds."

As was often the case, McPherson relaxed in Sherman's presence, and some of his nervous urgency drained off. As they talked, they concluded that if no enemy assault took place by 1:00 p.m., then it would not take place that day. Having achieved what he came for, McPherson took his leave from Sherman and rode off to meet with two of his three corps commanders for lunch.

As he rode south behind the lines held by Logan's Fifteenth Army Corps, McPherson saw troops and guns in the process of advancing into the trenches the Rebels used to occupy. Engineers and pioneers were reversing these trenches to face toward the city. Skirmishers north of the railroad were deploying beyond the new line of fortifications.

Just this morning, or really last night, the line of entrenchments his soldiers were now reversing and occupying had formed part of Atlanta's outer ring of defenses. Sometime during the night, those Rebel soldiers had removed themselves from his immediate front. On its face, it seemed to make little sense.

These were the same soldiers who had opposed him all the way from Decatur. They had resisted, skirmished, and harassed his lead elements even before they had entered Decatur and swung west along the Western and Atlantic Railroad. It was hard to understand this sudden change. What had been tough trenches held by grim, determined men who watched his own soldiers from less than a mile away were now empty and inviting. Was this a trap? Maybe he should slow this advance down until he knew for certain what awaited him.

The enemy withdrawal had not been total and complete though. Here and there along the line held by Generals Woods, Smith, and

Harrow's divisions, there had been brief firefights. As a result, there had been men killed, wounded, and frightened for a period of time. Yet once this forward movement was finished, his army would be in strong fortified positions.

In addition to his own powerful force, McPherson was comforted by the near presence of Sherman and of his friend General Schofield and his small Army of the Ohio just off to the north. They had been moving up from the Paden Plantation and Peavine Creek as he talked to Sherman this morning. Hood, who he had tutored back at West Point, must have pretty well exhausted himself yesterday since Thomas had pushed him down from the north across the rough banks of Peachtree Creek and then up the hillside. Old Sam Hood was beaten for the time being.

CHAPTER SIXTY-EIGHT

Confederacy | JOSEPH WHEELER

FAYETTEVILLE ROAD

JULY 22, 1864

MIDMORNING

Wheeler felt that his current orders were a much better mission, one much more suited to his talents. This was the kind of action that was worth riding in the front for. This was what Southern cavalry was all about. Backing up, digging in, retreating, defending in the face of a numerically superior, cautious foe as he had for the past several days was not why he had joined the cavalry. Now, riding in the van of a huge offensive designed by Hood to crush McPherson's slow moving Army of the Tennessee, he felt nearly boundless enthusiasm. It was good to be back on a horse and out of those shallow trenches on Bald Hill he had been sharing with Cleburne's infantry. He wished he could push his troopers along faster, but it was hot, and the horses and the men were nearly worn out.

His gloved fingers moved to his right side to find the holstered long barreled Savage Navy percussion cap revolver. He doubted he would fire it that day, but its secure presence was reassuring to him. He enjoyed loading it and especially placing each percussion cap on the nipples. The little caps fit so perfectly with a machined precision fit. It was a heavy pistol, but he liked the style of it with its hexagonal barrel and the unusual trigger guard. It had a business-like look to it, and he was confident he could knock a man off his feet or out of a saddle with it.

The plan for the day was a good one, and his role could well be a show stopper. Over the last several days, it had seemed to Wheeler that McPherson's army had been traveling light. Generally, the trains of an army moved with or near the rear of the troops they supported, but McPherson had only a few wagons supporting his three corps. Intelligence had reported that wagons and supplies were parked on the northeast side of Decatur in the cemetery, only a short distance from the courthouse. Wheeler just knew that the lightly guarded ordinance and supply wagons were a juicy target, and it was going to be a rich haul. The wagons would be filled with the material that were wanted and needed by the men of the Army of Tennessee. It would make headlines and maybe halt the thrust of at least part of Sherman's army.

Hardee had explained that the horsemen under Wheeler were also to screen and protect the right flank of Hardee's four divisions as Hardee's corps, in turn, flanked and then engulfed the left of the Union Army of the Tennessee. The Union forces that awaited him should mostly be Garrard's cavalry. Wheeler suspected they would have a section or two of artillery. Even with the guns, it seemed unlikely that a sustained defense would materialize. A hard-hitting initial action might run the Union soldiers off and let him snatch the wagons.

It was Hood's plan, and it seemed like a good plan to Wheeler. He especially liked the part when he and his fast riders were to play. With surprise, quickness, and greater numbers, his actions should lead to victory. He was confident his force of 2,200 troopers would rout Garrard's horsemen with speed and little loss of life to the fast moving Confederates.

Behind him was Ferguson's renegade brigade, and behind Ferguson's three regiments was Martin's division. Major General Martin continued to be sick, and Alfred Iverson Jr. continued to command in his place. The Georgia regiments of the brigade were now under the command of Colonel Charles Crews, who watched the world through melancholy eyes set in a delicate, fine-featured face. The five Georgia regiments had come off Bald Hill after Ferguson's Alabama troopers and were thus behind them in the line of march.

Third in line was Allen's Alabama brigade with his six regiments. New York-born and Alabama-raised, Allen graduated from Princeton in 1859. He read law and was operating a plantation when the war came. He entered Rebel service as a first lieutenant and was soon after promoted to the rank of major. After Shiloh, he was named colonel and commander of a regiment. He was wounded twice and promoted to brigadier general in 1864. At the same time, he became the commander of the Alabama brigade.

Wheeler's force was now moving easily on the Fayetteville Road that ran northeasterly toward Decatur. If the road seemed familiar to some in the command, it was. It had been over this same dirt road that only two days before, on July 20, Wheeler and his then-dismounted force had contested every step of Union General Frank Blair's Seventeenth Army Corps as it had moved toward Bald Hill and Atlanta.

Now, in the early morning of July 22, they marched. It was cool and pleasant, especially beneath the fully leafed trees that crowded the sides of the road and branched over the road itself. So far none of Wheeler's lead elements had seen any sight of Union pickets or vedettes. It seemed that maybe they were well behind the plodding Union forces that were pushing toward Atlanta from the east. Maybe their and Hardee's surprise would be completed.

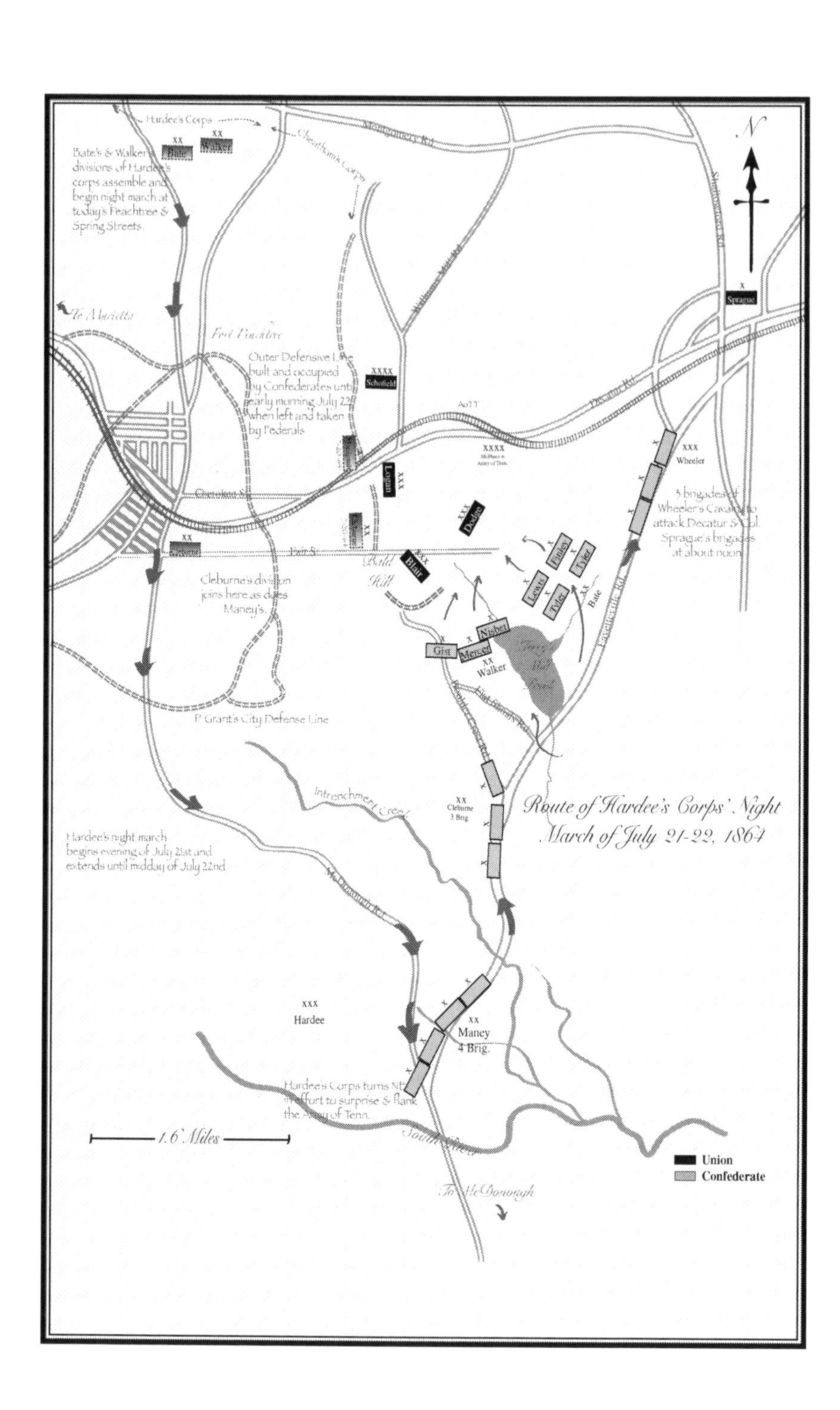

Hardee's Corps
Bate
Walker
Bate's & Walker's divisions of Hardee's corps assemble and begin night march at today's Peachtree & Spring Streets.
Cheatham's Corps
Montgomery Rd
N
Sprague
To Marietta
Fort Peachtree
Outer Defensive Line built and occupied by Confederates until early morning July 22 when left and taken by Federals
XXXX
Schofield
Decatur Rd
Logan
XXXX
Wheeler
Cherokee St.
Dodge
3 brigades of Wheeler's Cavalry to attack Decatur & Col. Sprague's brigades at about noon
Cleburne
Fair St.
Blair
Bald Hill
Finley
Tyler
Lewis
Tyler
Bate
Cleburne's division joins here as does Maney's.
Gist
Mercer
Nisbet
Walker
Terry's Mill Pond
Fayetteville Rd.
P. Grant's City Defense Line
Intrenchment Creek
Cleburne
3 Brig
Route of Hardee's Corps' Night March of July 21-22, 1864
Hardee's night march begins evening of July 21st and extends until midday of July 22nd
McDonough Rd.
Hardee
Maney
4 Brig.
Hardee's Corps turns NE in effort to surprise & flank the Army of Tenn.
1.6 Miles
South River
To McDonough
Union
Confederate

CHAPTER SIXTY-NINE

Confederacy | WILLIAM HARDEE & WILLIAM WALKER

HEADQUARTERS OF HARDEE'S CORPS

ALONG THE FAYETTEVILLE DECATUR ROAD NEAR THE SUGAR CREEK CROSSING

JULY 22, 1864

10:15 A.M.

CONFEDERACY, WILLIAM HARDEE

Hardee sat easily on his horse surrounded by a bevy of staff officers. The advance to the attack was not going well, and he knew it. The night march had been much too slow off the mark. It was just too damn far, and there had not been adequate time for this four-division force to move from hills above Peachtree Creek almost to Decatur. He had handled moving two divisions from Collier's Road as well as Maney's and Cleburne's divisions from the line on the east side of Atlanta without a hitch. That little show of tactical competence did not make up for a bad plan and unsatisfactory execution. The idea of it all made him flush with inner anger at himself. He was hot, and this inner burn only made it worse. Time had run out, and the order had to be modified.

His divisions ran from Cleburne on the left to Walker and Bate and then to Maney on the right. Ahead of him lay unbroken land thick with trees, briars, and vines. The terrain was covered with dense vegetation and trees so dense that one couldn't see twenty feet ahead. Beyond that thick land was the enemy, who—if Hood were right—were in the air. If they could hurry up, Hardee's force could soon attack into the near left flank and rear of McPherson's force at about a forty-five degree angle from the road, as he had been ordered.

Bate and Walker were supposed to begin the attack. Those troops should, by all rights, end up well in the center of the rear of the Army of the Tennessee's lines. They had the longest way to march and would be like the free end of a gate swinging in with great force. Cleburne's force would act in some regard as the hinge or pivot with less distance to travel to reach the troops of the Union Sixteenth Army Corps.

Hardee knew Hood wanted action, and time was wasting. Even if not enough time had been allotted, and any reasonable observer would know it had not, Hood still placed enormous pressure on Hardee to move, to get on with it, and to open the ball. Criticism even from someone like Hood was difficult to accept. Hardee preferred a more careful plan, but this is what he had to work with. He knew he had great soldiers. They would make even this poor plan work. Great soldiers could rise above even the circumstances they were forced to confront and wrest a victory out of these miserable circumstances. And, as soon as this effort was over, he knew that he would seek reassignment. With all Hardee's loyalty to the cause, he didn't think he could work for Hood any longer.

A group of horsemen approached quickly from up the road from the direction of Decatur. The horses looked as tired as the exhausted troops. One man stuck out. Hardee would know that man anyplace. It was Walker. Walker had always looked, to Hardee, a little like the picture he had seen of that crazy man John Brown who had struck hard at Harper's Ferry Arsenal. It was his eyes. They seem to blaze.

Up he rode, horse in a lather, and Walker gave a quick half salute. On his head was a black felt hat with the big black feather curling around. He sat on his horse well, ramrod straight.

"General, you must know that our fool guides have led us into a huge mill pond that lies nearly in the center of our line of march. It would take a little time, but it would be best if we could move down and over to our left to avoid the quagmire and the briars."

In a voice unusual for him, Hardee said roughly and with an edge, "No, sir. This movement has been delayed too long already."

Walker's eyes flashed, and somehow the salute came up as he wheeled his horse and set out back to his command. While Hardee may have been his corps commander and had an additional star, Walker by no means believed Hardee to be his superior. In Walker's mind, as it related to Hardee, superior wasn't in the running. Hardee had a vague sense about Walker's potential insubordination but had always relied on Walker's sense of professionalism.

CONFEDERACY, WILLIAM WALKER

As Walker rode along, his self control bleeding off and his rage coming to the surface, he said to his staff officer, Major Joe Cumming, "Major, did you hear that?"

"Yes, General Hardee forgot himself, sir."

"I will make him remember this insult. If I survive this battle, he shall answer to me for it."

Cumming rode along in silence for a while with Walker, who was venting a number of grievances. Suddenly, they were overtaken by one of the members of Hardee's staff.

"General, sir, General Hardee sends his most ardent regrets for his hasty and discourteous language. He begs me to say he would be here in person to apologize but knows you understand his presence is required elsewhere. He says further that he will beg your pardon in person and apologize to you personally at the first opportunity."

Major Cumming leaned over from his saddle to speak quietly in the ear of General Walker, "Sir, now that makes it all right."

Walker said, "No, it doesn't. Go back and tell Hardee I refused him."

Walker and Cumming pressed forward off the road and soon his four brigades were crashing through the vegetative hell and watery muck that was the terrain near Terry's Mill. With each step, his anger compounded at their guide and at Hardee, who he felt should have listened to him and done as he suggested. They had picked up their guide, Case Turner, back at Intrenchment Creek at Cobb's Mill. *"By God,"* Walker thought, *"if that man were a guide, I would damn well hate to meet somebody who was lost."* Walker, having worked himself into a rage, suddenly pulled his pistol from his hostler and aimed it at Turner.

"Damn you, sir. You said a little pond awaited us. This thing is more like an ocean than a pond. It is really more like a damned swamp. You, sir, knew it all along. You deserve to be shot like the lying dog you are."

Major Cumming splashed over and placed himself between the irate general and the terrified Turner. He said, "General, remember that Turner here told us about this horrible pond and advised against this route. It's not his fault. He only agreed to take us where we were ordered to go." He looked imploringly at Walker. "General, put away your pistol. You'll scare this old man to death."

Eyes fastened on the hapless civilian. Walker saw in him the entire basis for all his frustration. After a few moments, his senses reasserted themselves, and he relented. It had taken hours from the time he had moved his division off the Fayetteville Road at 5:00 a.m. to negotiate possibly the worst terrain he had ever encountered. The coolness of the early morning had been replaced by the boiling heat of the noonday. Decatur was still some four miles ahead, and these damned briars, muck, and marsh had conspired to exhaust already footsore and worn down troops.

"So much for Hood's original plan," Walker thought to himself. He knew that the boy's plan was far too ambitious when he had first heard about it. He was as much in favor of action as anyone—in fact, more in favor.

But he knew that commanders must temper their enthusiasm with judgment. Even under the best of circumstances with a well-marked road, accurate intelligence, good local knowledge, and well-rested, shod, and fed troops, the plan was too ambitious. With the state of the corps and the jungle of briars, the plan was a failure from the time it was announced. It had been almost impossible for his men to get through the briars growing around the millpond, and even as they made it through, Walker cursed Hardee.

Sweat ran down Walker's gaunt, full-bearded face from under his black felt hat and then down his back and chest. Without thinking much about it, he knew his sweat was tinged with the sweet smell of the peach brandy he had been nipping on since before the sun came up. He also knew he was sweating more freely because of drinking it too.

His horse had cuts on its legs and flanks, and he still had a few of the little hook-like thorns in his trousers. He was still angry about the way Hardee had treated him earlier in the day. How could one man's honor mean so little to Hardee? It was honor, after all, that lay at the very base of why this war was being fought in the first place. If the rights of the states and a man's individual honor weren't as connected as brothers, one to the other, a man didn't understand anything. If Walker survived today, he would demand to meet Hardee on a field of honor. Satisfaction, one way or the other, would be his.

So there he sat: tall, nearly elegant in the saddle, hot, and still angry. He was angry at Hardee, the way the war was going, his lack of appropriate recognition and advancement. He was mad about the delay, mad at the mud and the briars, just plain mad. *"By God, it is all an outrage, a total outrage,"* Walker thought.

He then received word of the presence of Federal skirmishers in his front, and that didn't make very much sense. There also wasn't supposed to be anyone between his division's right and the left of Bate's division so that they could both advance until they reached into the rear side of the entrenched Union lines. He and Bate should be far in the unsuspecting Federal rear. Certainly with all the miles marched, they would be. Hell, they were nearly in Decatur by now. This envelopment with all its faults must have put them well behind the Federal rear. The Union army should be nearly due west of him and maybe an hour away.

Now that they were all out of that thorn-and-blueberry-and-blackberry hell, it made sense for him to gain a little personal reconnaissance and determine for himself where he was and what lay to his front. *"Maybe that fool guide from the mill can pinpoint our location on the piece of a map I have,"* Walker thought. Of course, before anything else was done, his three brigades had to get themselves aligned correctly. Walker thought it would have been better to stay in column formation and go into a line of battle once they had cleared the infernal swamp rather than each man having to break trail for himself. But a line of battle was what had been ordered, so that is what they had done. Now, they just needed to improve the battle lines.

"Major Cumming, you and Captains Ross and Troup ride over there and tell each of the brigade commanders that we are nearly out of the woods. Tell them that they should continue up to the creek and then begin to move over toward the northeast and then improve their lines of battle. Find whoever is running Stevens Brigade and tell him to see if he can ease over closer to Bate's left. It'll probably be a little while yet, so let's keep everyone moving."

The three rode off, leaving Walker with his cousin Captain Talbot, his orderly, his civilian guide, and the members of his personal escort made up of Company F of the 10th Confederate under Lieutenant Bass. The small group of riders came up the steep end of the hill overlooking the large millpond they had just crossed. After an open space and 200 yards away, there was another forested area and, beyond that, more of these pleasant, rolling, wave-like hills.

Field glasses to his eyes, Walker peered at the terrain ahead of him, where he would shortly order troops to travel. He looked to his right where Bate's division was already organizing and then to his left over the area his men would soon occupy. The horse moved, making it difficult to keep the glasses on anything.

"It will be good to get this attack over. I look forward to a cigar and maybe Lucius can fry up some chicken," said the sweating general to himself.

CHAPTER SEVENTY

Union | JOHN W. SPRAGUE

2nd Brigade, 4th Division, Sixteenth Army Corps,
Army of the Tennessee

Georgia Railroad embankment, south of Decatur

July 22, 1864

11:30 a.m.

Unknown to Colonel John W. Sprague was the fact that an entire infantry corps and part of two divisions of cavalry were pushing northeast toward the village of Decatur. Whether he would have been relieved to know it was only the mounted element that was scheduled to assault Decatur and not Hardee's battle hardened corps of veterans can now only be speculated about. Colonel Sprague commanded the 2nd Brigade of the 4th Division of the Seventeenth Army Corps. His boss was Brigadier General John Fuller.

Sprague's brigade had come back to Decatur about noon the day before. His 2nd Brigade, with its three component regiments, had been pulled out of position along the railroad and returned to Decatur to guard the large Union wagon park. This logistical base was expanding, given its ideal location to support both McPherson and Schofield, but Decatur itself was not a big place. It had a ten-year-old, two-story courthouse, which was a handsome building and occupied the primary place in town. Just down the hill from the courthouse to the south and a little west, about halfway to the train tracks was the jail. It, too, was a building with two stories.

Sprague was very happy to have the independence of a separate command split off from the rest of the division. He was a serious man, and this was serious business. He knew this base area was going to grow soon because he was expecting his own 43rd Ohio under Colonel Wager Swayne to arrive in Decatur sometime today. They had in their care some 400 additional wagons, which were now making their way down the long road from Roswell, having crossed the river on the new Chattahoochee Bridge. Once the 43rd arrived, his brigade would be at its full fighting strength. He would have available to him the 35th New Jersey, the 63rd Ohio, the 25th Wisconsin, and the wagon train guards of the 43rd Ohio.

Sprague knew the 63rd Ohio well, as he had been its commander since January 1862. He was one of those many officers in the Union army who had survived those early days as a company grade officer and slowly advanced as boots were available to be filled. He had enough time to learn about command at lower levels to have developed into a pretty fair combat leader. Sprague enjoyed command. To him, it seemed mostly to be common sense.

Sprague had six companies of soldiers, two from each regiment, out as pickets on the roads south and west of the village. He would keep these companies sharp by replacing them with their sister companies from time to time. Too long in one spot or one activity can create complacency even in veteran troops. It was his sense that the way to the north was protected as well as the way to the west since the whole army was west of him and the roads to the north had been cleared of Rebels just yesterday. If trouble lurked, Sprague figured that it lay to the south and possibly to his east, so it was important to keep pickets in those areas.

Upon his arrival, after he ordered out his pickets, he then laid out the line where the entrenchments south of the village were to be constructed. He had added a line running from the eastern end, his left, to the north, all the way to the cemetery where the wagon park lay. Sprague would keep the men digging on that high ground just south of the railroad.

He was pleased that Garrard had ordered two sections, a total of four Parrott guns, to remain in town with his brigade. The Chicago Board of Trade Battery, under Lieutenant Trumbull Griffin, provided substantial firepower and was welcome to remain with Sprague as long as they could. After discussion with Griffin, he had placed them just north of the jail, facing south. The elevation of the hillside allowed an excellent field of fire in support of the regiments to the south of the railroad. The leftmost gun was next to the road that ran from the courthouse down to the tracks. Sprague's only other artillery was the two-gun section from Battery C of the 1st Michigan. These pieces were likewise rifled but were three-inch ordinance rifles rather than Parrott Rifles. These guns were south of the railroad near Dr. Hoyle's House and covered one of the two obvious routes of assault.

Supporting the four guns of the Board of Trade were three companies of the 63rd Ohio. Two more of the companies of the 63rd Ohio were on the hill to the right of Battery C. To the left of Battery C were four companies from the 25th Wisconsin. Beyond the 25th Wisconsin and across the Decatur Fayetteville Road was the 35th New Jersey.

Sprague watched with satisfaction as the de facto battalion made up of eight companies—four from his old unit, the 63rd Ohio, and four from the 25th Wisconsin—moved out. This force represented almost a third of his total, and he had ordered it out to make a reconnaissance to determine, if possible, what sort of enemy force existed down the tree-lined road that curved away to the southwest, the very same road the Seventeenth Army Corps under General Blair had passed two days before. The cavalry demonstration Blair encountered before the battle at Bald Hill had been real enough and might signal that something of substance was brewing.

On the other hand, it might represent nothing more than a small troop of cavalry searching for food or information. He hoped it was merely a roving band of Rebel horsemen out on a frolic, but one never knew. He had long since learned that active patrolling was the right thing under all circumstances even though the cavalry was not, in his opinion, made up of serious warriors and did not pose much threat in all probability. Decatur seemed a long way from the embattled but well-fortified Southerners some six or eight miles to the west in Atlanta.

Well, if there were Rebels down the road, he would know soon enough and could rapidly alert the huge wagon park behind him in the cemetery.

CHAPTER SEVENTY-ONE

Union | A WESTERN SHARPSHOOTER

SKIRMISH LINE, WEST OF SUGAR CREEK,

EAST OF ATLANTA

JULY 22, 1864

11:45 A.M.

Less than 800 feet away from the creek where Walker and his men were, a skirmisher from the 66th Illinois Veteran Infantry, known to some as the Western Sharpshooters, was stretched out prone. He lay in concealment in the tall grass on the forward edge of the hill, which sloped down to the valley of sluggish Sugar Creek. His slim, graceful, 16-shot Henry rifle lay to his front with its magazine tube balanced on a stone.

This skirmisher liked to shoot. He was blessed with the keen sight of youth and good genes. He remembered the Dimick American Deer Rifle that he had been armed with back in 1861. It had been a sweet piece. He could recall molding his own bullets and cutting his own patches. The first time he had come under fire had taken place just three days after Christmas in 1861. It was still fresh to him. They had been in Mount Zion, Missouri. He and about 150 of the sharpshooters armed with deer rifles had killed about 130 Rebels that day. It was easier than killing deer. Deer had the good sense to run. The Rebels had stayed to take the punishment.

The Dimick had been traded, and he and the rest of the regiment each spent fifty dollars for the stunning, new Henry. At least the army supplied the bullets for the thing. He had heard that the army brass was opposed to the use of the weapon on the basis that the men would waste the ammunition.

The Henry was without a doubt the most modern and advanced rifle around. Moreover, it had a special look. It had grace coupled with rapid-fire lethality. With few exceptions, the rest of the long arm weapons looked like one another and looked more like the flintlocks of the past. But the Henry was different in looks and action.

The rifle represented the peak of American technology and inventiveness. It was not unique in weight or length; it weighed 9.25 pounds empty and was 43.5 inches long. However, it was a lever-action, repeating rifle with a spring-loaded tubular magazine. The magazine was positioned under the barrel and held fifteen rimfire copper rounds. It fired a .44 caliber short bullet.

By pulling down the lever, which also served as the trigger guard, the soldier could extract the spent casing, place the next round near the chamber, and cock the weapon. Returning the lever back to the small of the stock pushed the round into the chamber, and the weapon was ready to fire. The movement of the lever was all done in one fluid motion, and practice meant the rifle might not even move from the firing position.

The efficiency of the new weapon was also a marvel. The rear sight cross bar could be elevated to acquire a target sight at a considerable distance. By keeping a round chambered and a full magazine, the weapon could deliver sixteen bullets as quickly as a man could find a target. In practice, the young skirmisher could consistently put five holes in a three-inch diameter circle at one hundred yards and knew that in a pinch, he could free twenty or so rounds in sixty seconds.

This young light infantryman enjoyed being out in front of the 66th Illinois. He enjoyed the freedom from hearing nearly endless complaints and being constantly ordered "close up" or "quiet in the ranks," from non-commissioned officers and smart aleck, high-pocket officers. He had never been around a group of grown men who were so unhappy and disappointed in everyone else. If all their corrections, complaints, and orders were any indication, they must be the unhappiest humans on the earth. It was better where he was. There were no flies, and the group could not yell orders at one another because of the quiet nature of their location and mission. He could stay in this position, comfortable, all day as long as his canteen held plenty of water.

Then, the sharpshooter sighted a group of horsemen coming up that little rise just off to the southeast. He figured it must be officers, and they had to be Rebs, even if the tall one had on an old blue Federal coat. The man didn't know who the Rebel was, but the man had field glasses up to his eyes and a black hat. The Rebel could be a general, at least a colonel, with the way those others all gee'd and hawed to be close to him.

The Illinois skirmisher had excellent eyes. He looked hard and knew he could see the dark saddlecloth and the reins of the bridle. He could make out the sword in its scabbard and the hilt of the weapon. He could distinguish the dark blue of the uniform coat and the black hat. His eye told him the group of men was about 250 yards away.

He had been a good shot with a rifle before the war. Since the war, with all the practice, he had improved. He had long ago learned to successfully estimate the distance to a target. Since his weapon had fired low when he got it, he had filed the German silver blade front sight in order to raise the strike of the bullet. Now, he adjusted the rear ladder sight and moved the rung up to his determined yardage. There was no breeze, and therefore no reason to drift the rear sight to adjust for windage.

He cleared his mind, as he often did in these situations, by reciting the rifle's nomenclature. This produced a calm in his mind and his lips moved almost in the form of a prayer. "*This piece weighs 9.8 pounds fully loaded and is 43.5 inches long. It is an individual shoulder-fired, lever-action, spring-loaded, magazine-fed repeating rifle. It fires sixteen .44 caliber 216-grain bullet, using a twenty-six-grain, black-powder-filled rimfire cartridge. It creates a muzzle velocity of 1,125 feet per second at the end of the weapon's twenty-one-inch barrel.*"

Now with the estimate of the distance at 250 yards, he thought that with a little luck and a little time, he just might be able to knock that skinny old man off his horse. With his right cheek welded to the smooth, dark, wooden stock and his keen right eye sighting on the distant horseman, he pulled the curved brass butt plate tighter into the natural pocket of his strong right shoulder.

The skirmisher had noticed, on past occasions, when he was alone and had the luxury of time that events seemed to slow down. Movement was halted to such an extent that every movement almost stood still and sounds diminished. He knew it was foolish, but he imagined that he could see the round in flight and see the strike of the bullet. He could see the dust puff, the cloth rend, the layers of material burn, the blood collapse behind the advance of the bullet, and then blood gush from the wound.

He had been in his position for some time, and as a result, his breathing and heart rate were at resting levels. Time was his friend. When he rushed, he needed to sight down the barrel and breathe once or twice in and out in order to be accurate. The rifle would rise and fall with the natural rhythm of his breathing. Not today—he was relaxed and at ease. His left hand on the rock allowed the weapon to rest rather than to be held.

The skirmisher knew that with this breath, he would fire. He slowly drew in the heavy warm air, stopped, began to exhale, and with his right index finger slowly applied pressure to the curved steel of the trigger. He took up a little trigger slack, let out a little more air from his lungs, halted his breathing process altogether, and gently squeezed the trigger. He felt a short, forceful jolt as the beautifully crafted Henry rifle kicked back. Then yes, by God, the man was down, off his horse. He knew it was a damn fine shot, especially from this distance and downhill at that. He cocked the rifle, and another round had been chambered. He was ready, but he knew no more similar targets would present themselves anytime soon, especially on that little rise down there by the creek.

Across the way, with an angry whine and a thump like a man's hand slapping the flank of a sweaty horse, the rapidly spinning .44 caliber round drove through a blue wool coat and a sweat-drenched shirt into the thin, straight body of General Walker. It was a devastating blow to a body that had absorbed so much.

Walker knew this was worse than any of the previous times he had been hit. Mexicans and Seminoles had all had a go at him, but he had always survived and more or less recovered.

He had been struck down before, but this time, he was dead before he even hit the ground, field glasses still clutched in his gloved hand. "Fighting Billy" Walker would not lead this assault on McPherson's rear, and the assault may have, in reality, ended then and there.

Chaos and consternation rose up among the command group, who had for so long served Walker.

CHAPTER SEVENTY-TWO

Union | GRENVILLE DODGE & JOHN FULLER

IN RESERVE, IN THE CENTER REAR OF THE SEVENTEENTH ARMY CORPS, HEADQUARTERS OF 4TH DIVISION OF THE SIXTEENTH ARMY CORPS

11:58 A.M.

JULY 22, 1864

UNION, GRENVILLE DODGE

Slender, energetic, and always active, Dodge wanted to push his horse to a faster clip. The youthful-looking major general liked being outside but was nonetheless looking forward to a light lunch with Brigadier General John Fuller. Dodge was soon to visit with the one commander he enjoyed out of his two divisions in his Sixteenth Army Corps.

The meal was to be a working opportunity to talk about the disposition of the corps' alignment, especially Fuller's division. With Sprague still in Decatur, Fuller's remained Dodge's only brigade. As he dismounted, he reflected on the situation.

Dodge had a meeting with McPherson earlier that morning at the headquarters of the Sixteenth Army Corps. McPherson had been filled with premonition about the battle he could feel would happen.

McPherson had said, "General, you know that as we pressed forward on Wednesday and Thursday and finally got lined up north of the railroad that your General Sweeny's division was squeezed out of line. What do you say we move his brigades down to the left of the Seventeenth Corps? I don't mind telling you that I have been worried about those boys south of Bald Hill just being in the air. I know Blair has them digging in, but it is still a bit light down there."

Dodge had replied, "Yes, sir. I think you are right. I will order Sweeny to come down to the rear of the army. There is a road that runs by Clay's house, north and south from the railway. I can move him this morning. Then, he and Fuller's one brigade can unite and extend our left and bolster Blair. I will get over there and lay out a line for entrenchment now."

"Let's look at the map."

Dodge had traced a line extending Blair's left and indicated the road that Sweeny could move his troops on. "Fuller has one brigade in Decatur. After your earlier orders, I moved him and his one remaining brigade here." Dodge had pointed to a place on the map near the rear of Leggett's division on Bald Hill. "He is camped right here on this road on this high ground. There seems to be a ridge line damn near every place you look around here."

"General Dodge, you know I have great faith in you and your troops. Sherman wants you out tearing up railroad tracks and ties. I know you are good at building it as well as tearing it up. But I have this sort of heavy feeling about today. I will feel better when your force is combined with Blair's and have added to our left flank. Sam Hood is unpredictable, and my instincts tell me to be wary and alert of the Rebels moving south of the city. Just get Sweeny down here as soon as you can. We don't have any cavalry out there to screen for us," McPherson had said.

Once Dodge was settled with Fuller, Fuller began providing Dodge with some English American hospitality at his headquarters tent. Dodge, always the "go-ahead" engineer, explained to Fuller where Fuller's brigade should go and where entrenchments should be dug. The map was imperfect, but Fuller understood his brigade should remove itself from its position to the rear of the center of Blair's Seventeenth Army Corps, where it was being held in reserve.

"John, I think McPherson is correct. He has been worrying about a calamity on Blair's left flank. By moving Sweeny's 2nd Division down from the far right of the Fifteenth AC to this point and combining it with yours here on Blair's left, we will be ready for any surprise," Dodge said.

Fuller replied, "Yes, sir, that makes sense. When then will Sweeny's division get here?"

"Well, he's now resting on this little north-south running road about a half mile south of the railroad and about three quarters of a mile from where we are. You can see where these two roads intersect. Since Blair won't move until tomorrow, I am going to have that 2nd Division bivouac where they are at the crossroad."

"Yes, sir."

"Now, John, tell me about the disposition of your soldiers."

"Colonel Sprague took his 2nd Brigade off to Decatur yesterday morning. From what I have seen, Sprague is up to running an independent brigade, so I stayed here with my old command. My pioneer troops have been entrenching on that Bald Hill and have also been helping get General Smith dug in south of the hill. The troops are in two lines behind Leggett's men as reserves to Blair's corps. I have already told Lieutenant Laird and the 14th Ohio Battery to park on the hill near the place Sweeny is now. We are in pretty good shape to help Blair should it come to a battle."

Dodge sat musing and said, "Well, it's all unclear to me. The Rebels seem to have left the line they held to our front last night. Maybe they are leaving Atlanta for good. I know that is what Sherman hopes."

Taking a bracing drink from his cup of coffee, Dodge looked up as a panting officer rushed up to the headquarters tent. "General Dodge, there is a fair amount of enemy cavalry over to the east and south of the 2nd Division. General Sweeny has set out skirmishers, and you can hear some of that firing."

"Go back and tell Sweeny to go into line where he is. I will send one of Fuller's regiments to take the ground to his right and to tie into the 2nd Division's line as it faces south. They can also provide some protection to the Sixteenth Corps' trains. Now, go! Hurry!" Dodge turned to Fuller. "General Fuller, do you understand this?"

"Yes, sir."

"Send a regiment over there immediately. Put them here on the right."

Dodge then left to personally organize the defense of the Sixteenth Army Corps. He was a hands-on leader and would disregard the rightful role of his subordinates to get the result accomplished a bit faster or better. In a way, Fuller was glad to see Dodge go and leave him alone to carry out the orders.

UNION, JOHN FULLER

The intensity of the firing from the east grew substantially during the next several minutes. It sounded to him as though it was a bigger fight than had first been thought. With the respect he had come to appreciate for the enemy troops, Fuller made a quick decision to move the entire 1st Brigade rather than only one regiment. Dodge was no longer there, and Fuller was not one to adhere to prior orders if it seemed circumstances on the ground warranted independent decision making. His experience told him that if one regiment were good, the mass and firepower of four would be even better. It would take just a little longer to move all four regiments, but it would provide considerably more flexibility and give him an edge in command and control since they would be with him, not removed at a distance. His decision made, he yelled for his adjutant to make it so.

This was exactly the type of situation Fuller excelled in. The circumstances were nearly tailor made for him and his unique set of martial skills. Anytime he could thrust himself and his troops into combat with surprise, speed, and mass, Fuller brought success. Back on December 31, 1862 at Parker's Crossroad, Tennessee, Fuller had led the Ohio regiments of Sherman's brigade. In direct contravention of orders to wait, he had rushed the Ohioans forward, south down the road toward the sounds of the guns. Just south of the crossroads, Brigadier General Nathan Bedford Forrest, the most adroit and able Confederate cavalry commander, had sprung a trap on the Union brigade under Colonel Cyrus Dunham. Forrest was in the process of chewing up Dunham's 3rd Brigade. Dunham's four regiments had been split up and almost surrounded.

Fuller arrived with flags flying, field guns going into hasty battery, and four hard charging regiments running down the hill through the crossroads and driving hard into Forrest's dismounted horsemen. As the blue-coated Union soldiers pressed the attack, they captured horses, artillery, and some three hundred stunned and amazed Confederates. In the process, they inflicted a near total defeat on the highly acclaimed Forrest.

Fuller naturally made decisions on the fly. He trusted his gut. He relied on his intuition. He often spoke hastily in lieu of more processed thoughts. The opportunity to lead troops into combat provided a jolt of energy to him. Once he made a decision, he became focused, and each action tended to follow as needed. Somehow Fuller knew when to strike, or perhaps it was that when he struck, it turned out to be the right time because of his zeal to thrust himself and his command into whatever melee was available.

As such, Fuller always seemed to rise to the occasion that was offered, and he soaked up the sense of accomplishment when the task was complete. Peers, once the work was done, might complain that anyone could have performed as Fuller had and then generally conceded that Fuller's action had been logical, reasonable, and quick. Fuller himself had great confidence in his leadership of regiment- and brigade-sized organizations. Today was no exception; he would wield his brigade with finesse.

CHAPTER SEVENTY-THREE

Union | JAMES MCPHERSON

AT THE RAILROAD ABOUT THREE QUARTERS OF A MILE IN THE REAR OF THE FIFTEENTH ARMY CORPS

JULY 22, 1864

11:30 A.M.

McPherson, his twenty-four-year-old Assistant Inspector General Lieutenant Colonel William Strong, their two orderlies, and several of the McPherson's staff rode toward the railroad. The group had just ridden from General Sherman's headquarters. It was not like a parade, but the review was, if anything, even more inspirational than one.

Troops and pioneers from the Fifteenth and Seventeenth Army Corps were busy reversing the fronts all along the more than one mile of recently abandoned Rebel lines. Building first-rate fortifications was now a strongly developed second nature to these veteran soldiers. McPherson had stopped and spoken with every brigade and division commander he had seen along the way. This ride clarified the situation for all present. Then, they turned their horses to move back to the northeast to their designated rendezvous point with Logan and Blair at the rear of the Union army.

McPherson was intelligent and introspective enough to know that while he could order and control the organized battle preparations that were currently underway, that control was largely an illusion. A general could get his troops lined up facing a certain direction, but once the enemy weapons began to light up and the minie balls and artillery shells began to impact, the control he exercised would vanish into thousands of individual actions. Control from the commander would be replaced by hope and dread and would return only when control was no longer really needed.

The corps commanders, their staffs, and several of the divisional commanders he had just seen were waiting for him. The combined riders ambled over to the group of oak trees about 200 yards south of the railroad. The oaks offered the only relief from the hot sun.

McPherson and the others present on horses began to dismount. Regardless of how much one enjoyed riding, it was a luxury to dismount and find a comfortable place to sit. In addition to Frank Blair and John Logan, McPherson saw with pleasure that his Adjutant General, Colonel Clark, was there as well as his artillery chief, Hickenlooper; his chief engineer, Captain Kilburn Knox; his signal officer, Rose; the Chief of Ordinance, Buel; Dr. Duncan; and two personal aides, Willard and Giles. McPherson thought that it was good to be with friends.

Then, McPherson noticed that Dodge was not present.

"I wish General Dodge were here so that I would know the precise location of his corps," said McPherson. Several men nodded their heads in agreement.

McPherson thought Dodge was sure and steady. Of the three political generals reporting to him, he liked the well-educated engineer the best. He recalled fondly the 700-foot bridge Dodge and his men had erected over the Chattahoochee down that steep riverbank at Roswell. Two days was all it took, and it was damn fine bridge. *"It would have been good to have Dodge here,"* McPherson thought, *"but I know Dodge's meeting with Fuller is needed."*

As he had with Sherman earlier that day, McPherson soon had everyone's attention as he discussed the recent change in command that had resulted from Hood replacing the cautious Johnston. McPherson spoke warmly of tutoring Hood in mathematics when Hood was but a big, blond, unpolished cadet from Kentucky.

"Maybe if I hadn't done such a good job, we wouldn't be facing him today. He might well have been shipped home," McPherson joked.

Official news of this change in the command of the Army of Tennessee had been brought just this morning in the form of a newspaper from Atlanta, dated July 18, 1864. Hood's reputation for dash and his bold adventuresome nature were known to most of those gathered under the trees. It was agreed that the extent to which the loss of his left leg and badly damaged arm had changed the man was at best speculation. As the talk continued, McPherson could not help but reflect on whether Hood's ambition had finally been outrun by this appointment and promotion. After all, how much glory and fame would attach to loss, defeat, and surrender? Hood might be game, but the defeat of the Confederacy and Hood in particular seemed foreordained to McPherson. It was merely an engineering problem to him—input and conclusion.

Hood was no Johnston. Rather, McPherson thought he was the opposite. McPherson had understood and had strongly approved of Johnston's skilled rearward movement from one well-prepared position to the next, all generally along the railroad. The government under Davis had to desire a substantial change to replace Johnston with Hood. Hood's personality tended to rashness, and he always seemed in a hurry. This was at odds with what McPherson thought an army commander should be.

McPherson knew himself fairly well and would admit that being careful had gotten him the command of the Union Army of the Tennessee, even if it didn't always win total praise from Sherman. Of course, there had been good reasons not to push forward hard and fast out of Snake Creek Gap and into Resaca. Hadn't Johnston beaten them to it? No matter, careful Joe Johnston was gone, and McPherson's army was quickly becoming secure in their improving defensive positions. This was a good place to be. In a wry moment, McPherson thought he would rather be in his boots than Hood's, especially since he could put two of them on the ground.

The road that the Fifteenth and Sixteenth Army Corps had recently come down followed a ridgeline. Down the elongated back of the ridge ran the Decatur Road and the railroad. The troops had climbed up one hill and down another as they approached the city, the hills rolling in an east to west manner. Now that the army was arrayed in a northwest to southeast arrangement, that line gently fell away from the railroad and rose first to one hill and then to the second, Bald Hill. Even now some men were starting to call this hill "Leggett's Hill" as a result of the heavy fighting by the 4th Division of yesterday. By the end of the day, it would have earned its name.

High ground was good and the Federal north-south line was on the high ground, generally overlooking the valley of Intrenchment Creek that ran between Atlanta and the Union line. Behind the line were other valleys of Sugar Creek.

McPherson smiled to himself as he thought about the junction of the Fifteenth and Seventeenth Army Corps. The men of Harrow's 4th

Division and those of Leggett's seemed fused in a clean strong manner. It was unlikely even a determined enemy could create a break where the two corps linked.

As he relaxed amid the talking and eating senior officers and his official family of staff, his mind indulged itself with a picture of the smiling, beautiful, young woman he would soon wed. She was wonderful, and he imagined his life with her. Once the overwhelming whirlwind of uncertainty was concluded, life would be quite satisfactory as he rose up the command structure of the peacetime army. The peacetime accomplishment of a once again united army under his skilled leadership would be a thing to behold and an opportunity worth seeking.

He motioned for Blair and Logan to come over to the table and look at the map. Going over their locations on the ground and on the map could do no harm. In case a supporting brigade had to be moved, it would be beneficial for both corps commanders to know as much as possible.

The railroad seemed to neatly bisect his Fifteenth Army Corps and confirmed the Army of the Tennessee was nearly due east of the city. The city was now protected by substantial earthen fortifications that, as he had seen from Bald Hill, were well manned and had substantial batteries. It seemed formidable and difficult, if not impossible, to breach by frontal attack. Siege seemed likely if Hood didn't somehow slip away.

McPherson wondered once more what Hood would do. Hood's sally of yesterday was powerful and unexpected. The premonition that a great battle would be fought on his left flank flooded over him again, and he reiterated his conviction to those looking at the map.

Logan spoke, "General, could I have one of those fine cigars you always seem to have with you?"

"Yes, sir, you may," replied McPherson. Somehow, Logan could make any man think Logan was doing the man a favor to smoke one of his cigars. Logan did have style. "Colonel Smith, let's get some of those cigars out for these distinguished gentlemen."

A short time later all who desired were in the process of enjoying a good cigar, compliments of McPherson. McPherson, still at the map table, wrote a note to Dodge. Upon finishing the note and dispatching it, McPherson turned his attention back to his cigar, which he savored. These were good men around him. *"If I lived to be one hundred," McPherson thought, "I would remember these men forever."*

From the southeast of the men and horses and from the left and rear of the army came the harsh crackle of musket fire. It was more than the lazy and occasional fire resulting from alert skirmishers. Rather, it was more concentrated serious firing that indicated a substantial group of men. The pleasantries of the lunch were quickly put aside as the generals and their staff called for and rushed their horses, moving off to return to their appointed places.

General McPherson, Lieutenant Colonel Strong, Captain Giles, Hickenlooper, and their orderlies rode toward the sound of the guns. The small party soon cleared the woods and emerged into an open field where a substantial part of the wagon trains that had not remained in Decatur were parked. Whether by design or not, shells were occasionally falling into the wagon park.

McPherson dispatched young Giles with instructions: "Get the people under control. Move as many of the wagons out of here and to the area north of the railroad." Soon, teamsters were shouting and whipping teams, which usually moved at much slower paces. The place was bedlam, and excitement and fear were evident.

Hickenlooper, the Sixteenth Army Corps artillery officer, was sent by McPherson to see to the immediate placement of Dodge's batteries. McPherson, Strong, and their orderlies moved to a position where the fighting could be seen. The hilltop position they occupied lay to the rear of the brigades of Union General Sweeny. The point they observed from was slightly higher and lay some 3,000 feet to the west of the battle. From this point, the way was clear before them, and the entire panorama of the battlefield could be seen. The area was all open, and two brigades, Rice's and Mersey's, were loosely formed in a line of battle.

One of Sweeny's brigades faced nearly east along Clay Road, which they had earlier marched down and then halted on. In the middle, facing east, was Sweeny's lead brigade, which McPherson believed to be commanded by Colonel August Mersey. Mersey's force extended Sweeny's line back toward the west by forming a right angle at the crossroad. The guns of the 14th Ohio Battery, under Rice, occupied the apex of the line. Those guns were now going into battery in preparation to begin their fight.

Moving toward the fight, McPherson saw the sole brigade of Fuller's 4th Division moving rapidly off the cut road to extend the right of

Mersey's line. It appeared to McPherson that those three brigades that made up Dodge's Sixteenth Army Corps had, by chance, been located on high ground surrounded by open field. He could also see a creek, or rather he could see the line of trees that clearly announced the existence of the watercourse, as it ran along the southwest edge of the hill as well as along the eastern slope.

CHAPTER SEVENTY-FOUR

Union | THOMAS W. SWEENY

Along Clay Road at the extreme left
of the Army of the Tennessee
July 22, 1864
About 12:30 p.m.

Slim, sitting straight in the saddle with only one arm, a red beard, and a profane vocabulary, forty-three-year-old Brigadier General Thomas W. Sweeny was angry. If he had but reflected on it, he was often angry. He was sometimes nearly mad. This latter stage was especially true if his fondness for whisky had been indulged too much.

"Goddamn Mister General Grenville Dodge and all his banking, railroading, and political friends." With his so-called Irish temper at full burn, General Sweeny was abusing his corps' commander, Dodge, under his breath as he punished himself with his recollection of the past day or so.

In Sweeny's opinion, anyone should be able to plan better than this group of jackasses running the Army of the Tennessee. Sweeny's entire adult life had been as a soldier. He was born in Ireland and immigrated to America when he was twelve. Circumstances had not allowed him the opportunities that would have been his as a graduate of the USMA, but nonetheless, he had spent nearly twenty years in the military service of his adopted country. During that time, he had risen from the position of a private soldier in the Independent Tomkins Blues to brigadier general in command of a Federal infantry division.

With the Blues, he had served in the war with Mexico and had lost his right arm, above the elbow, to the sharp knife of a surgeon in 1848. The amputation came as the result of a well-placed Mexican musket ball as he had fought his way forward in the storming of Churobusca.

Despite the loss of his arm, he was promoted to first lieutenant in the 2nd U.S. Infantry. After losing his right arm, he had really worked with his left arm and hand to be able to do as much or more than those with no such loss. By continuous effort, his left arm became more able than his right had ever been. With the reins under the stump of his right arm, he could guide his horse and swing a sword with his left. He was always ready to fight. He served in that unit until 1861. In January of that year, he was promoted to captain and then later to colonel.

He knew and had been a part of the old army. He knew about plans and planning. He was no "jumped-up" politician whose friendship with President Lincoln and an ability to build bridges qualified him to wear the twin stars of a major general. In all his time in the army, from Donelson to Shiloh to Cornith to Atlanta, never had his orders seemed so contrary and at odds with themselves as this moment. He blamed it all on Dodge.

On the morning of July 20, just two days ago, his 2nd Division had marched at route step off the Decatur-Atlanta road and over to the extreme right flank of the army. His 1st Brigade, under young and brand new Brigadier General Elliot W. Rice—another damned lawyer—had tied his troops into the right of Logan's Fifteenth Army Corps. Sweeny had made certain the 1st Division, under the command of Brigadier General Charles Woods, was on his left. Osterhaus, who normally ran the show at the 1st Division, was sick, and when he would return was anybody's guess. Woods was an improvement, if only because with Osterhaus gone, Sweeny didn't have to listen to Osterhaus' unique form of English, which mostly seemed to Sweeny to be German.

Off to his right, Sweeny had known there was a gap with no other military unit until one met the left of Schofield's Twenty-Third Army Corps, or as it was more grandly called, the Army of the Ohio. Sweeny had placed his 1st Brigade on the line and held his 2nd in reserve. His 3rd Brigade was absent. It was guarding Rome, Georgia, some eighty or so miles to the northwest.

On July 21, at about 2:00 p.m., he had moved his units forward and to the right where he made contact with Schofield. After tying his right into Schofield's left, Sweeny had remained in that location for the rest of the day and night. Then he had received orders from Dodge to move to the other end of the army. He had moved out with his 2nd Brigade, under Mersy, in the advance. The line of march had been led by the men of the 12th Illinois followed by the 81st Ohio and the "Western Sharpshooters."

Why in thunder had they been moved so far? It must be two miles, maybe more, and it was hot and dusty. Sweeny knew that he was angry with himself, his circumstances, younger officers, political generals, and the dandy – the list went on.

Despite his anger, though, he loved America. It was one nation to him, not lots of little countries loosely bound together for convenience. He found near joy and satisfaction upon his introduction to the Independent Tomkin Blues. He enjoyed the disciplined, all-male military activity. He had gone enthusiastically on the great western adventure to Mexico. After that, it was fighting Indians in the West. Then this great war had come along. His promotions were well deserved, and they had all been based, he was certain, on merit and accomplishment. His promotions were not like some of those still wet behind the ears: back-slapping politicians with more money and friends than with good sense.

Take that staff officer Dodge had sent to guide them. The officer didn't seem to know where the hell the 2nd Division was needed. It could have taken half a day for that staff flunky to decide where they should go once they had arrived at the little cross roads about a mile south of the railroad. As soon as his division had halted at the intersection he had put skirmishers out down the hill and toward the stream, as his instincts and the book had told him. Now, his division rested. Some men sat, and others stood taking their ease. Then, activity began to develop off to the east.

His skirmishers were fired on, and the alarm was raised that the Rebs were there in force. It had taken him no time to know what to do. With his left hand, he held and adjusted his field glasses. Through the lens, he could see the damned Rebels in the tree line.

He ordered Mersey's brigade moved, on the double, to form a right angle facing nearly south. He could see Fuller's 1st Brigade moving rapidly to deploy on his right. Mersey's brigade was then more or less facing south and was between Fuller's left and behind and around the six three-inch ordinance rifles of the 14th Ohio Battery. He ordered the 1st Brigade to face left and to assume a brigade front that faced generally to the east. He directed Captain Fred Welker, his division artillery officer, to place his six 12-pound Napoleons between the 2nd

Iowa and the 7th Iowa, which formed the left end of his line. His two brigades formed almost at a right angle with each other, and the 14th Ohio battery was located at the point where the line started north after having run in an easterly direction.

Unlike many situations, he didn't order his men to prepare trenches. The ground was high with the Federals in command of the crest. If a fight came, they could do it the old fashioned way: shoulder-to-shoulder and one line against the other. It would be like the American colonists against the British at Breed's Hill during the Revolution.

Skirmishers were out in front of the division without much conscious thought. Two companies of the 66th Illinois were sent out in front of the 2nd Brigade. These men were armed with the Henry repeating rifle. They were veterans and experience had taught them what to do. They all laid prone in the tall grass on the leading edge of the hill. The ground between his force and the tree line was open and provided no cover for the advancing Rebels. A creek ran along from north to south at the bottom of the ridge he occupied. Beyond it was a tree line and another hill.

Facing this accidental three-brigade force, down the hill and in the tree line, were the first two divisions of Hardee's corps. The divisions, which would soon assault embittered Thomas Sweeny, were those of General Bate and General Walker. Their combined six brigades of foot-weary, hot, nearly exhausted men had marched from just south of Peachtree Creek, some fifteen miles or so in the dark, hot night. They were as close to being correctly positioned as circumstances could have been foreseen, but McPherson's concerns had decisively altered those foreseeable circumstances—for the better.

"Get your guns in play now, Captain Welker. Eight hundred yards or so can be ideal for punishing those Rebel bastards before they can get to us," yelled Sweeny. Almost immediately the 14th Ohio and Battery H of the 1st Missouri began to spew smoke, noise, and hot steel down the hill and into the woods behind the tree line.

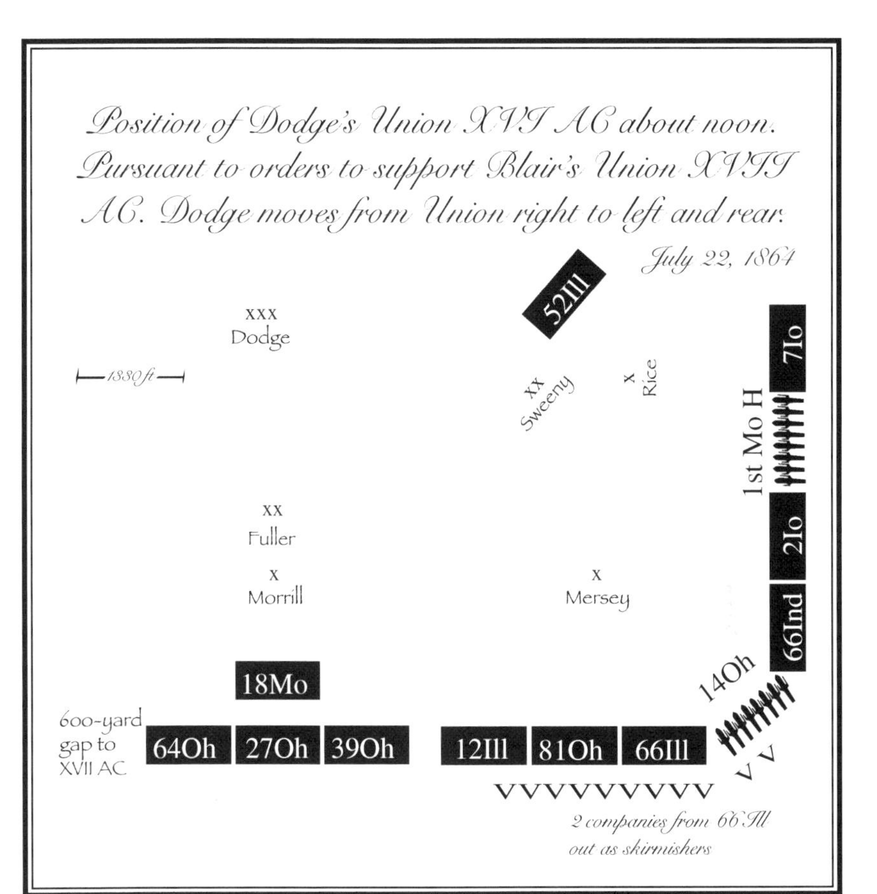
Position of Dodge's Union XVI AC about noon. Pursuant to orders to support Blair's Union XVII AC. Dodge moves from Union right to left and rear.
July 22, 1864
52Ill
XXX
Dodge
1830 ft
XX
Sweeny
X
Rice
7Io
1st Mo H
2Io
XX
Fuller
X
Morrill
X
Mersey
66Ind
14Oh
18Mo
600-yard gap to XVII AC
64Oh
27Oh
39Oh
12Ill
81Oh
66Ill
2 companies from 66 Ill out as skirmishers

CHAPTER SEVENTY-FIVE

Confederacy | *Union* | VARIOUS

BATE'S DIVISION OF HARDEE'S CORPS

THE EXTREME CONFEDERATE RIGHT,

NORTH OF TERRY'S MILL POND

JULY 22, 1864

12:30 P.M.

CONFEDERACY, WILLIAM BATE

William R. Bate had entered Southern service as a private. Like so many others, he had earlier military service as a lieutenant in the war with Mexico. During this service, his colonel was Frank Cheatham, who on this day was commanding a corps at the other end of the Confederate line. During the Mexican War, Bate had displayed personal courage by capturing the last flag taken in combat with a Mexican unit.

Upon return from the war, he had pursued farming and established a newspaper with a bellicose name, *The Tenth Legion*. He then joined the state legislature, after which he opened his own law office. On the day after the firing on Fort Sumter, Bate became part of Company I of the 2nd Tennessee. He was quickly elected captain of his company and soon became the commander of the regiment and its colonel.

During a charge against an infantry supported by artillery, Bate received a dangerous wound to his left leg. With two bones broken and an artery cut, he was in danger of losing his life. He kept his leg by offering to shoot the surgeon who had advised its amputation. Now at age thirty-eight, his left leg was so damaged that he could walk only with a crutch.

Bate had achieved his position of major general under Hardee as a result of being well liked and well known. He was intellectually committed to the cause of the Confederacy, and his considerable personal courage was an excellent platform to launch his ambitions from.

Before the battle started, Bate sat astride his mare after the miserable trek across the western side of Terry's Mill Pond. Bate's division had led the way and as a result had marched the longest in time and in distance from Peachtree Creek since the late afternoon of July 21. To General Bate, it felt like longer than only the previous day.

The day before yesterday, the senior command had relied on luck and hope rather than intelligence, and as a result, the division had accomplished little and was more or less defeated by the uncharted thickets. With this new plan, Bate had enough experience to know this envelopment around to the rear of the Union force was a gamble. The risks were made greater by the physical exertion it demanded and the nearly three days of marching, running, digging, and fighting. Marches and charges put a terrific strain even on the disciplined veterans, and the largely unsuccessful assault toward the creek used up energy and bled off the edge needed for really successful fighting. The exhaustion felt after combat was more than that of a full day's work in the sun. It was draining.

His corps commander, Hardee, had been clear about his orders. He was to form his division into two lines of battle, with his right on the homestead of Mrs. Parker on the country road leading to Decatur. On the signal, he was to move in the direction of Renfro's on the railroad. As he understood it, the railroad laid a mile and a half or so off to the north.

At least, that had been the plan. Before reaching Mrs. Parker's, one of Hardee's staff officers had ridden up and expressed Hardee's wishes to the effect that Bate's brigades needed to go no farther and that he was to organize them parallel to the road they had been moving on. Bate organized the lines with Lewis' brigade of Kentucky troops and two regiments of Finley's Floridians in the front line. Finley was on the right with Lewis on the left. Behind them, he ordered Cuthbert Slocumb's battery, his only artillery, and behind them was Tyler's brigade—now under the command of Colonel Smith. Next to them, he placed the other two regiments from Finley's Florida brigade.

Once he had his regiments in the order he desired, Bate had ordered them forward into the woods. After only a short time, it became obvious that while it was very difficult for infantry to move through the dense woods, that it was impossible for artillery to make any progress with its caissons, guns, and teams of horses and mules. Accordingly, the guns were ordered to take the left-hand road near Mrs. Parker's house and to unite with the rest of the division as soon as they could. With them were sent the 4th Georgia Sharpshooters under Major Theodore Caswell for support.

Once Bate had everything organized to his liking and the troops had moved off the road and into the trees, he had called a halt so that the men could rest in place. It was difficult to relax completely since the word was everywhere in the division that they would soon move forward to contact. A soldier found it hard to doze off when he knew the order to move forward was the next thing he would hear.

To make the matter just a little worse, Bate had been waiting for Walker's division to line up with his and then move in concert with Bate's division. As the time passed that morning, Bate had heard from Walker that Hardee now wanted Bate's division to move in concert with Walker's, not vice versa, and for Bate's division to "dress left," meaning essentially they would protect the left flank and drive the attack from the left. Bate had became concerned over the lack of clarity this advice offered, so he had sent a staff officer to discern the truth. This officer returned and confirmed that his effort would all be driven from the left. Walker was to watch for Cleburne's attack then move himself to be followed by Bate.

Moving forward, Bate's division had encountered undulating terrain and broad wet stream bottoms. The lack of personal knowledge or a reconnaissance as to the conditions that lay to his front in effect blinded Bate. The blindness was made darker by the dense woods, vines, and thorns. The three brigades fragmented as they came to the debris-choked mill pond, and the carefully constructed battle alignment became indistinct clumps and groups of men.

Now, Bate's mare lowered her head and cropped vegetation at its feet. Bate thought about lighting the cigar he held in his mouth. He squeezed his eyes shut on the recollection and slowly exhaled. The story of the unlighted cigar was well known to those who were close to the general. During a lull in the battle at Shiloh, Bate had asked his younger brother, Captain Humphrey Bate, to provide him with a light for his cigar. As the younger brother touched the tip of his own glowing cigar to the end of Bate's, a minie ball struck him a mortal wound, which he shortly died from.

The battle at Shiloh—during which his leg was injured—killed Bate's brother, his brother-in-law, and his cousin and wounded another cousin severely. Since the death of his brother, legend had it that General Bate had never lit another cigar.

Now with the cigar unlit and clamped resolutely in his teeth, he watched his exhausted men as they began to form into lines of battle. They didn't know exactly what was ahead for them, but it was fair to say they had survived the first fearsome skirmish with Mother Nature at Widow Terry's Mill Pond. Bate could only hope they would win the next contest as well.

Bate felt the pressure from Hardee to continue to move. This was combined with his own belief that haste contained the virtue of being able to strike the enemy before they had a chance to prepare for any such onslaught. Surprise was a tremendous ally in Bate's mind.

His teeth clamped harder on the wet end of the cigar. Bate involuntarily flinched slightly as he heard the single explosion of a rifle shot off to his left front. He asked for the time, and a staff officer was quick to reply. It was 12:15. It was good to know the time of the first shot when the report had to get written.

Although Bate's orders were somewhat vague, he knew his division was the one most likely to get into the Union rear, as he was on the extreme right of Hardee's several-miles-long line. He was preparing to move forward in a double line of battle marching west.

He thought back to a similar day only twenty some days before when his division ran into a buzz saw of dug-in Union troops at Dallas, Georgia. Those troops had been commanded by Generals Harrow, Smith, and Osterhaus—all under the able leadership of Black Jack Logan of the Fifteenth Army Corps. The troops he had attacked then, although he was not aware of it at this point, were the same Fifteenth Army Corps troops into whose rear this long secret night march was supposed to deliver him and his troops.

The soldiers moved forward, and the poorly developed battle line came under artillery fire from the crest of the hill overlooking the heavily tangled stream bottom. As the three brigades attempted an initial assault, the slow movement through the stream bottom meant the second line of battle caught up with the first, resulting in increasing confusion in the two lines.

Although not well coordinated, Bate's division was to be the first division into the fight again. Without much preamble, he sent the three brigades forward. He had seen the same terrain Major General

Walker saw just before his death and knew his troops had a long trek across Sugar Creek Valley and up the next ridge. From the treetops, he could see two batteries and a battle line of Federal troops. It wasn't really what he had expected. That area was supposed to be a clean, unfettered run up to the rear of the Federal army. But now, right where he would have put them himself if he had been directing the Federal defense was what appeared to be a strong Federal division ready for him. The supposed division was on the high ground backed up by, from what he could assume, superior artillery.

His two battle lines pushed back the light force of infantry, which were performing skirmisher duty. In fact, the skirmishers seemed to break away from him by their left flank, thereby uncovering the main battle line on the hill. As he watched, the Union skirmishers who still had loaded weapons stepped out one pace and faced the oncoming sweaty, dirty, ragged butternuts. At the same time, the men with unloaded pieces faced to the left and began moving off. The skirmishers fired, and as they began to move to the rear, he could see them begin to reload as they moved through the rear rank. That loose second rank now stood their ground and fired, and the drill was repeated. The officer running that skirmish line was pretty good. The soldiers seemed to have practiced the maneuver they were performing.

CONFEDERACY, JOHNNY GREEN

Johnny Green had been born in October of 1841 in Henderson County, Kentucky. Now twenty-three years later, he was a member of Company B of the 9th Kentucky Regiment, which in turn was part of the 1st Kentucky Brigade, also known as the Orphan Brigade. The brigade got its name because following the Battle of Stones River and upon seeing the broken condition of the 1st Kentucky, its division commander, Major General John Breckenridge, had cried out, "My orphans, my poor orphans."

Either as a result of this outcry or as a result of the isolation involved in being a Southern unit from a neutral state—or as a combination of both—the 1st Kentucky Brigade became known as the Orphan Brigade.

Today, the 9th Kentucky was at the right end of the brigade in the middle of its two sister organizations. Smith's brigade was on its left.

To the right was Brigadier General Jesse Finley's brigade of Floridians, some four regiments in all. Behind the Kentucky brigade, as a reserve, were four Tennessee regiments and one Confederate regiment of Maney's brigade led by Colonel Francis Walker.

Lewis' Orphan Brigade had started the long march last evening with more than 1,000 men, but some of those men, who had simply exhausted themselves, were spread at this point out over the sixteen-mile route of the punishing march. Some would join their companies during the day, but many were used up and would not be available for days. The men who were left were as good as veteran soldiers could be under the circumstances. On this bright, sun-filled noon, only around 800 men were present at the broken down fence that stood in front of Johnny Green.

With the halt, everyone had been attempting to catch their wind. Lots of the boys, who had carried their blanket rolls through the night and into the heat of the day, had thrown them off. Without the blanket roll, a man felt freer and less burdened. There was something about carrying a wool blanket in the heat that allowed one to forget what the cool the night would bring.

Green heard the pop and snap of sporadic firing from the open area beyond the tree line. The skirmishers had either found something substantial enough to shoot at or thought they had, but nothing much should be out in front except some wagons or small bodies of troops who need some encouragement to move on.

It was hard to see much in the thick woods, but as the line began to form behind the fence and the men directed their eyes toward what lay ahead, puffs of smoke from the skirmisher's rifles were seen over the tall grass. The order rang out up and down the line and was picked up by officers of the 9th Kentucky. Finally, here the fight was, hours beyond the sun's rising.

"Load, boys. Then let's get over that fence. Look yonder up the hill there. It's Yanks. When we get in close, give them a volley. I mean, a hard one now. Shoot low. Then we can get in among them and give them the bayonet."

Sure enough, there—some distance away in the bright sunshine—Union troops under Sweeny and Fuller could be seen on the hill with two batteries of artillery. The "them" of the orders were two lines of Union blue on an elevated area of terrain with the two batteries.

Right ahead of Green and his friends from Kentucky were the troops of Sweeny's 2nd Division of Dodge's Sixteenth Army Corps. Over to the left was Fuller's 4th Division, whose soldiers were, at that point, moving into position. To Green's immediate front were the rifles of Rice's 1st Brigade, who had fallen into a double line of battle between the guns of the 14th Ohio and Battery H of the 1st Missouri. The guns of this latter group were 12-pound Napoleons that performed their anti-personnel mission with canister and grape shot from their smoothbore pieces better than the rifled guns of the 14th Ohio. Rice had three regiments on the line. They were, from Rice's right to left, the 66th Indiana, 2nd Iowa, and the 7th Iowa. It was these soldiers Johnny Green could see on the hill as he began to climb the fence.

The portion of the fence Johnny was coming up against was too strong to tear down, so over it he went. His canteen got caught on the top rail as he dropped over to the Yankee side, and the canteen strap hung him around the neck so that he was unable to touch the ground. He made desperate efforts to free himself, all the while the whine and snap of balls and shots seemed to be passing all about him. No matter how hard he struggled, the strap seemed to hold him tight.

Suddenly a minie ball struck Green's shoulder strap, cutting it, and he fell to the ground. Without picking up his canteen, he ran to join the others in the 9th Kentucky as they double quicked across the field and up the hill.

CONFEDERACY, WILLIAM BATE

The six guns of the Union battery located toward the right end of the Federal line were beginning to fire their massive rounds of antipersonnel canister. The thick, white smoke created by the six guns firing about two rounds per minute seemed to blanket that ridge. But the long arm of the artillery reached out from beneath the smoke, and ragged holes were being torn in the fast advancing Southern troops.

As the range shortened from the original 800 yards that had separated the opposing forces to a distance more manageable by the individual riflemen, three Union regiments began to fire into the moving butternut ranks.

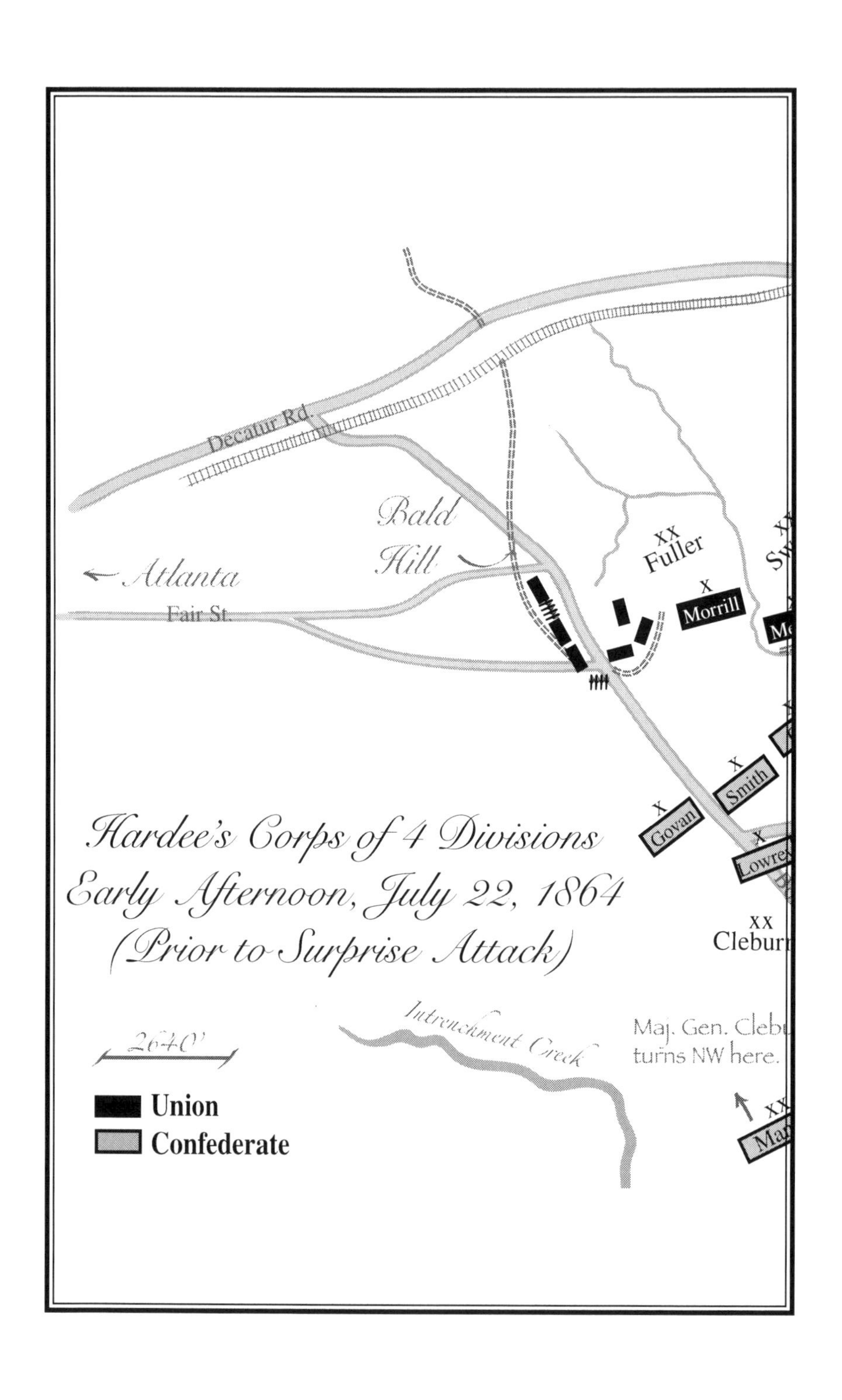
Decatur Rd.
Bald Hill
← Atlanta
Fair St.
XX
Fuller
X
Morrill
X
Smith
X
Govan
X
XX
Hardee's Corps of 4 Divisions
Early Afternoon, July 22, 1864
(Prior to Surprise Attack)
Intrenchment Creek
2640'
turns NW here.
Union
Confederate

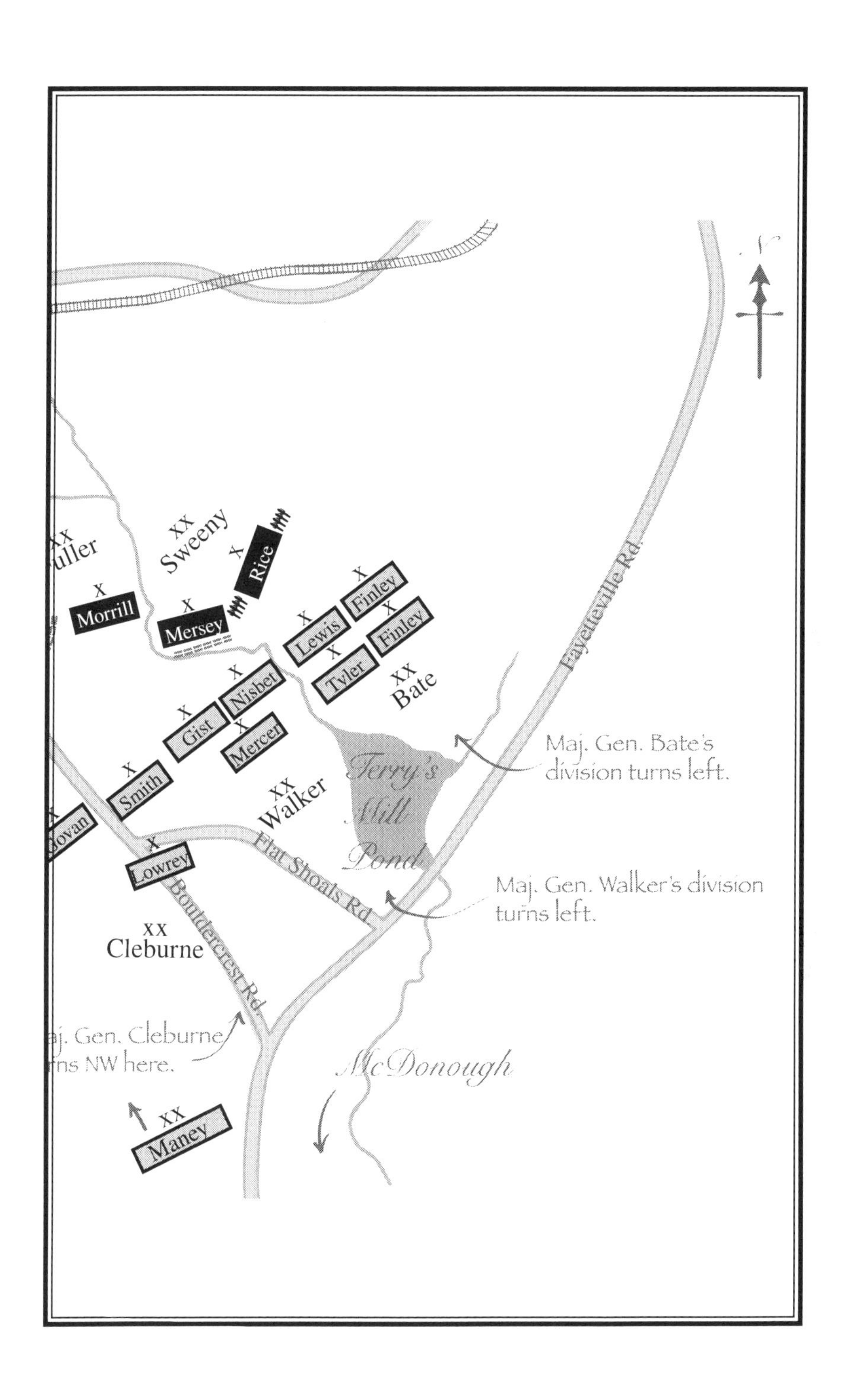
XX
Sweeny
X
Rice
X
Morrill
X
Mersey
X
Finley
X
Finley
X
Lewis
X
Tyler
XX
Bate
X
Nisbet
X
Gist
X
Mercer
X
Smith
XX
Walker
X
Lowrey
Flat Shoals Rd
Terry's Mill Pond
Fayetteville Rd.
Bouldercrest Rd.
XX
Cleburne
Maj. Gen. Bate's division turns left.
Maj. Gen. Walker's division turns left.
turns NW here.
XX
Maney
McDonough

UNION, ELLIOT RICE

Twenty-nine year old Brigadier General Elliot Rice had entered the Union army as a private in the 17th Iowa. By April of 1862, he was in command of that same regiment. Rice had received his promotion to brigadier general in June, only a month ago. The recognition of his achievement was substantially dampened as a result of the news of his brother's wounding at the Battle of Jenkins' Ferry. The injury done by the wound was made worse by a clumsy surgery performed upon his brother's return to Iowa. As a result, his brother died.

Rice was a veteran of a good deal of campaigning and had moved his brigade from the far right of the Union lines across the railroad and down Clay Road in an orderly and rapid fashion. Arriving at the crossroad, he had formed his hard marching brigade perpendicular to the line formed by Colonel Mersey's brigade. At the end of Rice's line, the six three-inch ordinance rifles of the 14th Ohio had gone into battery.

Rice had immediately sent forward his skirmishers and stood facing east with his three regiments and one battery. No time existed to dig even hasty works as the butternut division across the way had come out of the tree line almost at the time of his arrival. He could count nearly twenty regimental flags. That had to be what now passed for a Southern division.

Now the two ragged lines of gray and butternut troops were climbing up out of the valley toward his line. He began to think the fight might be more bitter than he had originally thought. Rice sent a runner back to find the 52nd Illinois regiment, which by his estimate should be arriving at the scene at any time. If they were walking, he wanted them to move on the double quick the rest of the way so that he could at least have some force to use as a reserve. A reserve thrown in at the right moment could stop this grim gray tide that was moving ever closer despite the rapid cannon fire and unrelenting aimed rifle fire.

Over his left shoulder, he saw the head of the blue column as the 52nd Illinois came at a near run. It was hellishly hot, and the heat seemed to shimmer off the vegetation, imposing a heaviness in the air that appeared to tug at the legs of the approaching troopers and hinder their approach. But on they came, and a cheer went up from the powder-blackened faces of the short, thin defensive line.

The timely arrival of the 52nd Illinois helped encourage the bone-weary attacking Rebel troops that the task was too formidable, even though the 52nd were not even yet placed in battle. The Confederate rearward drift began.

At almost the same time, Rice became aware that his rightmost regiment, the 66th Indiana, had simply run though all the ammunition they had. He immediately ordered the 7th Iowa to move from their position on his left to the place occupied by the 66th Indiana and for the 66th Indiana to change front. This would put the 66th Indiana in position to assist the men of the 1st Brigade of the 4th Division under General Fuller if the assault on Rice's rear and left flank should become more successful. The 52nd Illinois was placed in the position vacated by the 7th Iowa. The firing, except for chasing shots, seemed to be coming to an end.

On the hill behind the small two-division force of the Sixteenth Army Corps, McPherson had seen enough to know what the outcome would be on his left flank. He turned to ride to Blair's Seventeenth Army Corps, which was spread out defensively on the south end of Bald Hill.

CONFEDERACY, WILLIAM BATE

Bate felt the effect of the nearly three stress-filled, exhaustive days as he watched his three brigades reach close to the crest of the hill, falter, and then begin to recede. They had reached their culminating point. No reserves, heat, unimaginable terrain, and exhaustion all had combined to increase the friction that had inexorably slowed and then halted the tattered forward edge of his magnificent battle line. They began to drift back. Some men fell as they withdrew. The heavy fire volume from rifles and smoothbore cannons punished the merged retreating line of battle. The smells of fresh pumping blood, the stinging, bitter smoke, and the hollow suck and pound of the canister rounds left each soldier wondering how this brand of hell had flowered on this Georgia hillside. The Union's resolute, disciplined, and violent defense overpowered Bate's men, and they moved back down the hill. Slocumb's Confederate battery engaged the smoke obscured Union line, but this was too little, too late. Thus, the assault on the right end of Hardee's line ground down to nothing about an hour after it had begun.

The Tennessee brigade under Colonel Walker, which had been promised as reserves, finally arrived and reported to Bate. It was late and of no use at this end of the field. Hardee soon removed Walker's brigade as well as Smith's from Bate's control, leaving him with only the Orphan Brigade under Lewis and Finley's Florida brigade. The men collapsed in the cover of the trees and waited for what was next.

CHAPTER SEVENTY-SIX

Union | Confederacy

ALONG CLAY ROAD AT THE EXTREME LEFT OF THE UNION'S ARMY OF THE TENNESSEE

JULY 22, 1864

UNION

The six three-inch ordinance rifles of the 14th Ohio had begun to disgorge billows of white smoke, flame, and explosions as the Confederate soldiers moved forward in their initial attack. There was a cloud of smoke followed quickly by a flat thump, and out ahead near the tree line, one could see the impact of the rifled shells as the trees' limbs flew into the air, followed by geysers of dirt and flashes of color that first rose and then fell to mark the terminus of the shell. The individual reports of the guns gave way to a rolling roar as the battery began to achieve a rhythm.

West of McPherson's position rose the high dome of Bald Hill. Without thinking about it, he counted the time between the flash and the sound of the gun. Sound, traveling at 1,100 feet per second, was slower than the passage of light. The count of three confirmed that he was about 3,000 feet from the developing fight. As he watched the line some 700 to 800 feet down from the Union occupied hilltop Dodge was on, he could see the first of the now energized, hawk-faced, whipcord Rebel troops of Walker's division begin their assault. Rice's brigade, of Sweeny's division, also began firing downhill at those Southern regiments moving up the hill toward them.

McPherson saw lots of regimental flags, meaning perhaps more than a thousand Confederate soldiers were coming. Indeed, these soldiers were the 1,200 men of General Bate. They had marched the longest, both in time and distance, and were now the first into the fight.

The two Union brigades under Sweeny had not dug any hasty entrenchments, but rather had been resting prior to assuming their assigned places on the left of the Seventeenth Army Corps. They had assumed they were in the rear and were initially surprised to find themselves the focus of a major attack. Their fighting position was one of accident and happenstance. McPherson stood in his stirrups as though to see better. "It is a blessing Dodge had these men located so perfectly as to meet this surprise," McPherson said quietly, almost as a prayer.

Strong replied, "Blessing, fortune of war, or excellent generalship—they are here because you ordered them here or nearabouts. This is exactly what you have been predicting; this is the manifestation of your continuing unease, General. Damn good thing General Sherman listened when you pushed him earlier or those very soldiers down there would be tearing up track in Stone Mountain instead of closing the rear door of the Army of the Tennessee."

CONFEDERACY

The gray-and dun-colored soldiers were moving with resolution, and the Confederate en echelon attack occurred just as it had been ordered. The movement had started on McPherson's left with Bate's rightmost regiments moving first and the next brigades and divisions keying off their compatriots start.

The first attack started around midway out onto the open field. However, the return fire from the defending Federals drove the assaulting Confederate troops back to the cover of the tree line. There, amid smoke, shouted orders, and the metallic click and whir of ramrods, men bit into cartridge paper and with ease born of endless practice and rammed home the .57 caliber minie balls. Halfway up the field lay a line of dead and wounded. The line of men marked the flow of battle as the Rebels fell back, just as the tide is marked on a beach.

Ranks were being reformed and men exchanged expressions of surprise as to the presence and location of the Union force in what should have been vacant space. It should have been an open place that they were to advance over and then into the unsuspecting weak rear of the Federal army.

One could also hear the cries for help and cries for water from men who knew about death and wounds in a general sense but now knew about it in a personal and specific way. Some men cried, some prayed, some cussed, and some closed their eyes and remembered loved ones.

Surprise, that element commanders always seek for themselves, was in full operation on both sides of the line today. Surprise or not, the job still needed doing, and these hard old boys in gray were ready to have another go at it. It had been a hellish night march through the dirt, dust, and horse shit along a narrow road, all the while wondering if far ranging Yankee cavalry might come exploding into their ranks. Then they had moved through the briars, mud, and ooze around that mill. After all that, now they had run head long into this blue killing machine on that ridge in their front.

"Line up. Dress up those ranks."

"Forward...March." Commands rang out. By instinct and design, the torn regimental flags moved, and men followed. Mounted officers seemed to be everywhere. No shots were fired from the well-formed and disciplined troops. There was time enough for that when the lines converged. Overhead came the roar and noise of the Southern artillery pieces as shots rang out and over the advancing infantry.

As the attacking lines advanced, gaps showed themselves as the guns from the two Union batteries bucked, boomed, and flashed. One could see the rounds in flight if they were caught just so in the sun. The lines of infantry absorbed the cannon fire and closed up the ranks. As they moved forward, they left what had been whole men moments before and were now red pulp, blood, shattered bone, and horror.

At 100 to 150 yards, the coordinated return fire from the massed Union regiments swept into the thinning assaulting ranks. Few men remained on horseback now; they simply made too good a target. Regimental flags were at crazy angles to the ground as they fell from hand to hand. Everything was simply too much. Courage was everywhere, but fatigue, thirst, and the relentless, murdering massed fire from the high ground overcame it. All this combined with the blazing sun slowed, halted, and then dissolved the formerly well-ordered Southern men, as men made individual and collective decisions that it was too hot and the objective was too far and too hard to carry on. The open field was full of uncoordinated, individual, and entrepreneurial movement as the attack changed into a slow passionless movement to the retreat.

From the ridge, the Union regimental commanders of the 12th, 64th, and the 66th Illinois and the 81st, 39th, and 21st Ohio ordered their soldiers to load their rifles and, for those who had them, to fix bayonets. The preparatory order rang out followed by the order of execution: "Charge."

Hot cries rushed from their mouths as the Ohio and Illinois regiments ran forward into the disengaging Southern troops. The retreating Rebels ran for the cover of the tree line. The charging Yankee troops fired, and then some began to round up prisoners and tend to the wounded. The Union soldiers stood in the tall grass under the hot, metallic July sun. Grateful to be alive, they gulped water from canteens and began to move back up the hill.

UNION

McPherson and his orderly had watched the second assault without Strong, who had been sent to ascertain conditions on the left of Blair's line and to tell General Blair to hold with his Seventeenth Army Corps. Further, Strong was instructed to explain that McPherson intended to send troops to plug the hole existing between Fuller's brigade, from Dodge's corps, and the left of Blair's 4th Division. Strong had found Blair and Giles Smith near the end of Hill's brigade on the left of the trench line held by Blair's Seventeenth Army Corps.

Strong passed along McPherson's communication. Blair spoke after hearing what Strong had breathlessly related, "Tell General McPherson we intend to hold in place. Remind him that as I told him earlier, a substantial body of Rebel infantry has been seen moving out of Atlanta and onto my left flank since yesterday morning. I suspect the Rebels seek to get into our rear or find that gap between Fuller and Blair. Colonel, tell him that those Rebs are out there in force, no doubt about it."

Upon returning to the place he had left McPherson earlier, Strong reiterated Blair's message. As soon as he had finished, McPherson kicked his horse forward to personally go over the ground in question to see it for himself. This information was deeply troublesome, and McPherson needed to get firsthand knowledge of the situation. The gap must be filled in and soon.

The men rode back over the road they had traversed twice before: once this morning and again more recently on their way to lunch. For a newly cut military road, it was getting a lot of use. About midway down the road, McPherson turned left. He rode slowly down one of several finger-like ridges formed by Sugar Creek's many feeder streams.

McPherson knew this high ground would be a strong position for the defending troops, as he noted its positive terrain features. McPherson guided his horse back to the road. Once there, McPherson halted, and sitting astride the animal, he reviewed all he knew about the geography and the location of all his various units within his army.

Then he spoke, "Colonel Strong, go find General Logan. Explain how things stand at this moment. Especially impress on him this gap, this break, between the left of the main army and Dodge's three brigades. Tell him about the assault on Dodge's force. I want him to send Wangelin's brigade in here to connect the Seventeenth and the Sixteenth Army Corps. This ridge is a good place for the center of that connecting force. Wood's division is north of the railroad and more than a mile from here. You stay with Logan and guide Wangelin's brigade back to this position. I want their line to run from over there to Giles Smith's left. Once you have them established, come find me. I plan to be with Smith and Blair. We need those troops here now. Impress on Logan that all haste is called for."

Strong repeated McPherson's instructions, saluted, wheeled his horse, and rode with dispatch to find General Logan, the commander of the Fifteenth Army Corps.

With his aide, McPherson began his ride over to the exposed left wing of his army. It was about 2:00 p.m.

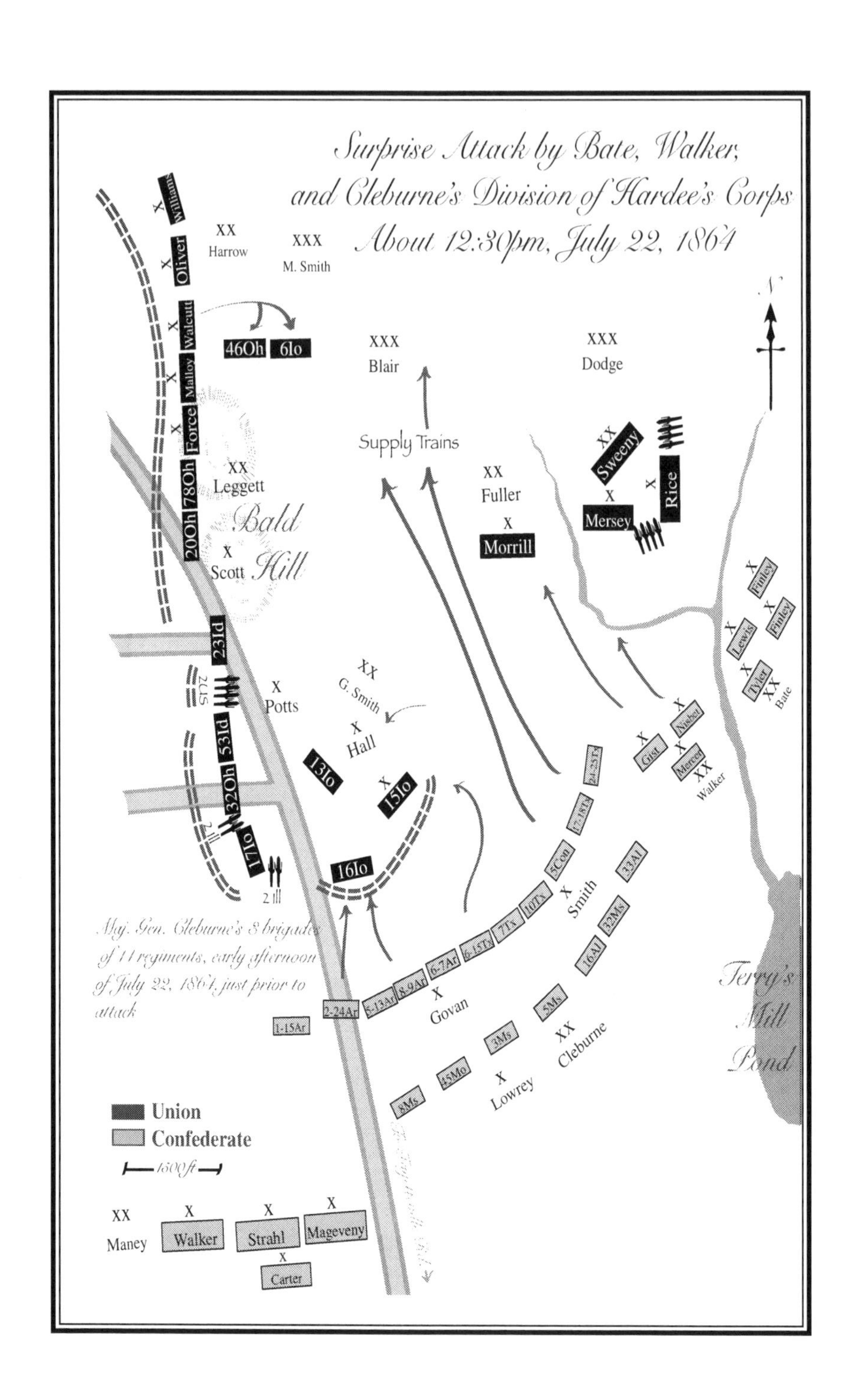
Surprise Attack by Bate, Walker, and Cleburne's Division of Hardee's Corps About 12:30pm, July 22, 1864
Williams
Oliver
Harrow
M. Smith
Walcutt
46Oh
6Io
Blair
Dodge
Malloy
Force
78Oh
20Oh
Leggett
Bald Hill
Scott
Supply Trains
Fuller
Morrill
Sweeny
Rice
Mersey
Finley
Lewis
Tyler
Bate
23Id
2US
Potts
G. Smith
Hall
53Id
32Oh
13Io
15Io
17Io
16Io
Gist
Nisbet
Mercer
Walker
24-25Tx
17-18Tx
5Con
10Tx
7Tx
6-15Tx
6-7Ar
8-9Ar
5-13Ar
2-24Ar
1-15Ar
Smith
33Al
32Ms
16Al
Govan
5Ms
3Ms
45Mo
8Ms
Cleburne
Lowrey
Terry's Mill Pond
Maj. Gen. Cleburne's 3 brigades of 11 regiments, early afternoon of July 22, 1864, just prior to attack
Union
Confederate
1500 ft
Maney
Walker
Strahl
Mageveny
Carter
To Fayetteville Rd.

CHAPTER SEVENTY-SEVEN

Confederacy | HUGH MERCER

In the tree line northwest of Terry's Mill Pond

along Sugar Creek

July 22, 1864

About 1:00 p.m.

Brigadier General Hugh Mercer was on horseback over to the right of his brigade. Mercer's brigade was serving as the divisional reserve and was posted in the rear of the brigade commanded by Brigadier States Rights Gist on the left and that of Colonel George Smith on the right. Mercer was the new division commander as a result of the death just a little ago of General Walker. This new responsibility rested heavily on his shoulders. He would not have chosen this role.

The division had been moving in a northeasterly direction, but now, as the blue Federal troops up on the hill ahead of them came into view, Mercer ordered the two lead brigades to pivot to the right to face the Federals more directly. Colonel Smith's brigade had less distance to pivot and so was finished before General Gist's soldiers even began to swing their brigade front around. The orders were clear: cross the open field, get across the creek, and clamber up the hill to take what seemed about 5,000 Federals with two six-gun batteries.

A more experienced division commander would have halted Colonel Smith and let Gist's brigade catch up, but this was not done, and Smith's regiments moved out through the underbrush. They went forward essentially alone. They were aggressive in the face of competent rifle and cannon fire.

Front to front was one thing, but their left flank was exposed to the blue regiments on the hill. Federal soldiers under General Fuller hammered away at the advancing Confederate flank in a manner nearly unopposed in the absence of Gist's brigade. Not only was their left flank uncovered by the lack of the regiments moving along with them, but Smith's forces represented the primary target and had fewer resources to reply on.

On the first assault, Colonel Smith was hit twice and had his horse killed under him. Command of the six regiments, in what was known as Steven's brigade, devolved to Colonel James Nisbet of the 66th Georgia. Then, Gist's brigade finally began to make its way up the hill into the smoke, noise, and gore. The four regiments were alone on the hillside, and the Federals went after them from the left, right, and front. Since they were late, they enjoyed the same solitary welcome observed by Smith's brigade. They got within 150 feet of the blue line when Gist was wounded, and the brigade slowly eased back down the hill over the bodies of those who had preceded them into the fight.

General Mercer, in command of the division, then ordered his old brigade into the fight. The brigade was not being ordered forward to exploit some opportunity, but rather was being fed piecemeal into the fray. The brigade was now under the command of Colonel Barkuloo. He had taken over when Mercer's original replacement, Colonel Olmstead of the 1st Georgia, was wounded in the head from a Union shell fragment.

General Mercer ordered his third and final brigade to attempt what had already been tried since both Gist's hard driving Georgians and South Carolinians and the tough Georgia Brigade had failed in the effort to dislodge the compact blue line. Perhaps had the Georgia Brigade waited for Gist's men to come up on its left and Mercer's four regiments had gone with them in one combined assault, then success would have awaited them. Piecemeal, they represented only so many targets to be chewed up in detail.

Colonel Barkuloo, who was ambitious but not overly reckless, led his men into the deep stream. His slender ranks quickly lost twenty or so men to the accurate fire of the artillery on the crest of the hill. Barkuloo saw the task as impossible and ordered his men to retreat before the attack was really underway.

General Mercer's command was pretty badly mauled and its leadership dispirited. Mercer was hot, tired, and discouraged. Nonetheless, he ordered Nisbet's brigade to form up on the left of Barkuloo's largely unbloodied troops with the remnants of Gist's brigade, now under Colonel James McCullough, on the left. Mercer intended that Walker's division would go forward as one in concert with Bate's division on its right. Just as this movement was forming, Mercer received orders for his former brigade to move off to their far left to reinforce Cleburne's division.

Restless and unwilling to wait, Nisbet and his six regiments went forward in conjunction with the division on his right. They went through the field, across the marshy stream, and then up that killing hill. This assault found itself on the right end of Dodge's "L" shaped two-division line. To be sure, this was a very light two-division force, but it was composed of three hard, veteran Union brigades. The Rebel force came right in front of the Union brigades. The leftmost Union brigade was under the direct, personal command of General Fuller, and the other was Mersey's brigade of Sweeny's 2nd Division. On came the ragged gray and butternut line until Nisbet and several of his men from the 66th Georgia found themselves surrounded by the 39th Ohio. Next to them, down to Nisbet's left, the 23rd Georgia ran headlong into the 64th Illinois from Fuller's left.

Walker's division was badly used. Losses included two general officers, Walker and Gist, and some nine field officers. These losses came on top of the losses on July 20. Captains and majors would now lead commands normally handled by colonels.

Fighting would continue until late into the afternoon, but the action that took Walker's life ended with the Union force on the hillcrest and the Confederates in the trees.

CHAPTER SEVENTY-EIGHT

Union | TOM TAYLOR

2ND DIVISION, FIFTEENTH ARMY CORPS

UNION SKIRMISH LINE, NORTH OF THE RAILROAD

JULY 22, 1864

12:30 P.M.

As Bate's men stood halted before the battle started, about 600 yards from the primary fortifications of the city of Atlanta and under a big oak tree, Major Tom Taylor lay dozing in the shade. The trench lines held by the Union forces to his rear were formerly those of the Confederate infantry that had held them until sometime last night when they moved back into Atlanta's fortifications. The Confederate skirmishers were out there somewhere to the front of the sleeping major.

Troops of 2nd Division of Logan's Fifteenth Army Corps, under the command of General Morgan Smith, had moved up and into the trenches as soon as the advanced Union skirmishers had discovered they were only lightly defended. These 2nd Division troops, mostly farm boys from Ohio and Illinois, were members of the 1st and 2nd Brigades. On their right was the four- gun battery of Captain DeGress, the same set of guns that fired the first artillery rounds into the city. DeGress had four 20-pound Parrott guns, heavy stuff and comforting to the infantry. The guns were in battery near the unfinished house abandoned earlier by Mr. Hurt. The guns were closely supported by the 30th Ohio Regiment. Facing Atlanta to the left of the Georgia railroad was a two-gun section of artillery. It was a section of Company A of the 2nd Missouri Light Artillery. This section of guns took up about fifty feet of space from the railroad toward the south, or the opposite direction from the wagon road.

Between the road and the railroad was an earthwork reinforced with logs. Moving north across the road was another section of artillery from the same Company A. Instead of a regiment in support of the artillery, only sixteen men were in place between the road and the railway behind those earthworks reinforced with logs. About twenty yards south of the railroad cut was a natural ravine that tied into the railroad. This ravine was filled with brush.

The 2nd Division had not chosen this ground, but they were there now and responsible for it. Near the end of the divisional line, a railroad cut through the main line of the division's works. The railroad line, in order to maintain a grade compatible with the locomotives of the day, had been cut at nearly a right angle. The cut was about fifteen feet deep. It was dry and firm on the bottom, and the tracks ran through its center. The width at the top of the cut was about forty-five feet. Between the wagon road that ran along the railroad and the lip of the cut was a distance of some sixty-five feet or so, and the road itself was about thirty-three feet wide. The cut and the road were clear and clean.

This cut fell into the sector that was the responsibility of the 1st Brigade, under the command of Colonel James S. Martin. Until two days ago, Martin had commanded the 111th Illinois, which rested as the regimental reserve for the skirmishers who were posted well to the front of the 2nd Brigade.

The senior leadership of the Union army, first among who was Sherman, were convinced that this new Confederate pull back meant the Army of Tennessee was abandoning the city. As with so many similar hopes, it represented a victory of hope over real evidence. Despite his personal doubts to the contrary, Logan, the charismatic commander of the Fifteenth Army Corps, had ordered both the 1st and 2nd Brigades of the 2nd Division to send a regiment each along the north and south sides of the railroad to advanced positions and lead the way into the city. As the new commander of the 1st Brigade, Colonel Martin had worked hard to provide this honor to his former command, the men of the 111th Illinois, who were now under the leadership of Major William M. Mabry.

The disposition of the soldiers was not a haphazard affair. The positioning had been ordered and then reviewed by both General Morgan Smith and General Joseph Lightburn, commander of the 2nd Brigade. Generals Smith and Lightburn were present the day before when Colonel

Wells S. Jones questioned the arrangement. Colonel Jones was interested primarily because his regiment, the 53rd Ohio, was the reserve for the division skirmish line arrayed to the south of the railroad.

After saluting, Colonel Jones commented, "General, don't you want to move my 53rd Ohio from out yonder to back here so that this cut and the road can be more completely covered? We could provide good support to that little four-gun battery."

The two generals turned and looked at the ground and the troops. General Smith replied, "No, Colonel Jones. I want the 53rd and you to remain where you have been placed. Hopefully, soon you and your Ohioans can march right into Atlanta where those tracks cut the Rebel's fortifications. We should be getting the word to advance anytime now."

Colonel Jones persisted, "What about those buildings ahead of our lines? That white house there. Do you see it? I think we would do well to burn them now to clear a better field of fire for our main line. My boys are close. Give me the order."

"Come, come, Colonel. Our position is strong, and we'll be moving forward just as soon as the way seems clear. Hood has left the city. It is ours for the taking. Don't worry about our troop disposition. Leave it with me."

The gap in the line remained.

Back at the oak tree, Major Tom Taylor continued to doze. Taylor had been up and moving at sunrise. He had pushed his skirmishers forward and drove the Rebels back first from their prepared positions and then back to their main line. He and his men remained in close contact with the enemy and stayed with them well enough to capture two prisoners and two lines of skirmish works. The enemy then fell back to the primary works around the city. He led and pushed his troops to stay close to the enemy so that it was only with difficulty that he could be fired upon without friendly fire striking the Rebels.

Taylor had also requested shovels to improve his works. They had been denied him based, it seemed, on the idea that the enemy was leaving the city. Taylor got one of Logan's senior aides to come see for himself. This view of things convinced the aide that perhaps the Confederates were not leaving the city, but the tools were nonetheless not forthcoming. After the exhilaration of being shot at and not hit, Taylor followed the old service axiom that one should sleep anytime the opportunity presented itself and relaxed under the oak.

At about 2:00 p.m., an order came to Colonel Martin to take three of his regiments from the 1st Brigade of the 2nd Division back to his left rear to assist the two very light divisions of Generals Sweeny and Fuller of Dodge's Sixteenth Army Corps. These two divisions were engaged with a substantial Rebel force near Bald Hill.

As things to his front were quiet, Martin decided he would lead the relief force to the aid of the Sixteenth Army Corps. He designated Lieutenant Colonel Samuel Mott, the commander of the 57th Ohio, as the acting commander of the 1st Brigade in his absence. The departure of the three veteran regiments—the 6th Missouri, 127th Illinois, and the 116th Illinois—left only the 55th and 57th Illinois regiments to fulfill the 1st Brigade's obligations and responsibility for their section of the line. The 111th Illinois, out in front, was now supported by only two regiments in the entrenched line. All three of those regiments were south of the railroad, which now formed a line of division between the 1st and 2nd Brigades.

Under the oak tree, the flies buzzed, and something aroused Taylor. He awakened slowly, feeling heavy and drugged. The heat was intense. His mind cleared and swam slowly up toward the bright sun. He knew he should awaken and arise, but he had enjoyed the deep sleep that had held him for a while. Then, as his mind engaged, he remembered where he was and quickly got to his feet.

There was some firing on the skirmish line—an occasional pop. Then, there was an explosion—a concussion—and hard clods of red dirt and debris smashed down around him. He was knocked down and over. Stunned but sound, Taylor looked about him. He saw two soldiers from the 47th Ohio, both injured. He scrambled to his feet, unsteady for a moment, and moved off over a small rise so he could see a bit better. Now he was aware of the sound of heavy firing from his left and rear. From the sound, it seemed to be more than a mile away, but it was difficult to know for certain.

He could see his command. He could also hear sounds of battle coming from down the line to the south. Smoke rose in the still sky. An experienced listener can sometimes form an idea as to the ebb and flow of battle by the sounds the person hears. The sounds that Taylor heard seemed to indicate the Federals were on the short end of the stick. Time passed, and he sensed that the Rebels had run out of steam. The sounds then took on a different note; it seemed to him that the defense was holding and that the butternuts had been halted. All this time, no action was taking place to disturb his line of skirmishers, and his flanks likewise were still supported.

As he had turned to look around and to his rear, a young captain exclaimed, "Major, look there. Isn't that a sight to behold?" It was. Moving out from the heavy fortified works around the city came a stream of men. Companies and then regiments began to form. The soldiers guided on their regimental battle flags. Soon, the regiments combined into brigades. Battle lines formed in such strength that Taylor was sure his men were facing a full division. In fact, though Taylor didn't know it, it was a full division. It was Hindman's division, one of the three under Cheatham, and was commanded by General John Brown.

The distance between the Union's 2nd Division skirmishers and the rapidly forming Rebel regiments was not great. From his position, the scene unfolded in a spectacular manner. It was most impressive to watch. Southern skirmishers moved out in front of the division. Soon, they were moving forward in the unhurried professional manner of men who had done this many times. The skirmish line began to deploy, and behind it, the heavy battle formation began to come to life.

Blue movement on the left caught the major's eye. *"Damn,"* he thought. The boys supporting his left flank from across the railroad began retreating without much effort to stem the Rebel advance. Taylor yelled above the noise and excitement to alert his own command. The gray line was advancing, and as it got within 250 yards or so of his force, his men began to slip back in an easy practiced fashion. They would obstruct this enemy advance as best they could. Major Taylor dispatched a runner back to his own division headquarters with the message that a major assault was taking place all along the divisional front.

As the Union skirmishers fell back, keeping up a light but steady volume of fire, they combined with their reserves. Once combined and now all engaged, the regiment-sized force shook themselves out back toward their fellows in the earthworks.

The Rebel line continued to press. The Union line would stop, fire, load, fire again, and then begin to again move to the rear. They were clear about their ultimate objective: the line of breastworks that occasional rounds would erupt from. That line of works more and more resembled safety. The Rebel line of battle was moving more rapidly as it seemed to slide forward. Southern regiments moved toward the houses on the north side of the railroad tracks, and a column of Rebels likewise were moving up the south side of the railroad.

The Federal skirmishers and the two regiments operating as their reserve retreated back to the main lines. On the north side of the tracks, the 53rd Ohio was placed in reserve as it moved through the main Union line. It turned, sorted itself out, loaded, and prepared to fight from this enhanced position. Communication across the railroad cut was nonexistent for the Union soldiers. The distance made cooperation between the two parts of the previously integrated force impossible.

Chaos reigned. The assault ebbed and flowed. Major Taylor happened to look at his pocket watch. It was 4:16 in the afternoon.

CHAPTER SEVENTY-NINE

Union | GILES SMITH

SEVENTEENTH ARMY CORPS ON THE SOUTHMOST END OF THE UNION LINE

JULY 22, 1864

12:45 P.M.

Giles Smith knew that the relocation of his division from the north, or right, side of Leggett's troops over to the left was the right thing to do. Leggett's forces could cover Bald Hill, but any military man knew that the south end of the Seventeenth Army Corps needed protection, which could only be provided by entrenched infantry. Of course, it would be great to have some cavalry operating out on their flank, but he knew they would have to do without them today.

He had placed Colonel Potts and his big brigade on his right to tie Potts into the troops of Leggett's 3rd division, which stretched north back up the mass of Bald Hill. Potts had the men of the 32nd Ohio and the 53rd Indiana facing east with the Indiana regiment on both sides of the battery that they had on loan from General Dodge's Sixteenth Army Corps.

Behind the 32nd Ohio and the 53rd Indiana and across the road, Potts had placed the 53rd Illinois and 3rd Iowa. General Smith then had Colonel Hall's Iowa Brigade veterans refuse their left, forming a reversed "J" or fishhook. This meant that the brigade bent around Potts' troops so that the 11th Iowa faced southwest with the 16th Iowa facing south and that the 15th Iowa faced southeast with the 3rd Iowa behind the other three in reserve. The 3rd Iowa should be able to support any of the three regiments to its front. The right of the 11th Iowa loosely tied into Potts' left and intersected with the northwest-southeast Old McDonough Road at a ninety degree angle, just below the area it connected to Flat Shoals Road, which ran between the regiments of the 16th and 15th Iowa.

Company F of the 2nd Illinois Light Artillery had two of its 12-pound guns facing south down Flat Shoals Road and two facing east toward Atlanta. This second section was between the left of Potts' brigade and the right of Hall's brigade. The Iowa troops had dug good works and prepared an abatis in their front. It all seemed to be in good order especially given the time that had been available.

The gap that existed off to Smith's left would soon be filled with Dodge's troops. Fuller's men, which even now were tucked in behind Leggett, would probably show up on his left and extend that line eastward. Both Potts' and Hall's brigades had skirmishers out. The pickets were placed in a way to protect the left and rear of the two brigades. They, in effect, formed a crescent generally facing east.

Smith understood his mission was to shore up the left flank of the Seventeenth Army Corps, and he believed his troops had done so. His strong defensive position was the military manifestation of McPherson's darkest worry. Smith was not sure anything would come of this at all, but the refused end of the line was stronger now than when they had arrived. He knew McPherson was concerned about this end of the field, and while he knew it should be attended to, he was not as enflamed over it as the army commander was. Smith was sure that they would be moving forward and into Atlanta before long.

Giles Smith was well aware of the Confederate lines about 1,000 yards to the west in front of Potts' two-regiment front. One could sense that if that line could be taken, the fortifications of the city were only 1,500 to 1,600 yards further and that somehow they were all very close. He wondered if a sharp frontal attack could dislodge the line ahead of him. Early in the morning of that day, Smith had sent skirmishers forward toward Atlanta. This was in conjunction with a similar movement managed by Leggett to his right. Some little success had been achieved in moving the Southerners, who had fallen back steadily when they were pushed.

Smith was contemplating moving Hall's two regiments forward to take the lightly defended Rebel lines but had not yet begun the process when some time after noon, musket fire began all along the skirmish line that had been established to the south and east of the dug-in 3rd Brigade. The skirmishers resisted, but in the intelligent way of a veteran, light, and alert force, gave way as the force and mass of Govan's Arkansas brigade of Cleburne's division surged up out of the dense forest and briars to drive in on the less-than-expecting Union skirmishers. The entire front from the 11th Iowa across the road to the 16th Iowa and then into Belknap's 15th Iowa troops was under a surprisingly strong attack. The Southerners—yelling, shooting and being supported by artillery fire—made good progress moving north in their assault.

Colonel Hall had his orders from Giles Smith to hold the front line. He understood that some help for his right flank would be sent from the 1st Brigade under Potts. With the directive and the promise in mind, Hall sent two companies from his reserved 13th Iowa to the left of the 11th Iowa and two more to the left of the 16th Iowa. These four companies from the 13th Iowa followed the company he had sent over to the left of the 15th Iowa. His reserve was fast dissipating.

Colonel Potts responded to the action taking place to his left and rear. He sent the three companies that made up the entire 3rd Iowa, under Captain Mathes, and the only two companies remaining of the 53rd Illinois rushing to the aid of Hall's left.

The fighting and firing was heavy, fast and hot along the entire U-shaped front of the 3rd Brigade. Potts' reserve were quickly overwhelmed and after a hard fight fell back to its works, leaving a number of killed, wounded, and captured in its wake. Among those who would answer no more bugle calls was brave Captain Mathes, who died in the early moments of the attack.

The five companies that made up the reserve for Potts' slender brigade retreated to their entrenchments. They were attacked throughout their relief assault, their withdrawal, and their re-entry into their works.

The 3rd Brigade had erected its earthworks along a line of about 200 yards where the 11th and the 16th Iowa lay. Behind that line was a second one of about the same length in which the 13th and the 15th Iowa waited. The Iowans had cut down all the small oaks to create a thick abatis along the front of their works so that the small oaks lay on their sides with their limbs facing forward. The effect and reality were formable, and the trees were positioned to prevent exactly the bold maneuver that was now being executed by the Southern soldiers. These were hard veteran Southern troops going into battle under the blue and white Hardee pattern flag, flown only by the regiments in Cleburne's division.

The Southern combined 1st and 15th Arkansas fell against the 11th Iowa, which lay in the first line of earthworks. The combined Confederate 2nd and 24th Arkansas smashed hard into the Union 16th Iowa, also in the first line, and the 15th Iowa was faced with the left half of the 5th and 13th Arkansas regiments.

The two groups, one behind formidable earthworks and the other struggling through the stumps and abatis, slugged it out for fifteen or twenty minutes. Each side fired as often as possible into the smoke-obscured, sun-blasted, loud, sweaty, and red-flashing hell. The exhausted Southerners were somehow exhilarated as they drove into the Union line.

The right half of the 5th and 13th Arkansas swung out and then, as though hinged on its left, closed around on to the left flank of the 15th Iowa, the same regiment its left half was attacking from the front, and flowed around into its rear. Even in their substantially depleted ranks, the mass and weight and sheer fighting prowess of the 5th and 13th Arkansas overwhelmed the 15th Iowa and the supporting troops from other regiments.

An order was passed and received, and the Union 3rd Brigade began to slide to the right. The 11th, the 13th, and the 15th Iowa all maintained their unit integrity and moved right into new positions in concert with the 1st Brigade. They were not beaten, but they had been overwhelmed and stunned.

In the works of the embattled 16th Iowa, which by its location on the first line made it the natural object of the attacking men from Arkansas, the 341 men under the command of Lieutenant Colonel Addison were in the fight of their lives.

The combined 2nd and 24th Arkansas with men from the combined 5th and 13th Arkansas on the right and part of the 1st and 15th Arkansas on the left were all in front of the earthworks, smashing and crashing through the abatis. They were then met with a well-aimed volley from the rear rank of the 16th Iowa, followed immediately by a second volley of over 200 muskets. Rifle fire was combined with canister from the four 12-pound Napoleons. There were two guns on either side of the 16th Iowa from the 2nd Illinois Light Battery. This fire came at a distance of no more than sixty yards and was excruciating in its intensity. Controlled, aimed, rapid rifle fire volleyed out of the works and was received in full measure by the dirty, begrimed butternut troops.

Weapons in the hands of the men of the 16th Iowa became so hot that powder flashed as it was poured from the paper cartridge into the weapon. Results of the rapid fire on the attackers were horrible. The worn out and exposed Arkansas boys could advance no more and sought cover on the ground and concealment in the abatis. Soon, it appeared that some of the Rebel troops, having had enough, sought to surrender. Gunfire slackened and ceased along the trench line of the 16th Iowa as soldiers from the 2nd and 24th Arkansas came forward with arms raised to surrender.

To the rear of the 16th Iowa, the 13th Iowa began to move off to the right, as did the 15th Iowa, in response to orders and very heavy enemy fire. The warriors of the 16th Iowa were, at least for the moment, victorious. But the ragged gray tide, which had now entered the works of the 16th Iowa with their hands raised, began to integrate themselves with the Confederate troops coming in from the rear and flank. The men of the 16th Iowa, although at first victorious, began to find their circumstances at odds with their original belief as more and more gun-toting Southern soldiers converged on their trench. Firefights erupted in the rear of the 16th Iowa by Rebels advancing from the trenches of the 13th Iowa, which had been deserted.

Lieutenant Colonel Sanders had received a request from Captain Smith to assist him in disarming a large number of sullen "prisoners" who had refused to lay down their arms and had moved to help. Yet when the men of the 2nd and 24th Arkansas begun to realize that perhaps their work was not yet over, Sanders found himself inside a tightening circle of smiling, steely-eyed men after he disarmed two Southerners.

"We won't hurt you, sir, if you surrender," said one Southerner.

Sanders, astonished at the reversal of his situation and the idea of surrender, broke through the ring of captors and ran toward the troops of the 16th Iowa to his right. As he ran, he hoped he could lead his men out of the entrenchment and off to the area originally on their right flank. As the men of the 16th Iowa combined, the hope in Sanders mind was dashed as he realized that he and what was left of his regiment were the only Union troops about. They were out of the fight. Surrender, rather than the victory he excepted, now washed over Sanders. He was outraged at the turn of events and at the circumstances, which had left his regiment alone on the field with the grimly smiling Rebels.

The men of the combined 2nd and 24th Arkansas, who had moments before been captured, were now taking the swords and side arms from the officers within the 16th Iowa, who found themselves prisoners of war. The action had started about 12:45 p.m. and had lasted about an hour. The south end of the Union line was in considerable disarray, and here the other end was in the hands of the men of Cleburne's division.

With the field theirs, Brigadier General Govan set about reforming his lines. The units were mingled, scattered, and considerably reduced in number. The line was reinstated along the second line of trenches taken from the enemy, that is, the lines formerly under the control of the 13th and 15th Iowa regiments. Prisoners and the wounded were removed to the rear of the Confederate forces. Govan was astonished by his success and concerned and saddened by the loss of what had been the brigade's senior, if youthful, leadership only hours earlier. Gone were Colonel John Murray of the 5th Arkansas, whose enthusiastic counterattack had led the way after the first repulse, and Lieutenant Colonel Anderson Watkins of the 8th Arkansas, who had died sword in hand in front of the 15th Iowa.

Wounded were Colonel Colquitt and Lieutenant Colonel Bill Martin, who led the leftmost regiment in the assault, the combined 1st and 15th Arkansas. Colonel Warfield and Lieutenant Colonel Basher of the 2nd and 24th Arkansas; Colonel Samuel Smith, Lieutenant Colonel Cameron, and Major Douglas of the 6th Arkansas; Captain White Washington of the 15th Arkansas; and Lieutenant Colonel Hutchinson of 19th Arkansas were injured as well. The process of the aftermath consumed about three hours. By the end of that time, the brigade had regained what it could of its strength.

The success of Govan's brigade should be put in context. With the advent of the rifled musket, the infantryman in defense had certain real advantages over the infantryman in the attack. The defender could kill at a range of 1,000 yards. He could reload and fire three or maybe four times in a minute. Attackers, on the other hand, could run, fire, halt, reload, and run again, or they could hold their fire until close to the defenders. A thousand yards of open flat field meant a single defender had between six and seven minutes to kill an attacker. This much time is available if one assumes an attacking soldier moves at the prescribed "double-quick time" of 165 steps per a minute, with each step being 33 inches in length.

With between six and seven minutes, a defender could get off twenty to twenty-six shots. Even if soldiers under fire could run the whole distance and cut the time in half, receiving ten to thirteen shots is a tremendous disadvantage to the attacker. If the defender is well positioned and protected by earthworks, so that he makes a very difficult target, his advantages are increased even more. Soldiers in McPherson's Army of the Tennessee and Hood's Army of Tennessee knew the truth about the tactical defense and attack even if their generals still believed that a double line of battle was an effective method to employ against a well-entrenched foe.

So for Govan's brigade to assault and wrest these trenches from these veteran troops was a superb accomplishment. They were aided by the very forest that impeded their advance. Under the cover the forest provided, the troops were able to get close before being subjected to Union rifle and cannon fire. In addition, their battlefront was longer than the front of the dug-in Federals. As a result, the boys from Arkansas were able to flank and then come in from the rear of the surprised Federals.

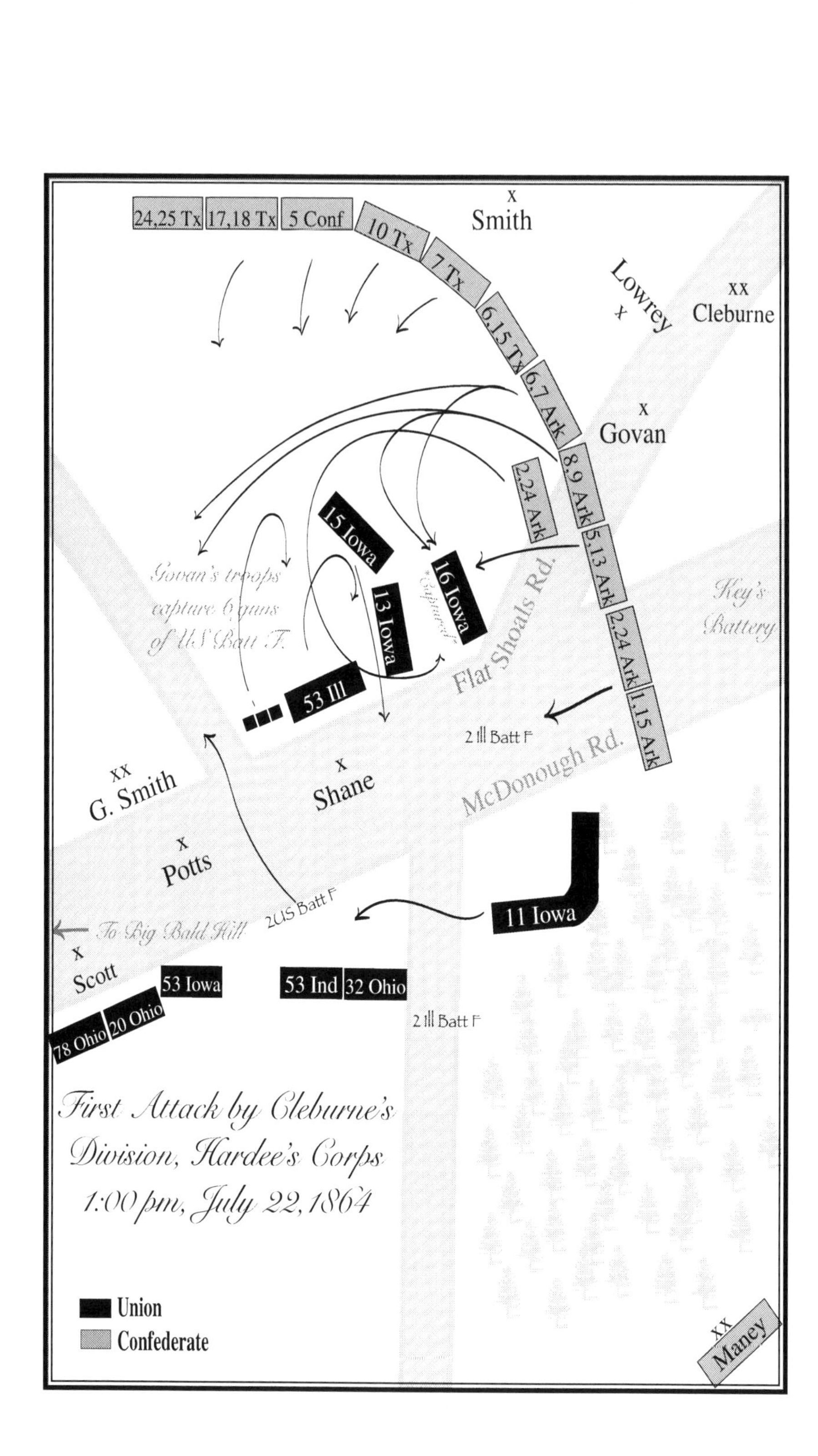

24,25 Tx
17,18 Tx
5 Conf
10 Tx
7 Tx
6,15 Tx
6,7 Ark
8,9 Ark
5,13 Ark
2,24 Ark
2,24 Ark
1,15 Ark
x
Smith
Lowrey
x
xx
Cleburne
x
Govan
Key's Battery
15 Iowa
16 Iowa
13 Iowa
53 Ill
Govan's troops capture 6 guns of US Batt F.
Flat Shoals Rd.
McDonough Rd.
2 Ill Batt F
xx
G. Smith
x
Shane
x
Potts
11 Iowa
2US Batt F
To Big Bald Hill
x
Scott
53 Iowa
53 Ind
32 Ohio
78 Ohio
20 Ohio
2 Ill Batt F
First Attack by Cleburne's Division, Hardee's Corps
1:00 pm, July 22, 1864
Union
Confederate
xx
Maney

CHAPTER EIGHTY

Union | BENJAMIN POTTS & OTHERS

THE SECOND POSITION OF THE 4TH DIVISION,

SEVENTEENTH ARMY CORPS

JULY 22, 1864

ABOUT 1:30 P.M.

UNION, BENJAMIN POTTS

Potts was a big bear of a man. He was thick through his chest and upper body and stood more than six feet tall. He was only twenty-eight and had become a colonel in the Union army by hard work and luck.

Right now, he felt some relative comfort in the location and position of his brigade. He had two regiments on the line facing west toward Atlanta. On his left was his old regiment, the 32nd Ohio, and next to it was the 53rd Indiana. In reserve to his rear, he had remnants of the 53rd Illinois and to their right, the 3rd Iowa. Last night, he had sent Major Allison and eight companies of the 53rd Illinois some two miles over to cover the left flank of the division.

He had been sorry to see the last of the 2nd U.S. Battery F with its six three-inch ordnance rifles depart. They had been well positioned but had been recalled only a little bit before to rejoin Fuller's 4th Division. He could understand why Fuller wanted those guns back, but he would have enjoyed keeping them a while longer. He knew how effective the artillery was. Just yesterday, the Rebel artillery on Bald Hill had punished him as his brigade had struggled to take that piece of high ground.

The men of Hall's brigade were catching hell right now, and Potts had been in complete agreement with his orders from his new boss Giles Smith. Smith had ordered Potts to send his reserve over to Hall's left flank in a desperate effort to shore up the 3rd Brigade before it gave way under the hammering from Pat Cleburne's Confederates. He had sent them, some five companies in all, to the 3rd's relief. Now, the largely disorganized troops of the 3rd Brigade were falling back toward Potts' own works. The small reserve force he had dispatched was now considerably reduced in size, and it came back bloodied and pulling wounded with them. As an organized force, the ad hoc battalion was no longer of any real significance.

As these mangled forces came streaming back across the road and into the trenches of the 32nd Ohio and 53rd Indiana, Potts realized the fight that he had hardly felt involved in was shifting rapidly into his area of responsibility. It was clear he was in for a fight. The enemy had attacked a veteran force well dug in and protected. That was quite a feat, as almost always the defender enjoyed a huge advantage. The hard realities spoke volumes about the foe he was confronting. The spirit of the Rebels must be supremely high, and their killing ability must be superb.

From the southwest, he knew he saw Rebel soldiers moving toward his position, so he had quickly organized his troops. The soldiers from the 11th Iowa, who were the first of Hall's forces to fall back on his trench line, joined in at the front of his line. This became Potts' base, and Potts skillfully began to arrange the retreating forces into a line perpendicular to the end of the 11th Iowa, which would run to the west toward the city. Potts mustered the 13th and the 15th Iowa from Hall's brigade to do just that. Hall's 15th and the 13th Iowa had essentially maintained their unit integrity, and Potts had the 15th Iowa on the right and the 13th Iowa on the left, tucked in against the 11th Iowa. Potts thought that this would provide some kind of defensive opportunity from the pursuing Confederates.

Energized, Potts, with his 53rd Indiana leading the way out of their trench, formed his brigade parallel to the line established by the men from Hall's 3rd Brigade. His 53rd Indiana was lined up north and west of Hall's 15th Iowa with his 32nd Ohio to its left, and what remained of the original five companies from the 3rd Iowa and the 53rd Illinois was tucked into the east end of his line. All these men faced south. The combined position of the Seventeenth Army Corps now resembled a "J" that had been tipped ninety degrees to rest on its side with the shaft on top. The longer shaft was north of the short line.

UNION, RUSSELL BENNETT

The cornfield where the Union soldiers found themselves provided concealment from the advancing Rebel forces. It also meant that those same attacking Rebels were invisible to the blue-clad soldiers who were awaiting them. Men in the 32nd Ohio were no different than those in the other Yankee regiments in their desire for intelligence on what was about to happen. Within the ranks of the 32nd Ohio was Russell Bennett.

He had earned the nickname the "Fighting Chaplain." He had two well-developed and equally strong beliefs: one in the power of God and the other in the power of arms. Unlike many chaplains, Bennett was always in the thick of the fight. He was sure his presence provided more spiritual service to his fellow soldiers than any good he might achieve behind the battle line.

His ministry included providing comfort to the dying and wounded, but he added the crack of his rifle to the chorus of the weapons in the hands of his fellow soldiers. Sometimes, he might be heard saying, "Bless us, Lord, for what we are about to receive," or its companion, "Bless us, Lord, for that which we are about to give." In either instance, his mates grinned or prayed silently.

Bible in one hand, rifle in the other, the chaplain was ready. Now, in the lull that sometimes falls over a battlefield, Bennett could be heard telling those around him on the ground to lie low and stay down. Bennett, with his Bible in his pocket and his rifle gripped in his right hand, edged his way forward through the cornstalks until he was about 150 feet or so forward of his regiment. Here, he found a stump that was high enough that if he stood on it, it provided him a vantage point that he could see the distant tree line from. There, he could see butternut troops advancing rapidly again toward the Union lines. He slipped back into the cornrows and returned to his line with the information that the Confederates were moving close.

"Aim low,"' he advised others, "and stay down." This advice was intoned as he stood, rifle at the ready. With one of the Mitchell boys of Company B reloading for him, Chaplain Bennett blazed away at the attacking Rebels. This action earned him considerable praise from the members of the 32nd Ohio.

UNION, CHARLES SMITH

For Corporal Charles Smith, yesterday's battle in the effort to capture the Rebel artillery and to take the hill held by Wheeler's dismounted cavalry had been the hottest, most deadly, and most exhausting fight of his nearly three years in service. More than sixty-five men had become casualties from Charles' regiment in the fight yesterday as they had fought to provide support to the left flank of the 3rd Division. So far, today seemed as though it would be harder than the day before. Worn out by yesterday's fight, he and the other members of Company I of Potts' 32nd Ohio had nonetheless been out as skirmishers at 3:30 in the early morning. They had joined with the skirmishers from the adjoining 3rd Division and had moved slowly toward Atlanta. They had skirmished with some Rebel cavalry and infantry and had made slow progress through the vines and brambles that obstructed their way. They had continued to move forward with no protection on their left flank until they encountered skirmishers from Hall's brigade.

Having both his left and right covered made Corporal Smith feel better. Smith believed that the men of Company I were as close to Atlanta as any men in the Union army was. The defensive works of the city were visible and lay only about a mile away. With a little luck, they would breech those walls today.

As the sun rose, hunger gnawed at him. Luck was with him as he found abundant blackberries nearly everywhere. Nature was a good provider. Smith loved the taste of warm blackberries, and he ate his fill. Time passed, and without warning, heavy musket fire erupted to the left and rear. The hard noise implied that a very active engagement was underway. This was not just some light firefight but the precursor to a battle.

They did not have to wait long before the skirmish line was under attack. The angle of the attack raised concern that they could be cut off from their brigade and this in turn prompted a slow steady retreat back toward the main body of Union troops. The successful attacking Confederates had followed up on their advantage, and for a time, the two opposing forces were close enough to exchange verbal taunts and insults in addition to their accurate rifle fire. Smith distinctly heard a strong Southern voice yell out, "Halt, you damned Yankee sons of bitches." Hot words, which in civilian life would have made a man stop and fight, in combat simply provided some additional impetus to continue on their way and not stand and surrender. The hard-pressed skirmishers from Company I were unable to reassemble with the 32nd Ohio but found a place in the line where their numbers and muskets were well received.

Charles Smith could not shake the image of one of his friends going down after having both legs blown off by a screaming artillery shell as they had retreated. Smith had been doused by a fine mist of blood, and bits of human meat and gore clung to his uniform. More horrifying was the fact that there was nothing he could do to help his rapidly dying friend. It seemed to Charles Smith that the butternut enemy was hitting the Federal line from the front, the rear, and the flank. It seemed that way to Smith because that was exactly what was happening.

CHAPTER EIGHTY-ONE

Union | *Confederacy* | VARIOUS

WEST OF THE 14TH OHIO BATTERY

JULY 22, 1864

12:30 P.M.

UNION, JOHN MORRILL

Prior to receiving the call to move out and the beginning of the battle, the men of the 1st Brigade, under Colonel John Morrill, had been taking their ease. As they understood their mission, they were going to shore up the tag end of the Seventeenth Army Corps' left flank. They were located to the east of the Seventeenth Army Corps' soldiers, who were still moving dirt around on the top of Bald Hill. Morrill's men were gathered east of the base of the hill.

The growing volume of fire rapidly dispelled what was at first believed to be the sounds of foragers shooting hogs, and the spirit of relaxation was replaced by an anxious enthusiasm to get into the fray. The brigade moved on the double quick from its location behind the Seventeenth Army Corps. The way was made more difficult by the wagons and other wheeled conveyances, which were moving pell-mell across the path of the brigade.

All was confusion and fear. Teamsters had little stomach for combat and were whipping their teams in an effort to get away from the shooting. The 1st Brigade quickly found itself formed with the 2nd Brigade of the 2nd Division of the Sixteenth Army Corps on its left. That 2nd Division was formed at more or less a right angle with the 1st Brigade of Sweeny's 2nd Division, and both the 1st and 2nd Brigades converged on and embraced the 14th Ohio Battery, which had been located on the hill earlier. In the trees opposite, Gist's brigade were spread. On the far left of that unit were the soldiers of Company I of the 16th South Carolina.

Colonel Morrill, under the close personal supervision of his superior commander Brigadier General Fuller, placed the regiments from left to right as follows: 39th Ohio, 22nd Ohio, and then the 64th Illinois with the 18th Missouri in reserve. The line swung back to its right. Sugar Creek cut through the brigade's area of operation and ran from the northwest to the southeast. The two Ohio regiments were south of Sugar Creek and overlooked a field. The 64th Illinois was north of the creek and was facing southwest, looking into a wooded area. The supply wagons and ambulances were racing away to the north of the brigade.

Skirmishers from the 1st Brigade went out immediately. They advanced across the open field and were quickly taken under rifle fire that came from the three brigades of Walker's division, which were assaulting from the tree line across the open field on the south side of the creek. The creek bed was a natural obstacle that tended to channel the attack up its southern side. Thus, Fuller's skirmishers from the 1st Brigade moved back from the forward pressure of the aimed rifle fire of the attackers to their lines.

The Union three-inch ordnance rifles of the fortuitously positioned battery on the hill above Sugar Creek were fast and accurate. Although not at their best in this closed-in, anti-personnel role, they were nonetheless deadly as their shells tore gaps in the advancing butternuts. Clouds of white smoke erupted and then hung about the guns. Their deep, flat reports punched the air with regularity. The heavy rifle fire and the enfilading rifled artillery fire compelled the shot-up, ragged line of Confederate infantry to retire to the trees.

On order, the three Federal regiments on the high ground lay down behind the crest of the ridge they occupied. Fuller ordered his troops to fix bayonets and explained that when the Rebel force was halfway across the field, they were to arise, fire a volley, and charge. Excitement and aggressiveness combined to create a contagion of its own that overwhelmed Fuller's reasoned orders. No sooner had the Southern troops emerged from the trees again than the high strung veterans of the 39th and 27th Ohio regiments stood up, aimed, fired, and rushed down the hill into the surprised oncoming Rebels without any thought. The two lines converged. Troops from Confederate Nisbet's 66th Georgia collided with and were engulfed and surrounded by Fuller's Ohioans.

"We have a general, boys," was heard by all who could above the hard noise of close combat. Talk buzzed from one man to the next, much to the amusement of the Georgia soldiers. Colonel Nisbet, like all colonels in the Confederate service, wore stars on the collar of his gray uniform coat as the insignia of his rank. The stars were unlike the silver eagle worn by full colonels in the Union army and were mistaken for the stars of a general officer by the Ohio soldiers who now surrounded him.

As Nisbet's hard-charging—but poorly informed—captors were celebrating, the right of the Federal line was being overlapped by rapidly advancing ragged butternut-clad soldiers.

UNION, JOHN FULLER

Fuller knew that a gap of some 500 to 600 yards existed between his brigade's right flank and the left of Giles Smith's division down the Union line. He was well informed as to the terrain and the distances since he had been camped on nearly the same ground recently and had just traversed it. The area between the two Federal corps was wooded, and two or more roads—which both generally ran from east to west—cut through the otherwise nearly impassable forest. Through this heavily wooded but undefended gap poured portions of Hardee's corps.

On the left of this fresh onslaught were Granbury's Texans, part of hard fighting Pat Cleburne's division, led by James Smith. On the right were the men of States Rights Gist's brigade of Walker's division. Although combat leadership was present in the form of company, regiment, and brigade officers, real leadership seemed to flow from individual soldiers and the noncommissioned officers above them. Men seemed to know that a breakthrough of substantial proportions was theirs for exploitation, and they moved forward on the run in an effort to achieve what now appeared to be the success Hood had imagined when he outlined his plan. These two broad streams of men were not coordinated on their edges, but they combined to create a maelstrom of a fast-moving, hard-hitting, hurtling mass of fearsome combat power.

The Union soldiers of Giles Smith's 4th Division were being hammered. The opportunity for the flanks of the Union's Sixteenth and Seventeenth Army Corps to find and join each other, if it had ever existed, was swept away as the Confederate vanguard of Govan's, James Smith's, and Gist's brigades smashed and shot their way forward.

Fuller, seeing the danger of the destructive flow of the butternut river to his right, ordered the 39th and the 27th Ohio regiments to fall back and change front to the right. This would place these two regiments at a right angle to the position they had earlier held and at right angle in front of the brigade commanded by Colonel Mersey, the 2nd Brigade of Sweeny's 2nd Division. But the two Ohio regiments were under a brisk fire from the troops on their flank, and it was impossible to maintain a well-dressed line of battle. For a moment, it seemed Fuller's maneuver would be swamped and overrun. The ranks of the 27th Ohio had to swing back over the longest distance, and these men moved in a dead run to the rear.

Fuller was greatly concerned that the veteran organization would simply keep running all the way to the rear and not stop at the imaginary line that existed so clearly in his mind. Their momentum might cause them to continue on to the top of the hill, where they would be ineffectual. Fuller, always directly involved and personally engaged, shouted at the regimental color bearer to move forward and then, with sword in his right hand, indicated in a forceful manner the line along which the 27th Ohio was to form itself. The 27th Ohio was well used to Fuller as he had formerly been their regimental commander.

It was vintage Fuller. He was not issuing orders from the hilltop to his brigade commander with the expectation that the regimental commanders and company commanders would be called together in turn and have the tactic explained. Rather he was in front, leading by example. He knew that to be successful, commanders needed to make a quick, positive decision, see how to do it, and then get it done. Fuller, because he was always there, making it go and getting it done, was respected by the men of the 27th Ohio. He knew them, and they knew him. They were confident that what he wanted to do could often be accomplished, and they were willing to do their best. His personal bravery and commitment created a strong foundation for his leadership. No doubt, this personal connection between the new division commander and his former regimental command enhanced Fuller's effectiveness.

The 27th Ohio completed their run to the line, aligned themselves, and assumed an aggressive line of battle—just as Fuller needed. The

39th Ohio, likewise, formed up to present a front that was two regiments in width. Bayonets were presented to the widening line of Rebel soldiers. The two Ohio regiments advanced, causing the Southern soldiers in their front to turn and move back to the woods they had earlier come from.

Confederate forces that were not yet engaged by Fuller's 27th and 39th Ohio continued to surge forward. Fuller's 64th Illinois, which had been on the right of the 27th Ohio before they had charged forward, as well as the 18th Missouri, which had been in reserve, now came into play. The 64th Illinois fell back so as to present a solid front with the 18th Missouri, which had already changed its south-facing front to the right so that it now faced to the west. Hardee's Confederate troops fell back and were now behind the fence line that ran north and south, separated the field from the woods, and offered some cover and concealment.

CONFEDERACY, STATES RIGHTS GIST

Brigadier General States Rights Gist commanded three regiments and the 8th Georgia Battalion. With his light hair and open face, he was a decided contrast to the lean, hard, dark-bearded face of his division commander, General Walker.

It was now three years to the day that Gist had fought successfully on the battlefield near Bull Run in Virginia. On that day, the South had demonstrated that the war was not to be the picnic so many had assumed. Now, three years later, he was leading the soldiers of his brigade into the undefended gap between the Union's Sixteenth and Seventeenth Army Corps.

To some degree, this was unintended. His soldiers had formed on the left of Walker's division, and the right of Cleburne's division was some distance to his left, too far away to provide support or pressure. There was heavy firing to his right, and no pressure to his left. Furthermore, the way the fields had been hacked out of the wilderness east of Atlanta provided a salient of trees that offered cover and concealment and a natural line of approach for Gist's brigade. The brigade had drifted to the left and managed to remain largely unnoticed in the trees that lay between the two exposed ends of Blair's and Dodge's corps.

CONFEDERACY, JAMES AND ANDREW MCEVER

Company A of Gist's 8th Georgia Battalion had been recruited mostly from the northwest Georgia counties of Gordon and Bartow. The company had been raised nearly three years before in September of 1861. James McEver and his older brother, Andrew McEver, had been with the unit since its inception. Now, the brothers were together behind the rail fence, where they were reloading and firing as rapidly as experience and position afforded.

The din of the combined rifle fire from the six or seven Confederate and Union regiments closely joined in this very real firefight and were nearly a continuous roar. The dirty white smoke was everywhere and lay thick near the ground. Some of the smoke rose in the air or was pushed up from below as new volumes were blasted out at ground level. The clouds of smoke then formed a low blanket over the hot, humid battlefield. The amount of fire coming from the right side of the Union line, particularly the rifles of the 64th Illinois, seemed particularly devastating and deadly.

The brothers were not afraid as they lay behind the poor cover provided by the fence rails, but each was glad the other was there. Thoughts about the continuation of the family bloodline might suggest that the brothers remain separate from one another in battle, but they had fought together for a long time and were comfortable with their closeness. They used ramrods to push balls down the barrel onto the black powder they poured out from the paper cartridges, which they had torn open with their teeth seconds before. As a result, a black ring of salty powder formed around their mouths. The powder, dirt, and sweat produced a grimness that would have made them unrecognizable to their mother. Andrew pointed the sight of their general, Gist, out to his brother as Gist rode up, black hat in hand, yelling and urging his weary troops forward.

"Damn, James. From the look of things, he wants us to get up and join him," said Andrew with mock seriousness.

"Yeah, and I'm happy right here," replied his brother. "Never was sure just how smart he was."

As the hawk-eyed men of the 8th Georgia Battalion, the 46th Georgia, and the 16th and 24th South Carolina regiments surged forward at Gist's shouted encouragement, they were met by a counterattack from the rapid-firing Henry rifles of Fuller's 64th Illinois. The Federals were only moments before ordered forward and to the left in order to place a heavy flanking fire into Gist's stubborn but weary soldiers.

At nearly the same time as a round tore into Gist and knocked him off his horse, a second round smashed into Andrew McEver. Cries of "Bring the General off" overcame the words from Andrew: "Brother, I'm hit."

Blood oozed from the wound above the knee of his left leg. As he lay moaning, James searched for the exit wound. Finding none, he tied his dirty, sweat-stained kerchief tightly around his brother's leg.

"I think you're going to live, Andrew. It didn't hit no artery," James said. Amid the singing sounds of death, James somehow got both rifles and—supporting Andrew—began to retreat from the dust, death, and smoke into the shadows of the hardwood stand that lay to the rear. The unleashed violence to the front and the flow of men removing the general served as encouragement to the rest of the men to move to the rear as well.

These actions served as a catalyst to the men of Gist's brigade as they removed themselves from the sheets of flame coming from the increasingly confident Union troops. Along the fence line lay heaps of wounded and dead and dying Confederate men. They lay at odd angles on the ground behind the fence, whose promise of cover had proven to be only an illusion.

UNION, JOHN FULLER

Gist's assault ran its course. The men of Fuller's brigade settled down to a defensive firing, which was accompanied by the never slacking fire from Lieutenant Laird's six rifled guns firing from the hilltop in their rear. General Fuller wondered about where the other six ordnance rifles of the 2nd US Battery F, under Captain Albert Murry, were. He remembered ordering their return as he had moved the brigade out from their bivouac toward the sounds of the guns. He knew he had not seen them nor had word from them since. Where were those guns? It would be good to have them here.

CHAPTER EIGHTY-TWO

Confederacy | JOSEPH WHEELER

One mile south of Decatur
on the Fayetteville Road
July 22, 1864
12:45 p.m.

Wheeler had ridden far enough up the Fayetteville Road to see fortifications, some artillery, and solid Yankee infantry standing in and near the freshly turned, red clay ditches. The new trenches ran along the high ground near the railroad track. Wheeler mused to himself that those soldiers looked not at all like the cavalry he had expected to see.

Wheeler turned to his subordinates, "Let's keep the brigades together. Go tell Iverson and Allen I want them to move off the road and move toward Decatur in a northeasterly direction. Let us see if we can get a force around those Yanks on their right. Tell General Ferguson to take his Alabama boys over to the left. It looks like a ridgeline. Tell him to spread out and move forward. I want to divide the artillery. Send one section with Ferguson. While it should support Ferguson, keep it close to the road here on Ferguson's right. Send the other section of artillery with the other two brigades on our right. These thick woods between us and Decatur work against us, so let's get off these worn-out horses and go kill that blue-bellied Yankee infantry with some infantry of our own. Do you understand me, Captain?"

The two young captains replied together, "Yes, sir." They moved off with dispatch to the respective brigades.

CHAPTER EIGHTY-THREE

Union | JEREMIAH RUSK

ABOUT ONE-HALF MILE SOUTHWEST OF DECATUR
ON THE FAYETTEVILLE ROAD
JULY 22, 1864
12:45 P.M.

Lieutenant Colonel Jeremiah Rusk had been excited about the opportunity to lead the four companies of the 63rd Ohio on this effort to find out what lay ahead on the road running from Decatur down toward the southwest. He had been somewhat disappointed when Sprague allowed Colonel Montgomery of the 25th Wisconsin to come with him so that, consequently, Rusk was still subordinate to someone. He had enjoyed the all-too-brief interlude as an independent acting battalion commander. He now led Companies B, E, F and I. At one time, this would have represented 400 men, but now it was considerably less. He knew Companies D and G were somewhere ahead of them on picket duty. They would serve as an early warning if danger really lurked ahead of them. Colonel Montgomery had even pushed his four companies out ahead of Rusk's battalion. *"Well, if mischief awaited,"* Rusk thought, *"then Montgomery's boys from Wisconsin would get bloody first."*

This was easy marching, and Rusk figured that the report of a heavy force coming this way had been exaggerated. Usually such information was more disconcerting in the reporting than in what actually happened. Experience had taught him that nothing was ever as bad or good as one was initially led to believe.

But then, he heard a scattered group of reports from rifled muskets down the road. To his well-tuned ears, a sense of building pressure seemed to exist. Then he saw him. Moving up the road toward him at a fast clip came Milton Montgomery on his horse.

"Rusk, we have run into a hornet's nest of them. I'm going to take my force and move it to the left of the road. You take the 63rd out to the right. Our pickets are coming back fast, and there is a lot of noise over to our left flank. I think it's important to try to hold them here and not let them get into the town. The terrain ahead is heavily wooded, and there is a ridge over there ahead of us. This should work to the advantage of a stout defense."

"Yes, sir," Rusk said, "and I will send someone back to Sprague with this information."

With confidence, the battalion moved into lines of battle on each side of the road and moved off to the west.

The Southern force, Wheeler's men, was moving forward quickly and on a wide front, and the Union battalion fired several volleys into the Confederate's oncoming force. It seemed to the opposing Union troops that they were up against first-class light infantry. The Union line of battle was not long enough or deep enough to resist the butternut pressure for long. Veteran troops know combat realities, and the blue line began to give ground and move back down the road toward Decatur as the troops realized they could not win.

The Confederates seemed well established on the ridge that lay before them. They were here in force and seemed determined. For all Rusk knew, the bastards had a section or two of guns up there with them. It was too much for four small companies even if they were veteran. The woods were too thick to see very much.

A horseman came pounding down the road with orders from Colonel Sprague: "Fall back and move to your left over that way to support the entrenchments. A heavy force is on its way."

They traded shots with the rapidly moving Southern troops and fell back. No caution was needed now that they moved back to the high ground just south of the railroad. Here, they rejoined the 1st Michigan gun sections and three companies of Montgomery's 25th Wisconsin.

Montgomery, on the left of the road, was forced back into some low, swampy ground. This low, wet spot broke up the clean and orderly rearward movement of his troops. Montgomery himself lost his horse to the miserable terrain as it was bogged down and could not escape. Montgomery retrieved his pistols from the saddle holsters and stood in the mud firing into the onrushing Southerners. He was hit in the arm and went down next to his mired horse.

Within minutes, the Rebels had him captured and were moving him to their rear. Cannon fire erupted from the ridge he had earlier approached, and now the same thing was taking place just down the road as the Rebel battery began to establish a rhythm.

The Union line was consolidating and putting up a substantial fight from the hill south of the rail line. The 35th New Jersey on the left changed their direction of front and fired as they retreated up the hill. From facing south and west, they bent back under flanking pressure so that they faced south and east. Captain Gilmore, along with a portion of the 63rd Ohio, was on the right of the New Jersey soldiers, who were holding on in a tight fight. Flanked on the left and right and somewhat concerned about being cut off and surrounded, the two guns of the 1st Michigan limbered up and moved north over the rails. The supporting infantry of the 63rd Ohio and 35th New Jersey followed suit, along with the disorganized remnants of the mixed battalion of eight rifle companies.

The retreating Union force fell back to rally around the four guns of the Chicago Board of Trade Battery and their supporting infantry, which were all in position just north of the town jail.

CHAPTER EIGHTY-FOUR

Union | COLONEL JOHN SPRAGUE

IN DECATUR

JULY 22, 1864

Colonel Sprague was actively involved in halting the retreating soldiers. He got them stopped, turned them around, and sent them forward to create a new defensive line. The two guns of the 1st Michigan rolled up unlimbered and began returning fire at the several sections of Confederate batteries. The four guns of the Chicago Board of Trade, despite their rifled barrels, sent round after round of canister into the swarming ranks of Joe Wheeler's dismounted troopers. Firing from the Union ranks was so fast and continuous that the veterans of the 35th New Jersey exhausted their ammunition supply as they endeavored to protect the square around the Decatur courthouse.

To the northeast of the town, in the huge wagon park, the noise of the Confederate assault motivated the teamsters and their animals. Without orders, but with a highly developed sense of self-preservation, the wagons started to roll. Sometimes, four wagons abreast would race north up the Roswell Road away from the fast-moving Rebels.

Sprague felt some confidence he could hold his line here in town but reasoned that his mission was to protect the wagons of the Fifteenth Army Corps as well as that part of the trains coming down from Roswell. To prevent the Rebels from gaining possession of these wagons and the many supplies they carried, it would be of importance to keep the enemy away from the fleeing wagons.

The defensive line retreated to the courthouse square with discipline in the face of a large, determined, and experienced force, which right now had the additional momentum that comes with success. The fighting raged on three sides of the courthouse. In the face of the ambitious Rebel force, Sprague retreated north of the square to a ridgeline.

Here, the forces that had been guarding the wagon train from Roswell, part of the 9th Illinois Mounted Infantry under Major Kuhn, arrived. They quickly set up a strong skirmish line west of the Roswell Road and north of Decatur. The trains coming from Roswell were directed to the west toward the rear area of the Eighteenth Army Corps and out of the way of Wheeler's dismounted cavalry.

The line of Union skirmishers, in concert with the halt and lame from Garrard's command and the members of the 1st Brigade band, began to actively serve as a blocking force. This point of stability allowed the retreating artillery and the disorganized infantry, which had soldiers from three different regiments pretty well mixed together, to pass to the next road junction. Some of the Union cavalry were armed with rapid-firing carbines, which swelled the base of fire from the blocking force.

Beyond the blocking force, at the next road junction, Sprague halted his disorganized force. This was the same road the wagon train had been directed down. Here, a crude but effective row of defensive works was thrown up. The 43rd Ohio, under Colonel Wager Swayne, fell in to add some organizational integrity to the milling members of the brigade. Soon, the battle line was being sorted out, and the 2nd Brigade settled down to await events.

About an hour and a half had passed since the reconnaissance battalion had first made contact. Standing in line behind his defensive works, Sprague reflected on the past ninety minutes. He figured that he had just done what Johnston's army had been doing for the last ninety days and what Wheeler's small force had been doing for the past several days. He had been using common sense to retreat to the next best place in the face of a determined enemy force. He had saved most of his command and held on to the logistical element he was to protect. He had saved the day but wondered if his reward would be like that of Joe Johnston's.

Sprague asked for returns from his subordinates and counted up his losses—some 240 killed and wounded. He assumed the large attacking force of Confederates had lost more and on top of that had failed to capture the highly prized wagons.

The sounds of heavy fighting off to the west could be heard, and he wondered what was going on. The butternuts that had come after him with such determination seemed to be pausing or perhaps even breaking off contact. Or, more likely, they were probably just catching their next wind before coming up for more. Still, it did seem that the mad activity was abating.

CHAPTER EIGHTY-FIVE

Confederacy | JOSEPH WHEELER

NORTH OF DECATUR ON SHALLOWFORD ROAD

JULY 22, 1864

1:15 P.M.

Wheeler sat easily on his sweaty mount. It seemed to Wheeler that he was just getting started. Sometimes, he wished he could have help and direction from one of the senior corps commanders, but not now. He had the damn blue bellies on the run. He had surprised them, pushed them into the village, and then out the other side. He thought they were disorganized enough that with a final push, he might rout them.

It was true that they had captured only a few wagons and that the spoils were not great, but he was clearly in the Yankee rear. He could turn and ride down Decatur Road, the same one he had fought two days worth of delaying action on, and be in the rear of the entire Union army. What a field day. He had for damn sure returned Decatur Courthouse to the proper jurisdiction under the flag of the Confederacy.

It also seemed to him that he must be easy to find. All three of Hardee's staff officers had found him within minutes of each other. All came with the same message from Hardee: "I need your help on my left. We are hard-pressed. Return to assist me in my direct assault."

It would take a little while, but he would get the word out to his exhausted troopers, line them up, and go off to help someone else.

If he could get some help or just control all of his horsemen instead, he could be slashing and killing Yankees outside the gates of Atlanta. It'd be fun to just chase these Yanks back to Roswell, but orders were orders. It would certainly be hard to say he had misunderstood all three sets of orders from old Hardee. He knew he best get on with it.

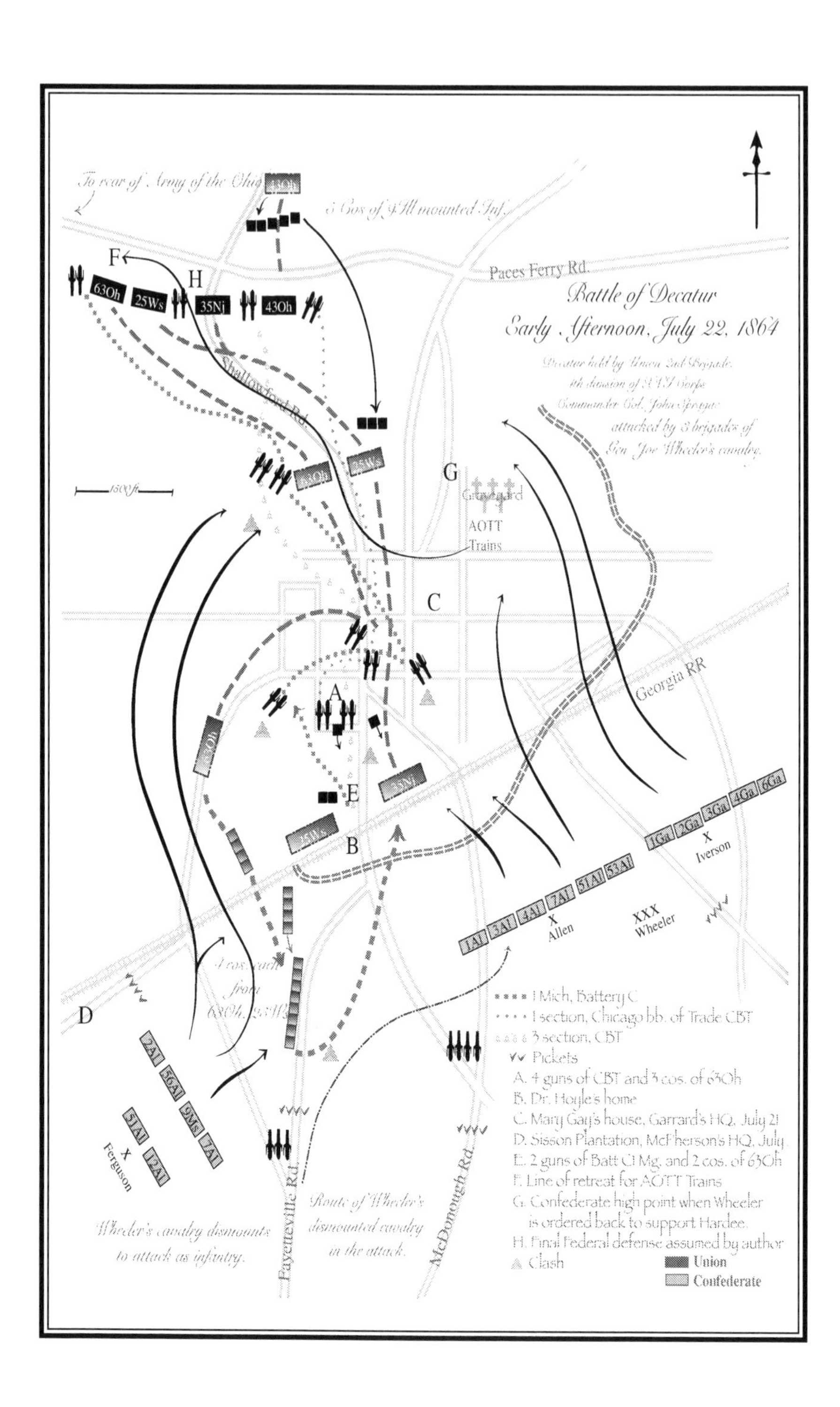
Battle of Decatur
Early Afternoon, July 22, 1864
Decatur held by Union 2nd Brigade,
4th division of XVI Corps
Commander Col. John Sprague
attacked by 3 brigades of
Gen Joe Wheeler's cavalry.
To rear of Army of the Ohio
43Oh
5 Cos of 9 Ill mounted Inf.
Paces Ferry Rd.
F
H
63Oh
25Ws
35Nj
43Oh
Shallowford Rd.
63Oh
25Ws
G
Graveyard
AOTT
Trains
1500 ft
C
Georgia RR
A
43Oh
E
35Nj
25Ws
B
1Ga
2Ga
3Ga
4Ga
6Ga
X
Iverson
1Al
3Al
4Al
7Al
51Al
53Al
X
Allen
XXX
Wheeler
4 cos. each
from
63Oh, 25Ws
D
2Al
56Al
9Ms
7Al
51Al
12Al
X
Ferguson
Fayetteville Rd.
McDonough Rd.
Wheeler's cavalry dismounts
to attack as infantry.
Route of Wheeler's
dismounted cavalry
in the attack.
1 Mich, Battery C
1 section, Chicago bb. of Trade CBT
3 section, CBT
Pickets
A. 4 guns of CBT and 3 cos. of 63Oh
B. Dr. Hoyle's home
C. Mary Gay's house, Garrard's HQ, July 21
D. Sisson Plantation, McPherson's HQ, July
E. 2 guns of Batt C1 Mg. and 2 cos. of 63Oh
F. Line of retreat for AOTT Trains
G. Confederate high point when Wheeler
is ordered back to support Hardee.
H. Final Federal defense assumed by author
Clash
Union
Confederate

CHAPTER EIGHTY-SIX

Confederacy | HOSEA GARRETT

NEAR THE REFUSED FEDERAL LINE, SOUTH OF BALD HILL

10TH TEXAS REGIMENT, SMITH'S TEXAS BRIGADE,

CLEBURNE'S DIVISION, HARDEE'S CORPS, ARMY OF TENNESSEE

12:52 P.M.

JULY 22, 1864

It seemed to First Lieutenant Hosea Garrett that while he had a great deal of respect for and devotion to courtly old General Johnston that they had been backing up ever since the Confederacy's Army of Tennessee had left that peaceful camp in Dalton. Now, with Hood's assumption of command, his 10th Texas had been going after the Yanks for the past week.

Garrett was in excellent health, and at thirty-two years of age, he was probably never going to have more strength then he had that day. Still, he and the 125 men of the regiment had marched all night and then took a short rest within the entrenchments of Atlanta after finally being able to disengage from the northern slope of Bald Hill that even now loomed up before him. Garrett knew that about a half-mile to his right were the troops of Major General Walker and in particular the brigade commanded by Gist. The undergrowth before them was dense. No clear field of fire or even paths seemed to exist. The way forward might not be impossible, but it would be hard going.

He wished he were still at Cobb's Mill, where the division had rested at daybreak and received an additional twenty rounds of ammunition. He was sure that if he had been allowed to move by the most direct route from the northwest side of Bald Hill to the southeast side, where he now was, the distance could not have been more than a mile. Yet to get to his present position, maybe 2,000 feet southeast of the hill, he had walked into Atlanta, then south for a long time, and then back north again. At best, he could tell the entire division and his brigade had walked at least twelve miles. He had mastered marching in his sleep, but he was still worn thin by all the geeing and hawing.

This was all compounded by having been under very heavy cannon and rifle fire for most of July 21. Usually, in his experience, cannon fire meant lots of noise and smoke but not a lot of human misery. Yesterday had been different. There had been a pesky Union battery off to his left, which had killed Texans right and left for most of the day. Somehow, they had seemed to be firing straight down the trench line.

The day before, they had been ready to join in the attack with the rest of Hardee's corps when that decision had been countermanded. They went from being ready to join in the fray to their front to marching to the new position on Bald Hill. They had marched, dug, and fought until they embarked on this last bit of marching about fourteen hours ago. He concluded that he had been on the go for more than forty-five hours now, but it seemed like a lifetime. He could only be grateful that he had not fallen back as many men had, and he was still with the men of his own regiment.

As the men rested, one of his messmates removed the top from his canteen.

"Boys, I have been saving this all night," he said, "This little jug is full of some red whiskey. It seems like the right time to drink it, maybe for the last time." He looked about, raised the canteen, and poured some of its contents into the cups held out to him.

Then he said, "Let's go strike a blow for liberty," and drank down the last swallow. The toast had sounded about right to Garrett, who didn't bother to wonder whether it was the consumption of whiskey or the killing they were about to do that constituted the blow for freedom.

Garrett hoped the brigade's young, thirty-three-year-old Brigadier General James A. Smith understood the plan of attack better than he himself did. He must, after all, since James Smith was a general. Smith's command, Granbury's Texas Brigade, was the rightmost brigade of Cleburne's famed division. It was made up of what were left of six Texas regiments and the 5th Confederates, who had recently joined. Several of the Texas units had originally been cavalry, but the horses had long since been replaced by their own legs. His 10th Texas was nearly in the middle of the brigade. Long ago, his regiment would have formed a front of nearly 300 yards and have been two lines deep.

Now, in a single line of battle, it occupied a fighting front of less than 125 yards, so depleted were the thin ranks. But these were the hardest and best of the boys who had left Texas. They were here because they survived and because the cause was dear to them. Behind the Texans was Lowrey's brigade.

To his left, Garrett knew were the men of Govan's brigade. Govan's brigade included the soldiers of the 1st and 15th Arkansas, who used to be under Polk before the fight at Mud Creek. It was the 1st Arkansas until it was renumbered the 15th Arkansas at Cornith, following the hard fight at Shiloh. The regiment had won many honors as the 15th Arkansas, and it remained close to Cleburne's heart.

Ahead of Cleburne's division stood the Giles Smith's 4th Division of the Seventeenth Army Corps of the Army of the Tennessee. The two veteran brigades at his command were well dug in at the left of a long Union line. Facing south and southwest at the end of the Union left was the brigade of Colonel William Hall. The brigade had four Iowa regiments: the 11th, 13th, 15th, and 16th. Immediately to their right was the 1st Brigade commanded by Benjamin Potts. Potts' regiments were the 23rd Indiana, the 53rd Indiana, and the 32nd Ohio. He also had the three companies of the 3rd Iowa. In close association were the fourteen guns of the three batteries of artillery of the 4th Division.

CHAPTER EIGHTY-SEVEN

Confederacy | RICHARD BEARD | *Union* | JAMES MCPHERSON

5TH CONFEDERATE REGIMENT

IN THE TREES, SOUTH OF BALD HILL

JULY 22, 1864

LITTLE PAST 1:00 P.M.

CONFEDERACY, RICHARD BEARD

It had been a hellish night last night. The hard, thin troops of the 5th Confederate, or what was left of it, had finally been able to disengage pursuant to Cleburne's order of early yesterday evening. They had lead the way back into the city of Atlanta for four or five dark and dusty miles, marched down McDonough Road, took a hard left, and then got to Intrenchment Creek. Here, there had been a mill and a chance to rest and fill up on water.

Following this brief respite, they all had picked up ammunition so that each man now had sixty rounds. They had then marched north and onto a road that ran back toward the south end of Bald Hill. They were but a short distance from where they had begun the exhausting night march. The 5th Confederate had rested and received the orders that they were to act as skirmishers for the division. This assignment, one they had performed many times, placed them on the far right and well in advance of the advancing battle line. They had set off in a march.

It was now well past 1:00 p.m., maybe as late as 1:45 in the afternoon. The 5th Confederate had been on the move for more than twelve hours, and that came on top of nearly two days of digging, marching, fighting, digging, and waiting. After such strenuous action, many men were stupid with exhaustion.

Major Richard J. Person led the regiment, and Captain Richard Beard led one of the companies. His company was in the process of arranging itself when the booming flat sound of artillery came from the far right. Alignment complete and the physical exhaustion momentarily forgotten, the entire brigade began to double quick through the thickly overgrown woods toward an enemy they knew lay waiting, but as yet, they could not see.

Federal skirmishers were encountered soon after, but the butternut skirmishers' progress was so fast the blue pickets were run through after nothing but a little shooting. Beyond the thin blue line of skirmishers, a narrow red clay wagon road cut a line through the woods nearly parallel to the 5th Regiment's line of battle. The Rebel line was walking now, out of breath from the initial run. Captain Beard lead his small company and cautioned them as they reached the verge of the road.

Suddenly, a group of hard-riding horsemen converged onto Beard's command. Beard, acting on instinct alone, stepped into the road, took in the lathered horses, and knew in an instant that he was confronting a high-ranking Union officer and his staff. Beard raised his sword in a manner to induce the now milling horsemen to surrender. Amid the uproar, Beard shouted, "Halt!"

UNION, JAMES MCPHERSON

Several Union signal corps officers had overtaken McPherson and his orderly A.J. Thompson in their ride toward General Giles Smith's line moments before. Captain Howard from the Army of the Tennessee and Lieutenant Sherfy from the Fifteenth Army Corps had caught up with and slowed their horses to move in concert with McPherson. The group of them progressed down the road toward Giles Smith and his 4th Division.

The small group of riders came sliding to a halt as more of the skinny, cold-eyed, bearded, and dirty men showed themselves along the road.

General McPherson raised his black slouch hat, nearly a salute, wheeled his big horse to the right, and with heel and spurs into his mount's flanks, began a gallop back up the road. His party turned with him.

Captain Beard spoke to the teenaged corporal at his side, "Kill him." Corporal Coleman raised his long rifled musket to his shoulder. He laid his right cheek aside the dusty wooden stock, aimed at the fleeing horseman, and gently squeezed the trigger. The .577 caliber ball spun out of the barrel ahead of the flash and struck the general in the back. The force of the round knocked McPherson from the saddle. Other shots from scattered Confederate men along the road roared out, smoke billowing from several firing weapons.

McPherson felt the heavy hammer blow to his back, flew up out of his saddle, and hit the ground hard on his face. He had willed his arms out to protect his face, but no response was forthcoming. He could hear the sounds of firing close at hand, the thud of horses' hooves, and the sound of running men. A hot rush from deep inside moved over him, and a heavy pressure seemed to grip him.

The warmth seemed inappropriate to him since his mind was certain he was on a snow-covered hill near his boyhood home. It was difficult to breathe. He was deep in the snow with his sled turned over. There, running toward him was sweet Emily Huffman, his lady love. She was holding him. McPherson thought it strange that she was here when he was just a small boy.

Darkness closed in. The black hat with its beautifully crafted Engineering Corps' insignia rolled as it hit the ground and came to rest a few feet from the general.

McPherson died at age thirty-three. He, a major general commanding the Army of the Tennessee, was an engineer at heart. He had kept his corps' insignia on his hat as a token of his loyalty to that proud group. Only the best of the West Point graduates were commissioned as engineers. In many ways, it signified much of what was good about McPherson, but it also revealed a hint of his deficiencies.

The 5th Confederate, failing to hear the shouted command for the regiment to move by the left flank, ran headlong into the Federal 64th Illinois of Morrill's brigade. These were the same soldiers who had worked over Walker's division and the brigade led by States Rights Gist earlier. Major Person and Captain Beard were almost immediately captured in the brief struggle that transpired. The flag was lost, and some forty men were captured.

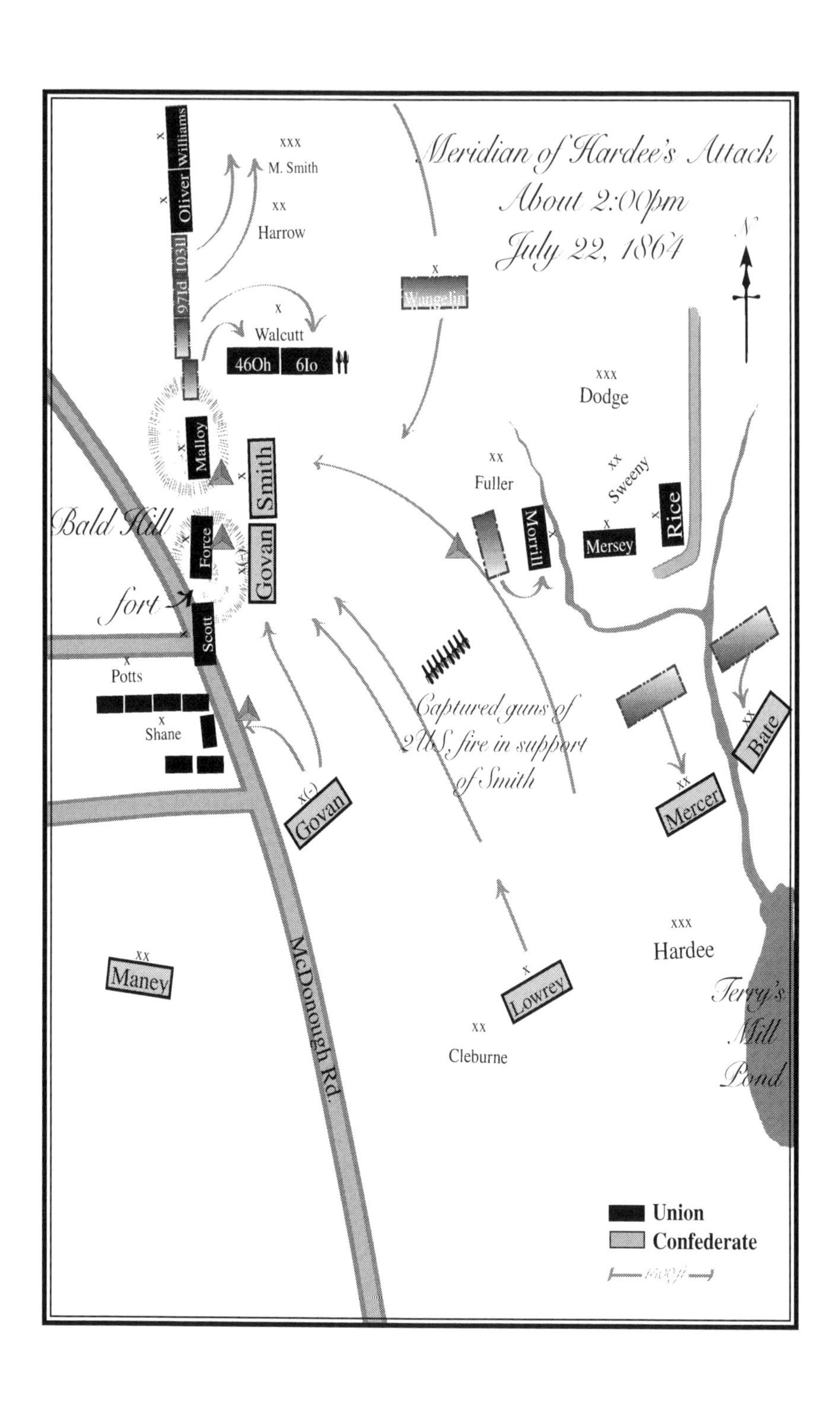

Meridian of Hardee's Attack
About 2:00pm
July 22, 1864
N
XXX
M. Smith
XX
Harrow
X
Williams
X
Oliver
97Id
103Il
X
Walcutt
46Oh
6Io
XXX
Dodge
X
Malloy
X
Smith
Bald Hill
X
Force
X(-)
Govan
fort
X
Scott
X
Potts
X
Shane
X(-)
Govan
XX
Fuller
Morrill
XX
Sweeny
X
Mersey
X
Rice
Captured guns of
2US, fire in support
of Smith
XX
Bate
XX
Mercer
XXX
Hardee
Terry's
Mill
Pond
X
Lowrey
XX
Cleburne
XX
Maney
McDonough Rd.
Union
Confederate

CHAPTER EIGHTY-EIGHT

Union | JOHN LOGAN

NEAR THE FIFTEENTH ARMY CORPS HEADQUARTERS

JULY 22, 1864

1:00 P.M.

The day was getting hot. The steam created by the damp interacting with the heat was gone, and the normal red dust was beginning to show itself.

Logan sat restlessly on his black warhorse, Old John, and thought about the changes thus far today. His three divisions had moved forward by echelon, from right to left, to take over the trenches abandoned during the night by the Rebels. He and McPherson had started and stopped in their preparations for the Fifteenth Army Corps to move out and follow Hood in what Sherman had predicted and hoped was Hood's retreat from Atlanta.

Logan didn't hold Sherman in the highest regard, and Sherman's prediction that the South would retreat flew in the face of what McPherson believed. Logan felt McPherson was far more likely to be correct. Logan knew only a little about Hood and didn't think retreat was part of his makeup, and it was now becoming increasingly clear that Sherman's hope was not taking place right now. Logan thought that Sherman occasionally fell into assuming his hopes were going to be realized rather than what was actually taking place on the ground. Sherman wanted Hood to give up Atlanta after the battle that had taken place south of Peachtree Creek on July 20, so Sherman had convinced himself again that was what must be taking place. Hood, not privy to Sherman's thoughts, was acting out his own version of things, which was mightily different from what Sherman was certain was going on. Logan thought it was far better to deal with the facts as they found them.

He felt, before he saw, the staff officer rushing toward him on a horse. Lieutenant Colonel William Clark, McPherson's adjutant, was flushed and strained. This was the second time today that Lieutenant Colonel Clark had been to see Logan. About an hour earlier, he had brought orders from General McPherson for General Logan to send a brigade to plug the space between Blair's left and Dodge's right. Logan had sent Colonel Wangelin and his 3rd Brigade of the 1st Division. Wangelin's departure would leave only eight regiments holding the 1st Division front.

Clark was breathing heavily as he stammered, "General McPherson is dead. General Sherman orders you to take command of the army. Hold on at all costs, and if you need reinforcements, call on him or General Schofield."

Clark had been riding hard and fast since he was informed that McPherson's horse, bloody from bullet wounds, had been found. He had ridden first to General Sherman's headquarters at the Howard House and from there back to the railroad to find Logan. Although he had become familiar with the terrain and the location of the various departments, army, and corps headquarters, he still had to ride more than two miles to find Sherman and then Logan, but he knew he was carrying the most important message of his army life.

Logan sat stunned for a moment as the officer rattled on about the loss of McPherson. The two of them, Logan and McPherson, had been together earlier in the day at about 10:00 this morning. Only about an hour ago, he, Blair, McPherson, and their staffs had been together in the shade of an oak grove. The two men had become friends since their time together around Vicksburg. They were different in many ways, but Logan respected his young commander and knew McPherson relied on him especially in a fight. He would always think of McPherson as a man with a twinkle in his eyes, and it was hard to believe McPherson was gone.

It could be an error. Time would tell. Often, rumors were unfounded, and yet Sherman must be damn sure of his facts, or such an order as he had just received would not have been given. This was unexpected, but in his practical mind, Logan began working out the sequence of actions that must now be accomplished.

Logan knew he must appoint General Morgan Smith as the new commander of the Fifteenth Army Corps, the same corps Logan had begun to personify. They must recover, if at all possible, McPherson's body. He must sort things out with Dodge and Blair on his left. He'd need to rally McPherson's staff around him as he moved out toward the sounds of heavy firing on that left flank, which McPherson had been so concerned about at lunch that day.

Now that flank was his problem, and McPherson's careful, cautious concern was the overarching circumstance to be sorted out. Hood's ability to deliver the unexpected had come crashing home in an irresistible manner. Sherman had misread this one. What was Hood up to? McPherson had clearly been right to be concerned. Logan didn't know Hood, but McPherson had talked about his friend so much that Logan believed he knew as much as could be known in a hearsay fashion.

As his horse moved under him, Logan knew that fighting the Army of Tennessee was the biggest job of his entire life. He wouldn't have the luxury of getting used to his new command, if he needed that. The whole army might be used up before he could get his hands around it.

As he rode to the point below and east of Bald Hill held by General Leggett of Blair's Seventeenth Army Corps, he yelled at one of the mounted staff officers, "We will get General McPherson's body back if it takes every man in the Fifteenth Corps!"

Logan's leadership was often unconscious. He intuitively knew the importance of recovering McPherson's body. McPherson was held in a nearly beloved status by his troops. It would soon become a rallying cry to "Remember McPherson," and this personalized—at a very basic human level—the reasons why the men of the army needed to try hard, sacrifice, fight back, and win. Logan didn't stop to think, but he knew it was the right way to begin. The rush of events demanded a quick and meaningful response. This one also took him forward to the point last under investigation by McPherson, where the enemy was making his presence felt in a hard, determined, and killing way. In the area McPherson was killed, in the very gap he was concerned about, Colonel Wangelin's brigade had moved rapidly and had run headlong into the attacking Southerners. Wangelin's regiments had pushed back the onrushing enemy until they took a slight rise, whereupon they constructed a hasty breastwork of rails. Wangelin's brigade was not enough to stop the Southern troops.

The Union tried to fix the exposed line south of Bald Hill. Prior to the assault, General Giles Smith had been breathing the very thin air of his exposed position at the extreme left end of the army. He had dug in along the road that ran along the ridge. Smith had then refused or bent back his line to the east, the curved part of which was composed of Hall's brigade. He had his pickets out about a mile and a half from his entrenched position.

Some of his pickets were actually behind his division, which corresponded to the front of General Sweeny's 2nd Division of the Sixteenth Army Corps, which was located in its bivouac about three-fourths of a mile to the rear and east of the Seventeenth Army Corps. This entire division had been on the extreme right of the Army of the Tennessee, linking the line between Schofield's Army of the Ohio and McPherson's Army of the Tennessee but had relocated one and a half miles or so to the southeast that morning. This relocation had placed them on the extreme-left flank of the army, awaiting the opportunity to move to position in the line. Sweeny was to buttress the thin Union left.

Troops had been sent to strengthen the line south of Bald Hill and Giles Smith had refused the end, but it was still inadequate against an assault from an enemy larger than a couple of regiments. This was the circumstance McPherson had feared. Despite efforts to correct it, the left flank was still essentially in the air, open to exactly the attack that was now underway.

CHAPTER EIGHTY-NINE

Union | WILLIAM HARROW | *Confederacy* | PATRICK CLEBURNE

HARROW'S 4TH DIVISION, FIFTEENTH ARMY CORPS,

ARMY OF THE TENNESSEE

ON BALD HILL

JULY 22, 1864

1:30 P.M.

UNION, WILLIAM HARROW

The time, in General William Harrow's mind, was July 2, 1863, a little over a year ago. The location was about midway down the line along Emmitsburg Road, south of Gettysburg, Pennsylvania. His brigade had been tucked in between three corps under Dan Sickles and one corps under Doubleday. He recalled staring out across the open field that separated Meade's Army of the Potomac from Bobby Lee's Army of Northern Virginia. Then, he had commanded a brigade under John Gibbon, commander of the 2nd Division of the Second Army Corps.

Now, on July 22, he had his own well-entrenched division. In both cases, he had faced generally to the west to view the Confederate forces, and in both cases, the road that he was positioned along ran essentially north and south. In his recollection, Pennsylvania had been greener than Atlanta. Atlanta was redder and dustier. The Pennsylvania countryside was richer with the neat, white-painted farms, well-fed cattle, and a Dutch cleanliness that was not here. The little town of Roswell was pretty, but it was different. Gettysburg was tame, and the outskirts of Atlanta were tangles of vines and thorns. It had been General Lee's aggressiveness that had resulted in battle there, and Johnston's relentless retreat that placed him and his 4th Division on line here.

The ground here was not as good from a defensive point of view as had been the ground at Gettysburg. Nonetheless, here he was positioned on the north side of Bald Hill, which anchored the Federal left much as had the Big and Little Round Tops a year ago. And this was a pretty good defensive position even if it was by happenstance, instead of selection.

After the battle in 1863, he had learned that John Hood had been shot off his horse down on the Federal far left, and as of a few days ago, that same former division commander was now in charge of the entire Southern force that thwarted the Federals here in Georgia. It had been a long year, and the attitude of the two forces had shifted almost completely. In 1863, it had seemed that Lee and his army could not make a mistake, and the poorly led Federal force had little faith in their own ability. Of course—and he was quick to say it—this western army was a harder, more resilient force than the men largely drawn from eastern United States. That eastern army never really seemed to get too far from Washington, D.C. This western army seemed at its best a long way from home. Like Lee's army, it had suffered few defeats and was extremely confident. The western army had produced Sherman and Grant, and the Eastern Theater had created John Bell Hood.

Here as was there, it had taken the better part of three days to bring this exercise to a hard boil. If the sounds to his left were anything to judge with, July 22 might be the hardest day of the past several. Harrow had formed an attachment to Charles Walcutt, who was his divisional artillery officer, and the two men often found themselves in each other's proximity. They were together now on the lower northern most hilltop of the two that made up the bald terrain feature. The small command group was all looking to the southeast, that is, down along and behind the dug-in Union line.

As they watched, an unusual scene developed. Teamsters—swearing and yelling loudly at the pounding animal in front of them, at those who raced along side, or at no one in particular—rushed to save themselves and their wagons. Wagons, ambulances, caissons, and all manner of wheeled military vehicles joined in the rushing parade. These were the same vehicles that had been parked in the open trains' area in the rear of the Seventeenth Army Corps, the very area that was supposed to be safe and now the Confederates had shown to be otherwise.

Only a few roads, some better than others, led from the safe area to what remained with the Army of the Tennessee. Pursuant to orders, many of the wagons had remained at the river near Roswell, and some of the wagons remained in the supposed safety of Decatur just three or four miles to the east. Pandemonium reigned as too many drivers tried to push too many teams and wagons down too few trails and roads in order to escape the onslaught of Confederates. A few of the wagoners had heard the instructions from McPherson's staff officer to remove themselves and their cargo. As powerful of a motivation as an order from a general officer can be, even more powerful was the pounding concussion of cannon fire overlaid with the sounds unique to musket and rifle fire. Drivers and their teams, who were more often ready to stop than to move forward, were all showing remarkably undisciplined quickness as they competed to get the hell away from the noise of death behind them.

As a result, it was not parade-ground perfection that resulted nor were the routes taken necessarily the ones that would have been selected if time had existed to study each avenue of departure. Combined with them were defeated soldiers from the 4th Division of the Sixteenth Army Corps, whose enthusiasm for standing and fighting had disappeared at least for the moment. It was less a retreat than a freewheeling, panicked gaggle of sweaty, beaten, reasonless men and a strange variety of wild-eyed horses and mules pulling canvas-topped wagons. It was a flood tide seeking an outlet.

The soldiers of Colonel Walcutt's 2nd Brigade of Harrow's 4th Division had never really seen the like of this scene before. Some of the men hooted and yelled at the runaway passersby. Harrow and several of the division staff officers including Griffiths, the divisional artillery officer, were standing near the southmost section of Parrott guns.

Lieutenant Gay, the commander of the 1st Iowa Battery, observed this unprecedented flight of the armies' trains and a large number of whipped, dispirited soldiers and called out, "Sir, should I bring my guns and caissons up?"

Harrow, the trial lawyer always quick with a response and seeing no need to wait for the person the question was addressed to, cried out, "Mr. Gay, by all means bring your caissons forward so that we all might go to hell together!" Of course, Walcutt had already had the presence of command to bring his regimental commanders together.

The situation seemed unbelievable, but at the same time, the realities were pressing in on all sides. Soon, the recently assumed line of defense that faced west toward Atlanta, which Walcutt's five regiments now occupied, was the only front not under assault. Earlier, Walcutt's 2nd Brigade had been at the left end of the 4th Division line but had later been tucked into the rearward angled line of Leggett's rightmost brigade, which was commanded by Manning Force. They had prepared for an attack from Atlanta. To now be on the receiving end of a northward moving flank attack in the middle of the Army of the Tennessee was not something they had ever planned.

Nonetheless, with musket fire advancing and some cannon fire obvious in the distance, the twenty-six-year-old Colonel Walcutt was getting his regiments repositioned. His plan, which quickly met with General Harrow's approval, was to relocate his regiments so that they would face south rather than west, essentially facing the left rear of the brigade. This was not a maneuver to be taken lightly. Troops were dug into their current position and would move to an unfortified position in the face of this seeming disaster, which was being driven toward them from the south.

The first step was to have the men in the five western regiments face to the rear in their trenches. Then Walcutt was to execute what amounted to a right wheel with the 40th Illinois, which was on the right end of the brigade, acting as the pivot. The far left of the brigade would swing like a gate until the brigade faced south, perpendicular to their former position. Orders flew to the 40th and 103rd Illinois and to the 97th Indiana, the 6th Iowa, and the 46th Ohio, and in less time than he had assumed it would take, the repositioning had occurred. The entire brigade was formed in a new line. The new line started near the left center of their former position. In this position, the 2nd Brigade could cover and protect the now increasingly vulnerable left flank of the 4th Division against what seemed to be incoming Confederates. This movement would at the same time buttress the right of Leggett's 3rd Division on Bald Hill.

The enemy was continuing to push the retreating Federals, and in some manner, Cleburne's troops captured stragglers, wagons, cannons, and other military stores. A caisson and its two-wheeled limber with its two ammunition chests were abandoned in the melee. The caisson was struck by an enemy shell launched from an unseen gun.

The explosion of the shell was amplified fifty to one hundred times with flame, smoke, and debris all blowing skyward in a spectacular and inspiring manner. Even the most experienced veteran ducked involuntarily as metal and wood rained down. The spare wheel on the rear of the caisson remained whole and rolled and spun down the hill after it had fallen from the sky.

With the 2nd Brigade front now changed to the left rear and spread out, the stable line began to act as a net for those men retreating toward it. Some men felt safe and stayed, and wagons went toward the rear, but with less speed and determination.

The men of Leggett's 3rd Division had turned around to engage the Rebel troops as they charged up the east side of Bald Hill in the attack. Because they were at a right angle and extended eastward and thus in the right position to, the troops of Walcutt's Illinois, Iowa, and Ohio regiments provided enfilade fire into the gully at the base of the hill, which hundreds of Confederate riflemen assembled at after their long and successful charge.

Two regiments—the 26th Illinois under Captain Bloomfield and the 70th Ohio under Major Bill Brown—from Oliver's 3rd Brigade of the 4th Division reported to Walcutt. These two regiments were put into the westward facing trenches, which had been vacated when the 2nd Brigade had moved. Just yesterday on July 21, General Force's brigade and those commanded by Scott and Malloy had stormed up the same hill. They, too, had crossed the open field, through the trees, and into the gully that lay on the base of the hill's eastern and southeastern approaches. Their assault had been aimed at the division of dismounted cavalry led by Brigadier General Alfred Iverson.

But this was a very different battle. Yesterday's early morning assault was made by well-rested, well-fed men who attacked with only one objective, and that objective was in sight from the beginning. Second, it had been a line of battle against dismounted horsemen in very shallow trenches to the extent the trenches barely existed at all. Reserves were there at the Union brigade, division, and corps levels if they had been needed. Today, on July 22, the sun was high in the sky. Smith's Texans, the attacking Confederates, had marched all night and attacked through difficult natural obstacles, smashed into Fuller's right flank, enjoyed some early success in the capture of the U.S. 2nd Battery F, routed the wagon park, and now, at the end of this assault, were attempting to climb a hill defended by well-entrenched veteran Union infantrymen. Even as they had left their line of departure, the Confederate troops had been a tired, road-worn, thin brigade. Now, after the disorganizing friction of combat, they were thinner still and breathing hard. Faces were drawn and haggard, eyes were red-rimmed, and black powder had formed greasy black marks around their lips.

The earlier fighting had the effect of compressing more blue troops into less space. Some had run as far as they could and were now ready to stand and fight if for no other reason than that they were exhausted. Colonel Walcutt's 2nd Brigade was now spread out on an east-west line at the north end of Bald Hill. Colonel Oliver of the 3rd Brigade of the 4th Division had augmented Walcutt by passing his 48th Illinois and his 99th Indiana regiments off to the 4th Brigade of his division. This line of some seven regiments was now digging in and had begun to account for itself.

The tired Confederate Texans of Brigadier General James Smith found themselves isolated from the rest of Cleburne's division, which were attacking another section. To make matters worse, they were being subject to accurate rifle fire from Bald Hill to their left and the west and from the increasing volume of effective fire from Walcutt's brigade in front of them to the north.

With the object of the butternut assault—the wagons—being to the Confederate troops' left, Smith's Texans had inclined leftward in their nearly unchecked advance. This brigade of Smith's Texans were the rightmost of Cleburne's 3,000-man force, so as they had moved forward across the road that they had earlier halted on, shot, and killed Union General McPherson, they were moving into the undefended gap between the Sixteenth and Seventeenth Army Corps. Particularly, to the Confederate's front right lay Fuller's brigade from the 4th Division of the Sixteenth Army Corps. Behind Fuller lay the collapsing left of General Giles Smith's division of the Seventeenth Army Corps.

Until now, it had been occupied by Union mounted messengers and staff offices as well as the six three-inch ordinance rifles of the 2nd U.S. Battery F and the 68th Ohio Infantry Regiment sent in to protect the trains of the Seventeenth Army Corps. All these had been washed over by the dirty, tattered, inelegant Texans and the 5th Confederates. This ragged but disciplined force had killed, captured, or routed all the Union force who were so poorly positioned as to be in that gap. With such little opposition, Cleburne's right had gone farther, deeper, and faster than Cleburne's left, which struggled with the well-entrenched forces of Blair's Seventeenth Army Corps before routing them back to their next defensive position. With the harder opposition on the left and the looming presence of Bald Hill exerting a pull, the soldiers of Cleburne's division pivoted like a gate toward the left.

As Smith's Texans—which knew how to maintain an appropriate alignment as well as any infantry brigade in either the Union or Confederate armies could—continued to move forward until its dress from left to right began to disintegrate. It became less and less a structured, functioning battle line and more and more of a line of skirmishers or individual riflemen. This was not so much a breakdown of discipline but more the friction of combat, the heat, and the distance covered. Smith's right then ran hard into the tested veterans of Logan's Fifteenth Army Corps. By now, enough time had passed that the blue line set up by Walcutt and Harrow had some hasty fortifications and were loaded and ready to engage. They stood and fired into the Texan men.

This was fire delivered from experienced troops who only had to hold onto the high ground to win. They delivered well-aimed gunfire into a group who, in order to win, had to move forward into the face of the massed rifle fire, all the while going up the hill. All this combined to make those Confederate soldiers' fire less effective and of much less volume. They were being punished by fire from both their front and left flank. It was too much to ask, and no reserves existed anywhere in Hardee's corps to reassert the powerful drive launched by Cleburne.

If infantry can be gallant in battle, the soldiers of Smith's Texas brigade were gallant that hot midday in Georgia. They were splendid in their tattered clothing and ragtag appearance and hell bound with their deadly rifled muskets. Failure was not a reflection of ability or steadfastness. Rather, it was the consequence of a plan that asked too much. It had always been an optimistic plan based more on hope than on careful intelligence about the facts on the ground. The massed fire was enough to fracture Smith's right. Large elements of the combined 17th and 18th Texas and of their battle mates from the 5th Confederates found themselves captured, surrounded by the begrimed western troops of Walcutt's brigade. In large part, they were there as a result of the isolation their enthusiasm and success had created for them.

CONFEDERACY, PATRICK CLEBURNE

People can't escape their personality, or at least, Cleburne couldn't. Cleburne's personality demanded that he provide personal, involved, hands-on leadership supplied at or close to the point of attack. So at the beginning of the assault, he was moving along with James Smith close behind Smith's Texans.

Cleburne was sure this afternoon's work was not going exactly as planned. Hardee should have resisted Hood's demands. The rifle fire and the very rapid cannon fire off to his right implied at least two divisions were involved. The plan had been for Bate and Walker to get into Sherman's rear. Since he had expected to be on Sherman's left flank, this two-division brawl was outside the scope of the operation as he had understood it.

The speed at which the plan of attack was required to unfold had left no time for reconnaissance, either of the ground or of the troop concentrations they were to face. The damned cavalry was good at tying up the road that he was supposed to march over. They did look good in parade, but for his money, they had not been helpful today. Wheeler should have provided intelligence as to the troops they would face. Cleburne preferred to know what he was up against, and finding out by moving forward in a line of battle was a poor substitute for knowing ahead of time. That was one of the reasons Cleburne was up there with his lead brigade.

The Union flank was supposed to be in the air. The heavy firing over to his right proved that something had been omitted from the calculus. The two divisions would probably not be helpful to Cleburne as he assaulted Bald Hill. They would not be working in direct concert with his three brigades, as planned, but were rather involved in something of their own, more than merely a skirmish line. It sounded like a battle of its own.

Cleburne had many problems—no reconnaissance, no maps of consequence, very difficult terrain, dense woods and undergrowth laced with briars, a wide front that was so spread out that divisions and subordinate units had no contact with the other's right or left, no corps' reserve, his own resentful compliance with Hood's orders, and exhausted troops. All of them presented opportunity for disaster. Combat was fraught with enough unknown and uncertainties even when a commander thought he had everything under control.

Smith's brigade plunged into the open ground near the base of Bald Hill. It seemed this line of march had met with no opposition of any strength and had streamed forward into a nearly undefended area. Cleburne concluded that there must be a gap between the Yankee forces. Then, back to his left and rear where Govan's troops should have found the Union flank, a substantial firefight erupted.

Fire from the right from Walcutt's brigade of the 4th Division of the Fifteenth Army Corps smashed into the attacking Texans. "*Too little,*" thought Cleburne. "*We are outnumbered and worn out, and this damn hill is too heavily defended.*" There was no shortage of individual courage, just not enough individuals. Mass was required but unavailable.

"Lieutenant," Cleburne yelled.

"Yes, sir?" said one of his young staff officers.

"General Lowrey's brigade should be back there 300 to 500 yards to our rear. I want you to find him and order him up here in support of Smith's Texans. We need them now. Do you understand me?"

"Yes, sir. I am to find Lowrey and have him bring up his brigade."

"Unless things are different when he gets here, I want those Alabama and Mississippi troops to drive ahead and provide the push we need to get up this hill."

The young lieutenant saluted and ran off to the rear.

Cleburne had been among the very best at the straight-ahead direct assault. Here, personal courage and a willingness to push forward in a determined rush to shock the enemy didn't mean victory. Companies and regiments required that form of leadership, but brigade commanders had to learn that more was required. They needed to begin to learn that combat mastery, the art of war, involves more than linear, direct attacks. Success requires a grander, more in-depth view of what is obscured and covered in smoke at best.

War was a demanding university, and combat, a compelling course of study. If a man lived, he had a chance to put his knowledge and newly acquired education to practical work. Cleburne knew he had progressed from a raw regimental commander to a competent divisional leader. He had learned that battle often turned on a single individual's efforts. As a regimental commander, his personal leadership could be seen and followed by his soldiers.

At the division level, it was impossible to merely lead by example. He could line them up and then send them forward, but his ability to make a difference was gone at the moment they departed. The one thing he could do was to be accessible and to understand the unfolding battle. He could also be able to maneuver with his reserve and to bring the relatively rested shock power to a point on the battlefield where it would yield dividends. Lowrey's brigade was to serve that purpose—one third of his force to be applied as he directed at more or less the time and place he selected.

But not today.

CHAPTER NINETY

Confederacy | JOHN M. BROWN

Along the Decatur Road and the Georgia Railroad
1st Georgia Line, Stovall's Georgia Brigade,
Clayton's division, Cheatham's corps,
Army of Tennessee
July 22, 1864
Before 2:00 p.m.

Part of the confusion relating to the names of some of the military organizations that arose in Georgia had to do with the railroad. Of course, the Western and Atlantic Railroad played a primary role in determining the route selected by Johnston in his retreat from Dalton as well as Sherman's selection of his avenue of approach toward Atlanta. Without the Western and Atlantic, the vast logistical requirements needed to feed, clothe, and equip the two massive groups of men on both sides simply could not be met. A reading of the location of the railroad's depots is like a review of the numerous actions and battles between the blue and gray forces.

The path of the Western and Atlantic Railroad was neither straight nor flat. Notwithstanding the mountainous terrain between Atlanta and Chattanooga, the running grade on the line was less than one percent. Lieutenant Colonel Stephen Long of the U.S. Army laid out the route, which twists and turns for 138 miles. It took more than ten years to complete the project. The cost of the undertaking was borne by the taxpayers of Georgia. The state owned the completed railroad. Perhaps because it was owned by the state and ran from Georgia to Tennessee, it was often referred to as the "State Line" or "State Road."

The earliest military organization in the state actually predated Georgia's secession from the Union. That group was the Georgia Militia. Each Georgia county was divided into militia districts that companies were formed from all able-bodied, white males between the ages of eighteen and forty-five. These men drilled periodically, and a geographical hierarchy of battalions, regiments, brigades, and divisions formed. The militia was called out in emergencies. This was similar to the militia in most of the states, north and south. The Georgia Militia fought in the American Revolution, in the War of 1812, and against Indians. By 1862, the Georgia Militia organization was folded into the Confederate Army. As a result of the Richmond government's need for troops, the age limit for the Georgia Militia was expanded to men from sixteen to sixty who were not in the national service. By the time of the Atlanta campaign, fiery Governor Brown had raised a new militia under Major General Gustavas Smith. This force was made up of exempt men. A full division of some 5,000 men was raised and was active as the Union army approached Atlanta.

Other state troops included the Georgia Army, which was established in 1861 and intended only for defensive use in Georgia. Brown later raised some 2,500 men for the 4th Brigade. This brigade almost immediately entered Confederate, rather than state, service. Governor Brown was not finished yet. He raised an 8,000-man force of men who enlisted for six months and who were also converted to Richmond's use. In addition, there was the Georgia State Guard and the Georgia Reserve Force.

The 1st State Line Regiment and the 2nd State Line Regiment were different than any of the organizations named above. They served for the entire war and were never merged entirely with the Confederate troops. These two regiments of State Line soldiers were created to guard the bridges and other important points along the Western and Atlantic Railroad, i.e., the State Line. Their duty extended to quelling local disturbances as they did in January of 1863 when a large body of armed outlaws, mostly deserters, was bent on seizing Dahlonega. Captain Galt of the 1st State Line Regiment raised a company of State Line troops, originally called the Blue Ridge Rangers and then Company D, to vanquish the outlaws. Acting as the Provost Marshall, they had rounded up deserters.

From the date of their organization until May 1864 when the Atlanta Campaign began, the men had helped keep the important rail line open. Trains moved, bridges were protected, and fortifications at some strategic points had been built. As more of the railroad lay in General Sherman's hands and less in the control of either the Confederate Army of Tennessee or of the state of Georgia, Governor Brown offered to loan these two regiments to General Joe Johnston. The two regiments were attached to the Army of Tennessee. The state of Georgia would continue to pay and clothe them, but the other aspects of their service would be provided, or directed, by the Confederacy.

The 1st State Line Regiment abandoned its position at Cartersville and at the Etowah River. Under Colonel Edward Galt, the 1st State Line Regiment fell back to defend the Chattahoochee Bridge crossing from July 5 until all the Army of Tennessee crossed the river on July 9. They had been involved in some skirmishing in this defensive guard duty.

The 1st State Line Regiment became part of Stovall's Georgia brigade. The brigade commander, Marcellus Stovall, was often ill and suffered from rheumatism, the same condition that had kept him from graduating from West Point. In his place, Colonel Abda Johnson of the 40th Georgia served as commander on an on-again, off-again basis.

Colonel Galt of the 1st State Line Regiment was wounded on July 20. The wound to his left arm was serious, and command went to the newly promoted Lieutenant Colonel John M. Brown, the youngest brother of Georgia's Governor Joe Brown. Thus, the unit was often derided as "Joe Brown's Pets."

Lieutenant Colonel Brown, with his long dark hair combed straight back so that his forehead seemed slightly larger than normal, was excited by all that was taking place this afternoon. Here, he was in command of the entire 1st State Line Regiment, and he was eager to prove himself. Young Lieutenant Colonel Brown had promised himself that no matter what duties there were to perform in the rear of the regiment, he would assign those duties to others, and he would lead from the front. He knew that only from the rear could a commander actually see everything that was taking place and correct it. Nonetheless, he believed the faith the men had demonstrated in electing him required him to lead by example. His position as commander and the reality that he was Governor Joe Brown's brother combined to encourage him to demonstrate his leadership rather than to order the regiment forward from behind.

Brown had been explaining this to his friend Captain Albert Howell. Howell was the senior regimental captain and hoped his words would carry weight with his friend. "Hell, John, we all know you're a good man, and we know you're plenty brave. You have nothing to prove to any of us."

Brown replied, "Albert, my brother would never forgive me if it even seemed a little bit like I was afraid to be up front—whether anyone ever spoke of it or not. My place is in front of this regiment this afternoon."

"I wish we could change your mind," Howell said. "But if you can't do that, then tell me again what Colonel Johnson said about our orders."

"As he understood it, we are to go straight ahead with the sun to our backs and the railroad tracks to our right. When we hit the Yankee lines, we are to kill them and sweep them aside," said Brown.

"Well at least it's a plan I can understand. Wish we had some time to inspect that mile of dirt between us and those blue bellies."

"We will be next to the 42nd Georgia, who will be on our left. Colonel Johnson is going to use the 43rd as skirmishers. The other three regiments will be on line to our right, and there won't be any real brigade reserve."

Howell looked out over the terrain, took a pull from his canteen, and said, "This damn waiting is hard. I know the boys in my company are ready to go."

Just over a short distance from the two State Line officers, troops from the 42nd Georgia started to build a fire. Private John Davis of Company G said, "Let's hurry and get this fire going. On a day as hot as this one, we shouldn't have to be building a damn fire to cook this pot of meat. It should just sit here and cook itself."

His brother retorted, "Hold your horses. I know you've been carrying that pot of meat since last night and want to finish it, and we will."

"Don't know exactly what kind of meat it is, but it damn sure needs cooking and eating soon. Hungry as I am, I could eat it raw, but I think it is mule meat. Unless we cook it first, I doubt we can eat it," said John Davis. His brother worked on the fire and then looked up.

Davis' brother said, "Brother, do you think we'll fight today?"

"Can't tell, but right now my fight is to cook this meat. Come on. Let's hurry."

CHAPTER NINETY-ONE

Confederacy | ARTHUR MANIGAULT

North of the railroad on the east side of Atlanta,
within the fortifications
July 22, 1864
2:00 p.m.

The brigade that bore Manigault's name was made up of two regiments of soldiers from his native South Carolina and three regiments from Alabama. The soldiers in his brigade had been in the sun almost all day. In this regard, they were like the men of the other three brigades of Hindman's division, now under the command of John C. Brown, of Cheatham's corps. All waited to be ordered forward out of the city defenses and into the uncertainty of battle. These butternut-clad boys had been at this game a long time now and could, Manigault believed, be counted on to stay as long as need be to convince the Union enemy that while the Union could not lose, they for certain could not win. Perhaps then they'd leave the South alone and go back home.

Manigault had been with these South Carolina troops since the beginning. He was a spare man who seemed taller than he actually was. He had sparse, thin hair, and he was dressed with dignity. He carried himself with a manner that told strangers he had long been a soldier. That was the image, and that was the truth. Like so many on both sides of this angry conflict, he had served as a lieutenant with his Palmetto Regiment in Mexico, had been at Charleston Harbor during the bombardment of Fort Sumter, and then served as colonel and commander of the 10th South Carolina Infantry Regiment.

Manigault believed that personal, involved individual leadership was required for success in combat. Leadership was important. It was essential even. Manigault wondered about Major General John Brown, a Tennessean who—although a friend of Hood's—possessed some level of leadership. However Brown turned out, Manigault knew that he would be better than Hindman, who while talented had taken a first-rate division and driven it into the ground with his scheming and political maneuvering. Relief greeted Hindman's departure some twenty days ago, and Manigault for one was glad to be rid of him and have Brown in his place.

Maney often wished he knew more about what was going on. His brigade had moved across the river and had for a while been positioned on the east-west line north of Atlanta. There, they had waited for a decision from Joe Johnston or his Union counterpart. How it all fit was unknown to him, but he knew John Bell Hood and doubted his abilities. He wished they had not lost Johnston.

It seemed they had been moving to the right for days and had finally reached the railroad on July 20. He mentally marked the date. He needed to remember these things so he could write about this war later. After reaching the railroad, his men had toiled in the heat to create earthworks where only brick-like clay existed before.

About 3:00 that afternoon of July 22, Manigault's attention had been directed from his immediate front to the action taking place off to his left. The boom of artillery and the smoke and bark of rifles seemed a long way off, maybe three or three and a half miles to his left. The sound seemed to be coming from the general area he had marched through two days ago. The best he could tell, the sounds came from over by Peachtree Road where it crossed that big creek. Exactly what was taking place could not be known, given the distance and the lack of communication, but clearly a major exchange was occurring.

For not the first time, Manigault reflected that it would be helpful and interesting to see the entire array of the two big armies as they faced each other. His men fought who was right in front of them. Often after the first exchange of rifle fire, the smoke was so thick that when combined with the contours of the terrain, the trees, and the vegetation, the enemy became more of a concept than a battle line or individual soldiers. His own vision should, in theory at least, cover the entire brigade front. The awful truth was that he was often restricted to what was right in front of him as well. Ideally, he should have some control over his regiments as they fought, and certainly in the defense, he felt some greater degree of control. In the assault, even if he purposely followed rather than led from the front, the illusion of command seemed to disappear as smoke, fearsome noise, death, destruction, and disorientation enveloped him.

The hard fighting that was going on over to his left seemed in many ways to have no impact or effect on him at all. It was more real than a newspaper story, but along his defensive position, it was at most an interesting distraction. He could imagine the soldiers struggling through the tangles and the minie balls whining about like those cursed yellow-jacketed hornets that often seemed to be more dangerous than the lead slugs that filled the air.

A balloon or a good perch high in a tree on a hill would provide a seat that one could see the whole thing spread out from. He needed a vantage point that would allow the general commanding to move brigades and regiments more like chess pieces on a well-understood board and less like a blind man resisting an assault by a band of small street ruffians. Maps helped and served as a partial substitute for clear vision, but good maps were usually not available. Even when good, the maps only represented the chessboard, and they quickly broke down in their usefulness when movement started along a line. They became useless when the first contact was made with the enemy, and units began to maneuver in response to being shot at. Thus it had always been—unless armies drew up facing each other on an open plain. They were a long way from an open plain here, where the undulating earth and the scrub trees made even the most keen-eyed youth as impotent as an old man who needed a stick to help him find his way.

Yesterday, Thursday, July 21, the pressure had seemed to increase on the front he protected. The competing Union troops had dug in as they approached and had field artillery in position with more soldiers spread out in regimental size groups to Manigault's front.

As night had fallen, orders came down the chain of command from Hood's headquarters to Cheatham's corps to Brown's division and finally to his brigade. There was no discussion, no inspection of his fine defensive position, but rather he was to give up what he had hewn from the red clay and march back into the works more closely surrounding Atlanta. This movement took a good portion of the evening, and sorting everyone out in the dark took still more time. These tasks were made more difficult by the willingness of each veteran soldier to sit down and then go to sleep. All good soldiers knew that in or near combat, they should always relieve themselves, eat, and sleep whenever the opportunity presented itself.

As the dawn came, it had been easier to see exactly where his regiments were, and Manigault and his regimental commanders soon had the men up, cooking and eating breakfast, and then working on the fortifications. Smoke from breakfast cooking fires had mixed with the smoke from the artillery to create a haze. The haze had not been thick enough to obscure the reality that the same Federal troops they had faced yesterday were now taking over the defenses the Southern soldiers had constructed and then abandoned the night before. Those same trenches were being reversed, and the blue Union force was now closer and more threatening.

Throughout the day, artillery that was controlled at the corps and division level was being placed from Cheatham's newly shortened line. It was well enough placed, manned, and fired to discourage any serious attempts by the Federals to cross the area that separated the forces and that lay between the lines.

The day wore along. There had been a brief rain shower early in the morning, but by 2:00 p.m., no evidence of that short, fresh respite lingered at all. Exactly what plans existed or what awaited the Confederate brigades was not apparent, so soldiers ate, cleaned weapons, watched, slept, and kept their heads down. Suddenly, Manigault jerked his head to the right. The sound of combat some miles off to the southeast arrested his attention.

"Sounds like more action over that way than we have here along our front," Manigault said to no one in particular. Maybe that makes some sense after all. His mind retreated to the long lines made by the men of Hardee's corps that he had seen and bumped into last night as he had moved his sleepy troops back into the walls of the city. Hardee had been moving south through the city, leaving the lines to the north to be held by Stewart's corps. It had looked like Hood had moved three or four divisions of Hardee's down to the south of the city and around to the Union left. The noise was simply too angry to merely be Wheeler's dismounted horsemen standing up to an advancing Union line.

To the small group around him, he said, "Reckon those boys have been moving all night from the time we saw them last night until now?" Moving back into the city walls was no barn dance, but at least he could sleep most of the night. Those poor devils must have been marching for twelve hours or more. He bet Hardee being there was a surprise to those Union boys. If Hardee were lucky, maybe he could get behind them before they had time to organize. So far this fight over the last two or three days has passed them by in the main line. Maybe July 22 would be different.

Orders came for the division and brigades to hold themselves in readiness. It was the brigades' mission to leave the safety of the breastworks, advance until they found the enemy, and drive the enemy from the works, which they would occupy until further orders reach them. The understanding that the enemy they were to find were in the same works the brigade had earlier left and that those Union soldiers stood on the same ground the Confederates had formerly held, had given up without a fight, and now must fight to regain did not enhance morale. The futility of this was overpowering. The division would line up with Deas' brigade on the right. This brigade was made up entirely of regiments from Alabama. Since illness had retired Brigadier General Zachariah Deas, the unit was then under the command of Colonel John Coltart, who had formerly led the 50th Alabama. Coltart would guide on the railroad that lay to the left of his seven Alabama regiments. Behind Coltart, providing support and some heft once the enemy was struck, was the slender force commanded by Colonel William Brantley with troops from Mississippi. Brantley was under some stress, as he had just assumed command of the Walthall Brigade after Colonel Sam Benton had been struck in the foot and chest by rounds from a Yankee sharpshooter earlier in the day.

His own troops would also guide on the railroad, but they would keep it to the right. The job of staying close to the tracks would fall to the 10th South Carolina. Next to the 10th would be their sister regiment, Manigault's own 19th South Carolina. To their left would march the 34th Alabama and then came the 24th Alabama on the left of the brigade. The 28th Alabama would be out in front of the brigade, fulfilling the role of skirmishers. These troops would gradually fall back into the following Alabama and South Carolina forces as resistance to their front increased as they drew close to the Federal entrenchment.

Colonel Sharp's men would follow and provide support with Tucker's Mississippi brigade. General Brown's division would attack, following the railroad, with a two-brigade front. Two brigades would follow with half the force on one side of the railroad and the other half across the tracks.

At about 4:00 p.m., the division was ordered forward. The first 2,500 feet or so was over familiar ground, which was essentially open. Skirmishers were out and quick work was made of this initial part of the advance. The Union forces had their own pickets and skirmishers out and had some two regiments providing a skirmisher reserve. North of the track as part of this reserve was the 53rd Ohio. To the south lay the men of the 111th Illinois.

CHAPTER NINETY-TWO

Confederacy | JACOB SHARP

MEETING OF THE BRIGADE COMMANDERS
OF HINDMAN'S DIVISION, CHEATHAM'S CORPS
INSIDE THE EASTERN FORTIFICATIONS OF ATLANTA
JULY 22, 1864
2:30 P.M.

As the brigade commanders of Hindman's division received their orders, Colonel Jacob Sharp discovered his brigade of Mississippi troops would follow Manigault's. Sharp's soldiers were known as Tucker's Mississippi Brigade after the brigade's original commander, General William Tucker, who had been wounded at Resaca on May 14, 1864. Colonel Sharp had under his command five Mississippi regiments and a group of sharpshooters, who usually served as the pickets and skirmishers for the brigade.

Colonel Sharp was thirty-one years old and had practiced law after leaving the University of Alabama in 1851. He had been elected captain after enlisting as a private in the 44th Mississippi. The 44th Mississippi was now one of his regiments along with his others: the 7th, 9th, 10th, and 41st Mississippi as well as the 9th Mississippi Sharpshooters.

This afternoon, the plan called for his brigade to be positioned about a hundred yards behind Manigault's brigade. The support provided by his brigade would be needed as contact was made with enemy and additional mass would be needed to force the dug-in Yankees out of their red clay pits.

Sharp thought about the coming assault. The terrain between the city walls and the line of Union defenders was gently wave-like. Some of the area had trees, and some of the area was open. Some of the land was swampy and gathered water in the rainy season. It wasn't bad ground since the rolling hills offered some protection as it dipped and rose and would allow battle lines to be reformed without the deadly interference of direct fire.

Colonel Sharp knew that a cut existed for the railroad track as it entered the defensive line they were to assault, and he wondered if it provided access to the rear of the Union lines. If the Yankees were smart, it probably wouldn't. It was more likely heavily defended, but it was something to investigate should his force get to that point. If it were open, then he could cut through the line without being seen and create havoc in the Union rear.

CHAPTER NINETY-THREE

Confederacy | GEORGE MANEY

HEADQUARTER OF MANEY'S BRIGADE OF
CHEATHAM'S DIVISION
WEST OF FLAT SHOALS ROAD
IN THE TREE LINE SOUTHWEST OF THE
SEVENTEENTH ARMY CORPS
ABOUT 3:00 P.M.

When Maney had been promoted to brigadier general, he had not felt junior to anyone, but now as the newest divisional commander in Hardee's corps, around men who had been major generals long enough to be comfortable with their rank, position, authority, and place, he was the least senior among them. He had been a brigade commander of the Tennessee brigade, Maney's Tennessee brigade, which was still called after him. He had been at ease running his five regiments.

Clearly, this divisional command was a bigger job. He had expected he would grow into it, but on July 21, 1864, only two days into this new task, he had realized that the job had yet to conform to him. Like new boots, he knew in time they would mold to his feet, but now they were stiff and bruised him. The old pair may have been nearly played out, but they were soft and familiar. He doubted that he was the equal to Cleburne or even old General Walker. He felt more equal to his fellow Tennessean General Bate than the others. But it still rankled when Hardee said that his old brigade would be used as support for General Bate's division and that his other brigade, Wright's brigade under Colonel Carter, would act as reserve for Cleburne's division.

Being the junior in operational control, his command and his division were reduced to merely two brigades. It had been human nature for Hardee to strip brigades from the inexperienced Maney. After all, Hardee had thought Cleburne was as good a general as existed and that troops under his leadership would push harder, faster, and farther than anyone else.

"Well, it does no good to complain," Maney thought. He would do the best he could. It was Hardee's show, and Maney would endeavor to become worthy of his place within it.

Maney reflected on what he could have done differently two days earlier on the south bank of Peachtree Creek. With Vaughan's brigade on the left and Wright's brigade on the right, he had pushed them down the hill toward the Federals. He had kept Strahl's and his old brigade, now under Walker, in reserve. His role was a simple frontal assault with Loring's division on his left and Walker's on his right. His men had gone forward through the valley up the hill and down until they ran into fortified positions with hard, well-armed men behind them. Given the thickness of the ground cover, some of the advantage that went to the defense had been nullified. Attacking well-defended earthworks, no matter how recently constructed, was not a job that paid well. His attack, his first as a divisional commander, had petered out. The entire attack had seemed wasteful, and by and large, he felt he had acquitted himself satisfactorily.

He knew he had handled the night march well enough, though he wondered how all that marching had enhanced the situation. How did disengaging from the enemy and marching west into the city, then south at the end of Hardee's corps, down the long hill toward the Yellow River, back again north, then across the creek at Cobb's Mill, and now back to the south end of the Bald Hill improve the ability of his footsore and exhausted men to fight? The plan seemed half-baked at best.

Yet he knew he should put the best face on matters he could, if only for the men's spirits. Maybe the execution of the plan would prove its value, but the south end of the hill didn't look much less defended from this vantage point than it had looked yesterday from only a few compass points and less than a mile distance away.

Now, he and his men would wait here in the woods for Hardee's orders. His men would get some much needed rest and do all the little things that could be done before they threw themselves at the Union Seventeenth Army Corps, which were somewhere off to the northeast.

Noise from the conflict had gotten quieter down to his right, and the mid-afternoon sun now beat down on an already well-baked earth.

Heat from the ground rose to meet the sun's rays, and the breathless afternoon seemed like it might never give way to the cool of the evening. At least, his boys had enjoyed some rest under the shade of the trees.

Maney and his division had not yet been used. Hardee had withheld any direct order to attack, and this lack of orders held Maney back. Though Maney's men weren't a reserve, Hardee could use him to exploit an advantage. At this point, Cleburne's troops had been in almost constant action for three or four hours now. They had achieved some success, and the Union regimental flags that had earlier been seen flying in the fishhook formed by the Federal Seventeenth Army Corps could no longer be seen.

A messenger came panting up to Maney and his little cluster of staff and aides. "General's compliments," gasped the always courteous aide. "General Hardee had received word that the damn Yanks may be forming to hit Cleburne's left. In conjunction with Cleburne, you should advance against them beginning in about fifteen minutes. General Hardee wants to know if your men can be counted on."

"Tell him we are ready to go," barked Maney.

CHAPTER NINETY-FOUR

Union | BENJAMIN POTTS | *Confederacy* | GEORGE MANEY

THIRD POSITION OF THE 15TH IOWA

ALONG THE NORTH-SOUTH ROAD

JULY 22, 1864

ABOUT 3:00 P.M.

UNION, BENJAMIN POTTS

The assault from the southeast by Govan's Arkansans of Cleburne's division had resulted in the 15th Iowa and the rest of Colonel Hall's 3rd Brigade of the 4th Division being flanked from their double line of running trenches. These trenches had been hastily prepared and continuously perfected since the brigade arrived before the attack. They had been dug perpendicular to the road that just served so well as an avenue of approach for the Southern forces.

Fleeing for their lives from the attack of Govan's brigade of yelling and shooting Confederates, the troops of the Union 3rd Brigade had crossed the road and established new lines. These new positions ran parallel to the road and to the trenches occupied by Colonel Potts' and his 1st Brigade.

The 15th Iowa had taken the south end of the new line and the 13th Iowa came up snugly to the left of the 15th. The 11th Iowa occupied the trench earlier constructed for the 53rd Indiana. These three regiments faced to the east, the direction their enemy had appeared from, even though the trenches were built to face the other way.

The 1st Brigade was now not much more than two veteran regiments interspersed with the remnants of two more. The brief encounters Potts's 1st Brigade had with the attacking Confederates had been costly. Most of the men in the ten companies who were sent forward as relief to the refused right of the Seventeenth Army Corps were almost immediately killed, captured, or wounded. The combat had been quick, hard, and deadly as the Union troops were ground up and swept through by the fast-moving Rebels. The survivors who escaped the onslaught retreated without order back to the line established by the 53rd Indiana and the 32nd Ohio.

Potts's 1st Brigade had formed a second line of trenches parallel to the routed but slowly regrouping Iowans from the 3rd Brigade. These two lines of works were on the west side of McDonough Road. In effect, the two brigades were now back to back with the men in the 1st Brigade facing west toward Atlanta and the new arrivals in the 3rd Brigade facing back to the east from the area they had just left in disorganization and defeat.

Mauled, breathing hard, and confused by the events and the well-executed attack by these tattered fiends from hell, the officers and sergeants began to shake the two brigades out. The regrouping and reorganizing was accomplished with lots of yelling and cursing as the men found friends and comrades from their companies and regiments and order was slowly reasserted.

Time passed, and the Confederate pressure coming from the east—that is, the deadly rifle fire from Govan's brigade—abated. As the Arkansas brigade ebbed back toward the trenches they had earlier won and then swept over, the two Union parallel lines on the west side of McDonough Road sensed that the next danger might come from a different quarter. Accordingly, the troops were rearranged.

The 15th Iowa moved from the security of its north-south trench and formed a south-facing line of battle perpendicular to its former position. The 15th Iowa moved far enough to the west to allow the 13th Iowa to form on its left so that the two units completed a two-regiment front. The 11th Iowa remained in the north-south trenches so that the three regiments in the 3rd Brigade formed an "⊔" with two regiments facing south and the 11th Iowa facing east.

About seventy-five yards to the north, the 1st Brigade stretched out parallel to the 13th Iowa and 15th Iowa, facing south. From left to right, Potts assembled what remained of his 53rd Illinois, 3rd Iowa, and the nearly full strength of his 32nd Ohio and the 53rd Indiana. This line, too, was on the west side of the McDonough Road, and it was about one regimental front longer than the 3rd Brigade's line seventy-five yards south of it.

GEORGE MANEY, CONFEDERACY

Maney's division had made the long exhausting night march and now, like Cleburne's division, was attacking essentially the same ground they had defended the day before. They had been at the right end of the Confederate line guarding the city. In truth, had his division been simply ordered into the defenses of Atlanta and allowed to sleep, they would not be in a very different position except now they were worn out from the march.

Maney's division was positioned at the extreme left of Hardee's corps. The attack had started down on the right somewhere with either Walker's or Bate's division and had moved westerly to the left through Cleburne's division, and now it was his turn. One of the problems with such a method of attack is that once your neighboring unit had been struck, it was a signal that you were likely to be next. *"Well, if the boys in blue were ready for me,"* Maney thought, *"I suppose I am ready for them."*

The ground here was essentially level and had been planted with corn. The southern boundary of the cornfield was the east-west running Fairground Road that led from Atlanta to an intersection with McDonough Road. Soldiers gazing beyond the road saw the same thick forest that shielded the movements of Cleburne's division as it had pushed north from the Fayetteville Road hours before. It was from this position in the thick woods that the two brigades under Maney lay waiting to be ordered forward.

Maney would attack with his entire force. The brigades were lined up one behind the other. Vaughn's brigade, under the command of Magevney, was drawn up in a conventional double line of battle. Companies from the 11th Tennessee, 29th Tennessee, the combined 11th and 47th Tennessee, and the combined 13 and 14th Tennessee made up the assault force. The combined 13th and 14th had furnished both Vaughn and his successor Magevney. Behind this lead brigade, the men of Strahl's five regiments rested.

Strahl had his unit formed in double battle lines too, close enough behind Magevney's brigade to add his men's mass to the attack but not so close that his troops would be killed or injured by the same rounds aimed at either of the leading brigades' two lines of battle. Strahl had been leading this brigade since before Chickamauga and was relaxed and comfortable in his ability to lead men. He had become more religious as the war progressed and, having been baptized before the start of the campaign, was at peace with his God.

The order of "forward march" was given, and from the dark of the woods, the Tennessee boys moved forward for the first time since arriving on the new battlefield. Out from the dark shade of the tree line, across the Fairground Road, and into the cornfield came the two brigades of Confederate troops. Moving quickly, they smashed into the thin ranks of the still dazed Iowans of Smith's 4th Division. The begrimed blue and gray forces combined. The rightmost of Maney's lines smashed into the 15th and 13th Iowa. After only a few volleys, the Federal regiments retired to the original trench line, the same line they had moved out of only a short time before.

The fight was intense with the two lines blazing away at each other, but it was over soon. The Confederate front was wider and extended beyond the Federal right. Even the natural advantage of the defense was inadequate to prevent the Tennessee troops from sending the seven regiments making up the 4th Division reeling back to the north and back toward the crest of Bald Hill.

It was enough for the exhausted Tennesseans as well. With the successful rout of the Union troops, the Tennessee brigades lacked the ability or energy to pursue them. The Southern troops moved back to the shade of the trees to enjoy the victory. The wounded and prisoners needed to be sorted out, and this provided a military reason to rest.

CHAPTER NINETY-FIVE

Union | WILLIAM BELKNAP | *Confederacy* | WILLIAM LAMPLEY

FIFTH POSITION OF THE 4TH DIVISION,

SEVENTEENTH ARMY CORPS

JULY 22, 1864

ABOUT 3:00 P.M.

UNION, WILLIAM BELKNAP

At the same time Maney's two brigades were attacking from the southwest, Cleburne's men were also in action. Lowrey's brigade, under the command of Brigadier General Mark Lowrey, and Granbury's Texas Brigade, under the command of James Smith, were closing in on the southeastern approaches to Bald Hill. It was a rare event: two Confederate divisions attacking the Union's Seventeenth Army Corps at the same time and same area with Maney moving from the southwest and Cleburne from the southeast. Was this an example of Hardee's military professionalism manifesting itself or happenstance? No one was quite sure. Either way, the result was terrific and effective.

The 1st and 3rd Brigades of the 4th Division of the Seventeenth Army Corps held their unique sort of "U" shaped position until the 15th Iowa was flanked by Maney's forces, and it became apparent that men from Cleburne's division had joined the fight and also must be defended against. The 3rd Brigade, under Hall, finally bowed to the distasteful way things were, moved back to the McDonough Road, and took up the positions alongside the road that had been occupied by the men of Scott's 2nd Brigade of the 3rd Division earlier in the day. This movement allowed everyone to fall back to the north toward Bald Hill.

It had the effect of reducing the area being defended by the Federal forces, and as the forces compressed, the defense slowly stiffened.

The 15th Iowa was on the right end of the line with the 13th Iowa in the middle and the 11th Iowa on the left. The black-faced, weary defenders peered off to the east, the direction they now faced. Behind them on the west side of the road lay the men of the 1st Brigade, who were searching the ground toward Atlanta. The two brigades lay back to back, separated by the expanse of the road. The division was in the air. This more precarious position was not as sound as the position that they had been driven from earlier. Those previous individual regimental positions had been thoughtfully and skillfully prepared. This new position had no thought or preparation connected with it except that it was there and it provided some shelter from the yelling, screaming, killing butternut soldiers who pressed them from both sides. The men of the 4th Division had retreated or been pushed back into this place and began to hold on to it more tenaciously as the force compressed. They were shocked at the terrible, furious nature of the attack and were surprised at the manner that they had been handled.

Union Colonel William Belknap knew it was too damn early in the afternoon for this thing to be over, and he was gladdened that the companies were sorting themselves out. He could see that weapons were being cleaned and reloaded as the 15th Iowa settled down for whatever hand the fates had dealt this hot, still afternoon.

Belknap was a big, round, robust, redheaded lawyer with personality to match his physic. He was possessed with an open-handed form of personal leadership. He understood about politics and could be counted on at any formal occasion. This was an occasion with all the importance of a gathering of the highest state and national leaders. He knew his role as commander of the 15th Iowa required his keenest personal attention to its placement and its well-being. Here the bright flashes of light were created by artillery fire, not light from a chandelier, and the intoxication he felt was not the result of liquor but rather the exhilaration of close combat.

Being on the end of the line like this was an unsatisfactory part of life. There weren't enough soldiers here to make any difference to the outcome of the fight, and Belknap concluded that he might as well fight with what he had and do the best he could. This was no calculated political decision but only a hard, practical one that he could only accept. He would do his best and was confident his troops would follow his lead and command.

He had not ordered it, but the regiment was arranging itself into two lines, more or less, and he knew immediately by looking at the men on the wall of the ditch what was taking place. Shooters were on the step, and at the line behind them, those who were just perhaps a bit less bold were loading rifles as fast as they could and passing them forward in exchange for an empty one. No one organized it, but the men knew themselves and each other, and so the defensive face of the 15th Iowa was set and hardened toward the repeatedly attacking Southerners.

Here the screaming, mean-faced Rebels came. This charging group looked almost fresh to Belknap's eyes. To some degree, they were. This was the brigade that had been behind those of Govan and Smith, and as yet had not killed, wounded, captured, or routed anyone. Intermingled on the left side of the butternut line were troops from Wright's brigade, now being led by Colonel Carter. These men were Tennesseans from Maney's division who had been broken off from their division and used as Cleburne's reserves.

The clash between the hard-running Tennesseans, Alabamians, and the boys from Mississippi as they smashed into the entrenched farm boys from Iowa was like a hammer striking an anvil. The anvil didn't move, the hammer recoiled, and a numbing shock took over as the two forces combined. Aimed rifle shots at close range cut through the quickly moving Southerners. The Confederate line thinned as it wheeled on its leftmost side and stretched out to its right, as though centrifugal force itself was at work.

The blue line in the trenches held steady behind the dirt wall, and half of them fired, aimed, and fired again as fast as a weapon could be reloaded and returned to them. It was a hard fact of war. Men with courage behind dirt walls can dish out huge amounts of killing punishment to likewise resolute and courageous men who are brave enough or driven enough to attack them.

Cleburne's troops came forward twice and fell back. In the brief smoke-laden lull, the loaders slipped over the embankment and seized rifles from the hands of good Southern boys who no longer needed them. Additional weapons enabled a larger volume of fire to be thrown at the next attacking wave of the men of Lowrey's brigade.

Belknap himself was hoarse from yelling what he assumed were inspirational words as he ranged up and down the trench line. Suddenly, before him, coming like the devil himself was a Rebel colonel. He was out front, yelling to his men to follow. Behind him were lots of soldiers, but most of them were on the ground—many dead or wished they were. Still he ran on, sword in hand, hat off, with energy and strength as though through personal example, his troops could overcome exhaustion, wounds, and death to storm the trenches of the dug-in Union infantry.

CONFEDERACY, WILLIAM LAMPLEY

Still leading the charge and by some stroke of magic not blasted to his death, the Confederate Colonel Lampley looked back over his shoulder to see the position of his troops after he finished shouting. They were gone. What had happened? Lampley of the 45th Arkansas couldn't believe it. His men must have quit and run off. He cursed them, "Goddamn, you bastards! Come on!" He was still moving forward toward the red trench filled with blue soldiers.

Then a huge hand reached toward him, grabbed him, and hauled him over the mounded earth. A red-faced Yankee colonel screamed at him, "Look at your men. They are all dead. Don't curse them. They gave all they had."

Lampley sagged against his captor—Belknap—and sunk to the ground. Lieutenant Colonel Andrew Gwynne of the 38th Tennessee soon joined Lampley. Both commanders had led their regiments to the wall bristling with Iowa rifles and survived. The dead and dying of the 38th and 45th Arkansas had not been so fortunate. Around them, the battle continued to rage up and down the line on both sides of the road.

Captain Thomas Key, who commanded eight guns of Hotchkiss' battalion, had been successful in moving his battery up the Flat Shoals Road. He had been in support of Cleburne's division and had been firing with considerable effect into the trenches held by the Union 4th Division. The weight of Lowrey's reinforced brigade and its successful route of attack combined with the artillery fire made it an impossible force to stand before.

For the third time in as many hours, the Union 4th Division began to move northward to reduce further contact with the men of Cleburne's division. More than 500 men lay on the battlefield and could not answer the bugle calls and voice commands to fall back and to assemble to the south.

The troops of Smith's division moved north up the road toward the anticipated safety of Bald Hill. They had helped take the hill just the day before and now moved to repair the lines they had earlier held. They were giving up real estate and were doing so under killing pressure. These veteran Union soldiers were not used to going backwards.

Belknap's troops took their place in the new line running east and west and had the comfort of knowing the 1st Brigade was scattered out to their left and rear and that a portion of the Fifteenth Army Corps was just down the way. It was 6:00, and it had been a long, hot, man-killing day.

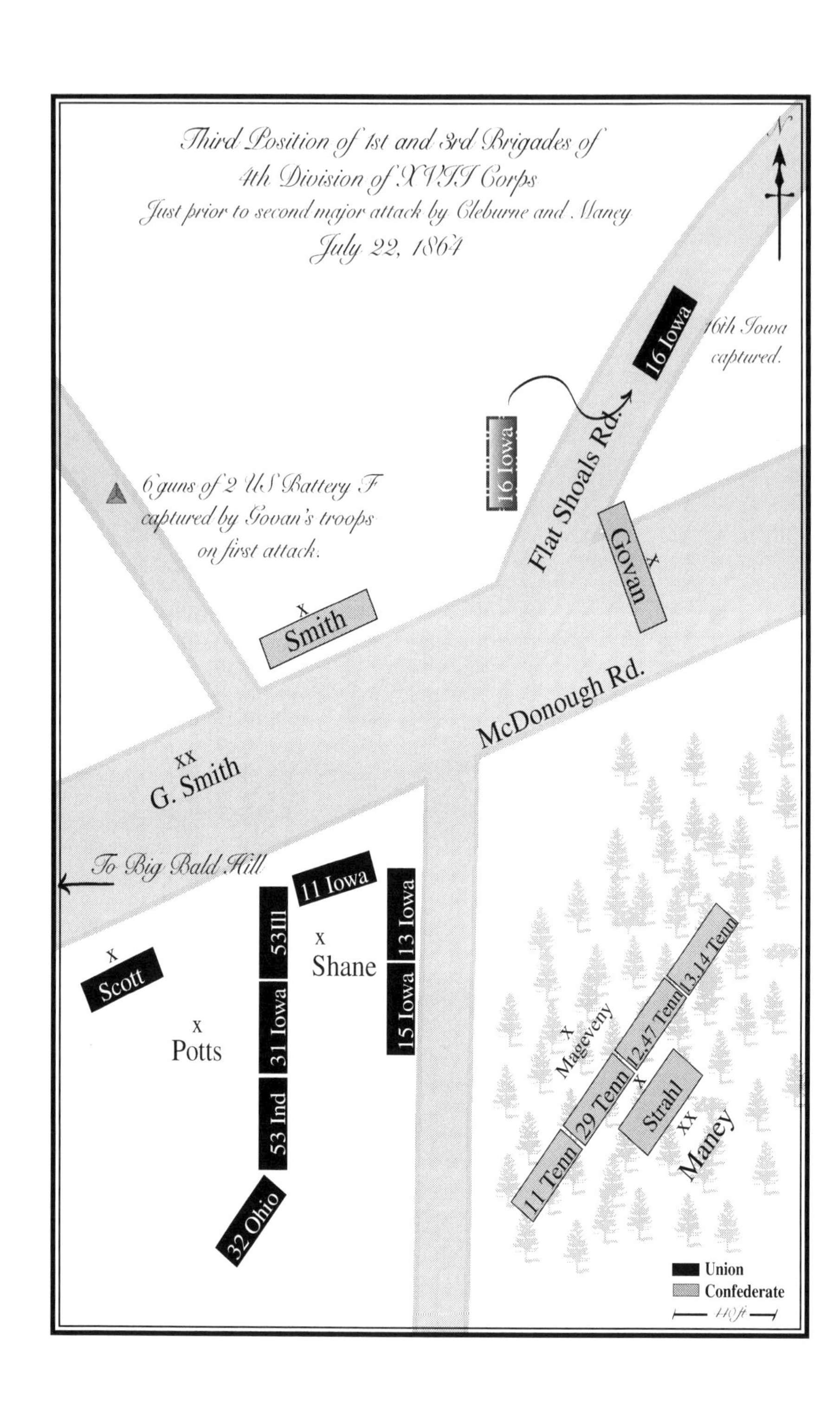
Third Position of 1st and 3rd Brigades of
4th Division of XVII Corps
Just prior to second major attack by Cleburne and Maney
July 22, 1864
N
16 Iowa
16th Iowa
captured.
16 Iowa
Flat Shoals Rd.
6 guns of 2 US Battery F
captured by Govan's troops
on first attack.
Govan
x
x
Smith
McDonough Rd.
xx
G. Smith
To Big Bald Hill
11 Iowa
13 Iowa
53Ill
x
Shane
x
Scott
15 Iowa
31 Iowa
x
Potts
3,14 Tenn
x
Mageveny
12,47 Tenn
x
29 Tenn
Strahl
xx
Maney
53 Ind
11 Tenn
32 Ohio
Union
Confederate
140 ft

CHAPTER NINETY-SIX

Confederacy | GEORGE MANEY

MANEY'S HEADQUARTER OF CHEATHAM'S DIVISION

WEST OF FLAT SHOALS ROAD

IN THE TREE LINE SOUTHWEST OF

THE SEVENTEENTH ARMY CORPS

ABOUT 3:00 P.M.

As Hall's men fell back into their original works, the skirmishers and men of the 11th Iowa were still engaged with Cleburne's men, firing at them from the east side of their trench. The end of the Union line was not completely enveloped, but it was receiving fire from both the east and southwest. It was under a sustained attack from that force firing from the southwest.

As the two Confederate Tennessee brigades moved forward, their ranks were increasingly being engaged by the veteran troops from Potts' brigade, who were standing in the corn field. That fire was being added to by that of the 11th Iowa in the better protected trenches. The 11th Iowa had the advantage of not being directly under attack and thus could provide an enfilading fire into the right of Maney's division. Potts had about 1,000 men in his four-regiment brigade, and they stood resolutely to their task. They could fire more rapidly standing still than could the dusty, screaming, smoke enveloped gray-backs moving steadily toward them. Men in both organizations were killed and wounded as the two forces shot into each other.

The two lines drew close. The Confederates then had the time to stand, fire, reload, and fire again, but their forward thrust was largely gone. They slowly fell back, firing as they went. Those who were able helped the wounded to retreat. Not beaten but exhausted from the heat, exertion, and Yankee resistance, they drifted back across the east-west Atlanta road and into the cover of the woods.

It was 4:00 p.m., but it seemed like the sun had not moved. This lack of movement was contested by the dead and dying on the ground, who could testify that time had indeed passed.

CHAPTER NINETY-SEVEN

Confederacy | GUSTAVUS W. SMITH

ONE MILE DUE WEST OF BALD HILL

CITY FORTIFICATION HELD BY THE GEORGIA MILITIA

JULY 22, 1864

3:00 P.M.

When Longstreet, Jackson, Kirby Smith, and three others were all promoted to lieutenant general on October 11, 1862 and he was not, Gustavus W. Smith resigned his commission. All those promoted were his junior, and none were as deserving of recognition as he. In January of 1863, Smith accepted the position of major general of Georgia Militia, which was extended by Governor Joe Brown. As Johnston moved south of the Etowah River, Governor Brown called for all civilian officers of the state of Georgia and the militia to assemble in Atlanta.

These 3,000 men were initially organized under Major General Wayne. Wayne was a competent professional who had graduated from West Point in 1838. He had won brevets to major for gallantry at Contreras and Churubusco in Mexico. He had resigned from the national service with the advent of the war and been appointed Adjutant and Inspector General for Georgia by Governor Brown. The group that assembled had been exempt from conscription in Georgia. There was some grumbling as the required military forms began to exert themselves. The men were informed that following the election of their officers that if they were dissatisfied with their own non-election, then they would be sent to the nearby Confederate conscription camp.

On June 1, 1864, General Smith assumed command of all the militia. While the training of these raw militia soldiers was going on, a former subordinate in the New York City Streets Department visited Smith.

This gentleman advised him that General Johnston needed the militia to operate with the Confederate cavalry on the flanks of the Army of Tennessee to allow the army to remain entrenched near Marietta without the danger of being flanked. Major General Smith with his militia force and Captain Anderson's battery had assumed a position some five or six miles from Johnston's flank on the north side of the Chattahoochee. The unproven militia had performed reasonably well there and elsewhere. It was good experience for what was planned today.

General Gustavus Smith saw Reynolds' brigade, which was the unit immediately to his left, move forward with the others in Stevenson's division. General Smith, acting on his own authority without any direction from Hood, ordered his militia into line of battle. The militia moved forward over the parapet toward the Union forces who occupied the west side of the looming Bald Hill.

General Smith's four brigades moved forward as did the four 12-pound guns of the Anderson's battery. The Southern troops moved forward about three-quarters of a mile to within 400 yards or so of the Federal lines on Bald Hill. Smith's Georgia Militia was soon isolated. The troops on his right, Maney's, had carried out their assault from the southwest of Bald Hill and Stevenson's four brigades had fallen back after a short confrontation with Harrow's 4th Division of Union troops. The militia, dressed in their obviously civilian clothing, held their position and would exchange fire with the enemy until about 6:00 p.m. At that time, Smith would receive an order from Hood to return to the fortification they had come from.

Although the outcome would be inconclusive to him, General Smith would be pleased by the performance of his force and would hope that General Hood would recognize their gallant action in correspondence with Governor Brown.

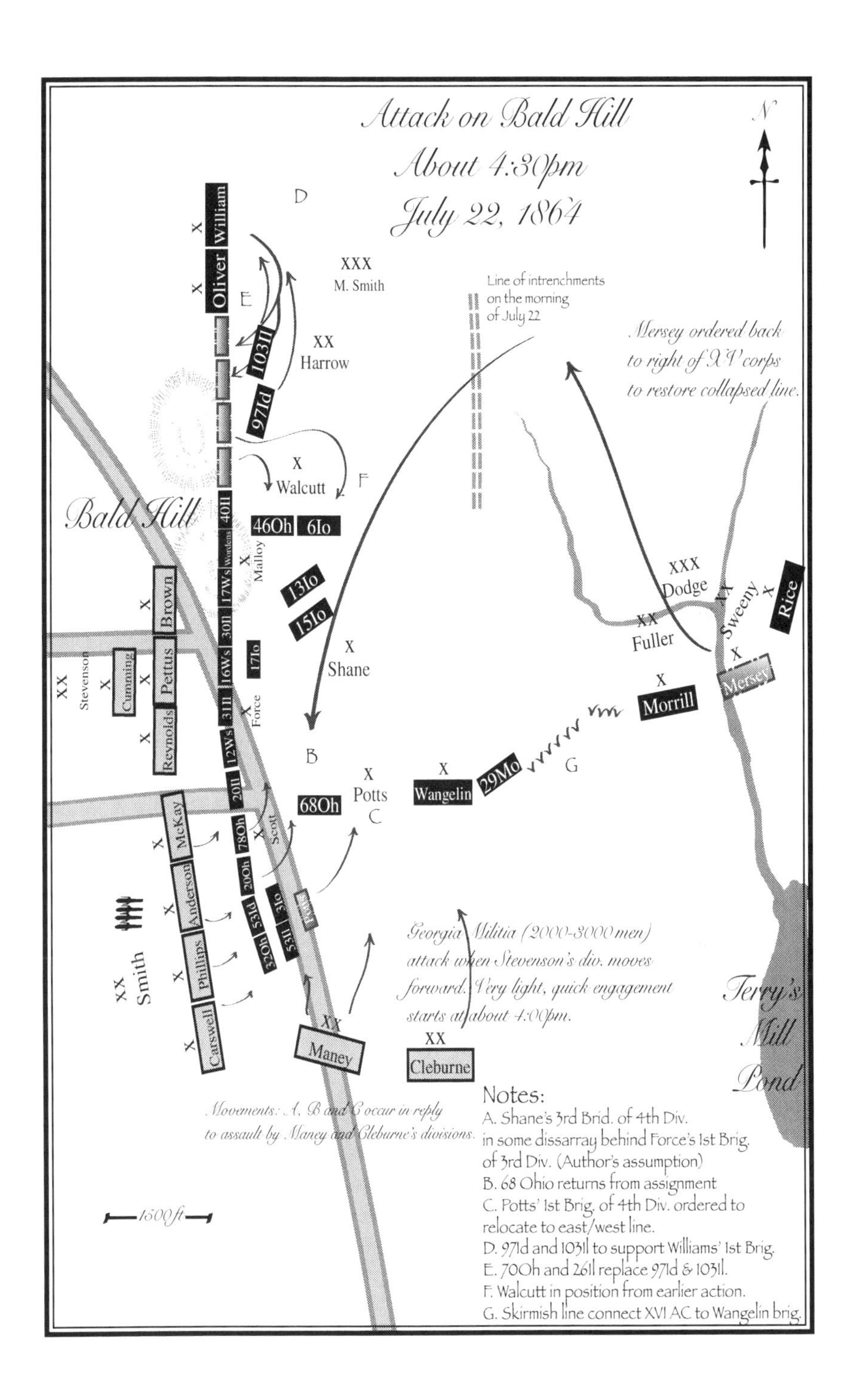

Attack on Bald Hill
About 4:30pm
July 22, 1864
N
Line of intrenchments on the morning of July 22
Mersey ordered back to right of XV corps to restore collapsed line.
XXX M. Smith
XX Harrow
X Walcutt
X Malloy
X Shane
X Force
X Potts
X Wangelin
X Morrill
XXX Dodge
XX Fuller
XX Sweeny
X Rice
X Mersey
Oliver
William
103Il
97Id
40Il
46Oh
6Io
Wordens
17Ws
30Il
16Ws
31Il
12Ws
20Il
78Oh
20Oh
53Id
32Oh
53Il
3Io
13Io
15Io
17Io
68Oh
29Mo
Scott
Bald Hill
Brown
Pettus
Cumming
Reynolds
XX Stevenson
McKay
Anderson
Phillips
Carswell
XX Smith
XX Maney
XX Cleburne
Georgia Militia (2000-3000 men) attack when Stevenson's div. moves forward. Very light, quick engagement starts at about 4:00pm.
Terry's Mill Pond
Movements: A, B and C occur in reply to assault by Maney and Cleburne's divisions.
1500 ft
Notes:
A. Shane's 3rd Brid. of 4th Div. in some dissarray behind Force's 1st Brig. of 3rd Div. (Author's assumption)
B. 68 Ohio returns from assignment
C. Potts' 1st Brig. of 4th Div. ordered to relocate to east/west line.
D. 97Id and 103Il to support Williams' 1st Brig.
E. 70Oh and 26Il replace 97Id & 103Il.
F. Walcutt in position from earlier action.
G. Skirmish line connect XVI AC to Wangelin brig.

CHAPTER NINETY-EIGHT

CONFEDERACY

North of the railroad on the east side of Atlanta,
between Atlanta fortifications
July 22, 1864
4:00 p.m.

Manigault's Confederate troops stepped off with enthusiasm to regain the trenches around Atlanta they had abandoned the night before. Skirmishers were out in front, and his four regiments were now moving in a line of battle. The brigade guided, as it usually did, on its regimental flags with everyone occasionally looking right to stay with the 10th South Carolina as it moved along with the railroad on its right.

The Federal skirmishers and their infantry support were already on the move to their own rear. They had been out pretty far from their lines in hopes that they were going to lead the way into the city. Now, they were on their way back to the safety of the men and the trenches. The two-gun section of the blue artillery banged away, but their efforts seemed tentative with more rearward looks than an aggressive gun crew would exhibit. On the other hand, they could see an entire Rebel division and maybe more coming at them. Discretion may be the better part of valor in such a situation.

Now with Rebels coming closer with the obvious intent of advance, the guns near the two-story brick house—the huge 20-pound Parrott rifles—began an accurate, angry response to the dust-covered Rebel troops. The big rifles were part of the battery under the command of Captain DeGress, the same guns that had fired into the city days before when McPherson's army was moving toward the city.

On the south side of the railroad tracks, the other two Confederate brigades of Hindman's division, those commanded by Colonel Coltart and Colonel Brantley, were likewise moving into the blue skirmish line ahead of them. Their orders were to keep the rail line on their left so that Coltart's brigade would hit the Union line nearly at the same time and in an adjacent place as Manigault's and hopefully break it.

Perhaps it was the fire from DeGress's 20-pound Parrotts to the left of Manigault's troops that exercised some push or force toward the tracks, but Manigault's troops adhered resolutely to their planned point of attack. Coltart's Alabama troops on the south side of the tracks, on the other hand, slowly moved away from that same railroad. The tracks curved to the left into those soldiers moving along the north side and away from Coltart's men. The 25th Alabama, the leftmost of the regiments making up the Alabama brigade, also found the way they were ordered to go blocked by small buildings and fences. This all combined to induce a southward or right-hand drift in the course of the attacking troops and resulted in the entire brigade edging more and more to the right. This course left a growing gap in the middle of Hindman's division, right at the primary thrust of the attack. By the time Coltart's Alabama brigade had pushed its way up to the Union skirmishers' reserve regiment, the rightward drift had created a gap from the railroad, which amounted to about 150 yards on the brigade's left.

Fire—both well-aimed minie balls and artillery fires—was hot, accurate, and increasingly heavy. It was with some relief that Manigault's brigade found cover in a substantial depression only 150 to 200 yards from the death-dealing Union entrenchments. Here, in the middle of the battle, this brigade found relative safety in the cover afforded by this swampy-bottomed, natural declivity. The Southern regiments then realigned themselves, reloaded their weapons, consumed gulps of water through powder-blackened lips, and prepared for the last rush into the sheets of fire ahead of them. Even among these veterans, there was no doubt that many rifles were double-shotted and barrels might explode. For many, it would no doubt be the last rest they had before permanently resting. They knew it would soon be terrible.

Yelling and moving quickly, no longer in the near perfect parade ground fashion they had started in, the Alabama and South Carolina boys moved out of the natural protection of the big cut and off toward their enemy. Manigault's brigade found itself under more and more punishing fire. As they moved ever closer to the little white house, veteran Union troops of the 47th Ohio and their sister regiment, the

45th Ohio, blazed away from the cover of their entrenchment and the concealment provided by the wood-frame house. The white house slowly evolved into a Rebel asset, however, as the lean, hard men from South Carolina began to use the exterior for offsetting cover and concealment, just as the Union soldiers were doing.

The Confederate regimental commander of the 10th South Carolina, Colonel James Pressley, studied the situation and concluded that the first and second stories of the little wooden white house offered an important tactical advantage. It combined cover, some concealment, and an unobstructed view down on the defending Ohio regiments. It was manmade high ground. Pressley ordered troops from his combined 10th and 19th South Carolina regiment to get into the house and up the stairs and then to hammer the Federal soldiers in the trenches below. Soon, the Confederates were in the building, and fire erupted from all the openings in the place. Given the unobstructed field of fire, their shooting was very effective.

Because the troops in Manigault's brigade had slowed, they were soon being pressed from behind by Sharp's rapidly moving Confederate troops. As Sharp's men added to the volume of Rebel rifle fire, the fire from the second floor of the white house intensified, and the 54th and 47th Ohio Regiments began to come apart. Then, troops from some of the rightmost of Sharp's Alabama brigade were pushed off the roadway by the natural flow of things and found themselves in the almost perfectly prepared avenue of approach: the cut for the railway.

It was unbelievable—a clear path below the line of sight of the Union soldiers on the top of the left and right banks. If the white house had offered an advantage of high ground, the railway bed provided the opposite advantage, that of a defilade. Troops could pass through this defile without being seen. Only by accident could they be hit by gunfire. Through this gap poured some of Sharp's Alabama men. This approach quickly gained the butternut-clad troops an easy entryway past the flank of the two ends of the 2nd Division and into the soft rear of the two unconnected ends of Lightburn's Federal 2nd Brigade. Like a hot knife through butter, the Southern troops began to emerge out of their hidden passage. They flooded into the unsuspecting flanks and rear of the 47th Ohio, the poorly led and largely unsupported two sections of Battery A of the 1st Illinois Light Artillery on the north side, and the two guns of the same Battery A and the 55th Ohio on the south side. These were the same troops under fire from the Rebels in the white house.

This sudden, unexpected, and now very close rifle-firing Rebel force was concealed in large measure by the white smoke that lay close to the ground and thus caused the 47th Ohio on the north side of the cut to begin to break away in fear and surprise. Their commander, Colonel Augustus Perry, was captured as the regiment was pushed out of its entrenchment away from the railroad. The regiment gained momentum as it retreated back to the line it had occupied earlier in the day. With the loss of Colonel Perry, Major Taylor—who had earlier commanded the 2nd Division skirmishers and who had earlier in the afternoon been napping under the oak—was appointed as the new commander of the 47th Ohio.

The blue force of the 54th Ohio then was attacked on the front side and rear by those same Rebel forces. Shaken by the attack, the 54th Ohio retreated as well, leaving dead, wounded, and the soon-to-be-captured in its wake. After that, the four Napoleons of Battery A were overrun, re-limbered, and moved off to the rear by Pressley's 10th South Carolina amid cheers and excitement. Regimental flags and cannons were high prizes in the deadly game played in combat. With the capture of these guns, it was obvious who the victors were, at least here and now.

In the wild melee that resulted as the South Carolina boys climbed over the Federal works, Colonel Pressley had been hit in the shoulder and suffered a wound that would remove him from the war. Command passed to Lieutenant Colonel Cornelius Walker.

Now, the gray tide was running fast and true as it swept northward with determination, rolling up into the flanks of each successive northern regiment in a classic infantry style. They ran right through the line of the 57th Ohio, the 37th Ohio, and the 53rd Ohio. The 53rd Ohio had earlier fallen back through the trenches on the north side of the tracks from their forward posting to be the regimental support for the skirmishers and form a reserve for the 2nd Brigade. From this second reserve position behind the 37th Ohio, they had reformed, shaken themselves out, and then almost immediately found themselves on line and in the fight. The 53rd Ohio was engaged in brisk, hot work, and initially some success was seen. Success was short lived, however, and before long, the howling troops from South Carolina and Alabama descended on their left flank.

Troops from Companies A, F, and D were in direct support of the DeGress Battery at the rightmost extreme of the 2nd Division. The guns were not fielded in a regulation front but drawn more closely together, given the circumstances of their area. The battery was separated from the 1st Brigade, the brigade on the left of the 1st Division of the Fifteenth Army Corps, by about 250 yards of low, swampy ground. This low area formed a natural barrier between the two divisions and would be at best a difficult area to traverse. Consequently, it would be a very poor avenue of approach for anyone attacking. It would also make receiving support from the right difficult.

CHAPTER NINETY-NINE

Union | JOHN HENRY PUCK & SAM MOTT

THIRD FLOOR OF THE BIG BRICK HOUSE NEAR THE RAILROAD

JULY 22, 1864

4:00 P.M.

UNION, JOHN HENRY PUCK

Before the onslaught of Rebel troops, the men of the 37th Ohio Infantry Regiment had been hard at work reversing the forward side of the entrenchment the Rebel forces had abandoned the night before. The regiment was now under the command of Major Charles Hipp. The men, after sixty days under him, had become used to Hipp. He had matured, and his leadership had firmed. A bit south, closer to the Atlanta-Decatur road and the railroad, troops from the 2nd Brigade had moved the trenches to the west toward Atlanta so that the trench was now in the front of the big brick house. The 37th Ohio was at the far right of the 2nd Brigade of the 2nd Division line. Just north of them was a marshy area full of brambles that covered an area that was 200 yards wide. The briars and swampy ground didn't seem to be a likely avenue of approach. As a result, no one was posted within the low-lying area.

Rebel activity had seemed to be picking up at the front of the 2nd Division, and the battle sounds off to the southeast had not really let up since about noon. Even the veterans were somewhat uneasy, but most of the men attempted a manly nonchalance. The word had gone out up and down the line of the 37th Ohio that Major Hipp was seeking volunteers to move over to the big brick house near the Atlanta-Decatur road. These volunteers would serve as sharpshooters. From Company C and G, some twelve to fifteen fellows stepped forward. This group included Private John Henry Puck. He fancied himself a pretty good shot and was interested in visiting the fine brick dwelling. It would be interesting to go inside. With some dispatch, the volunteers moved behind the battery and moved down the line parallel to the 30th Ohio and the 54th Ohio. Along the way, they came upon a spring. Puck and several others drank their fill and filled their canteens. One never knew when they would again be released to get more water. It could be a long afternoon.

The young men all moved into the house and up the stairs to the third and final story. Almost immediately, each soldier broke through the wall before him to the outside to have a hole to fire through. The orders were to keep a sharp lookout to the front, and the squad of soldiers arranged themselves accordingly.

"John Henry, look at that," called out the boy to Puck's left. Puck looked. There, moving toward them with flags flying and skirmishers out in front came what looked like the whole Rebel army. It was the brigade commanded by Manigault. The troops from the 37th Ohio brought their weapons up and began to blaze away, as did those in the entrenchments before them. Out ahead of the Union lines, their own skirmishers were flying back through their own lines. The fire from the trenches was decisive, and the butternut-clad force responded by going to ground.

Behind the first line of assault, a second brigade-sized unit appeared. These were Sharp's Mississippians. This attacking Rebel force found cover from the storm of flying metal that filled the sky. They used the white house and the undulating nature of the terrain. Just as water naturally seeks an outlet, so did the combined forces of Sharp and Manigault. The butternut troops ebbed and then naturally flowed up the railroad cut dividing the Union forces, unbeknownst to the Union troops until they were under attack.

The men of the 37th Ohio peered intently ahead, braced for the next assault. They knew the next tide would come in fifteen or twenty minutes following the natural lull in the battle storm. Eyes stained and shoulders pressed forward into their rifle butts in the effort of searching for targets. Time passed, and it seemed that the fight was over and that the Union forces had held their newly acquired trenches. Then firing to the left and rear of the big brick house came, but that firing also soon faded away. The silence was confusing. Private Puck left his firing position, walked to the other side of the house, and stuck his head out. To his amazement and surprise, he saw the backyard and works filled with Rebels.

"Fellows, our boys have left us here alone, and the place has more Rebels than a dog has fleas. We have got to get out of here," Puck cried out. Rifles in hand, the squad descended the stairs as fast as they could. As the Union soldiers reached the second floor, the troops from the 10th South Carolina and 19th South Carolina, under Colonel Pressley, were moving into the house on the first floor.

There were five big windows on the backside of the house. Without much thought, Puck and five or six others went out those windows as quick as they could. Puck chose the centermost window to make his exit. He was followed by two others before he hit the ground. Their landing was softened by the knapsacks that the 37th Ohio and others had piled there when they had taken off their packs to reverse the Rebel line. The landing sent the men sprawling with the Rebels watching from the windows above them. Puck was sure the game was up. From thoughts of Union victory, just minutes before, he knew now he would be shot or captured.

One of the Southern soldiers in a group by the right hand corner of the house raised his rifle and yelled the command to halt. That word was like the sound of a starter's pistol in a foot race. Puck and some others ducked and ran without a backward glance or a second thought. The next 400 yards rearward was covered about as fast as a young man could move, or at least this was the belief of Puck as he finally halted, now in the company of other retreating Federals.

Private Puck and several of the other sharpshooters moved with the tide of routed Federal soldiers eastward toward the line they had occupied earlier in the day. All of the regiments—the 47th Ohio, 54th Ohio, and, to a lesser degree, men from the 30th Illinois—were part of the flood of discouraged and shocked Union soldiers. As it became obvious that the onrushing gray troops would be successful in their rout of the Ohio soldiers, the artillerymen and infantry soldiers spiked the six big guns and killed many of the artillery horses as they stood in their traces with limbers and caissons. Around the guns on the ground were fourteen artillery men whose heroism and sense of duty had kept them at their work when lesser men found their presence was urgently needed elsewhere.

Within the five Ohio regiments north of the railroad, all was now substantial confusion as men from one regiment mixed with those from others. Officers tried to reassert some order. Here and there, officers were attempting to form units or groups of men to return to the fight. All were retreating rearward toward the line they had left earlier that day. As an immediately effective fighting force, the 2nd Brigade of the 2nd Division had ceased to exist for the time being. The group of hard, lean Rebels were congratulating themselves as they gulped water and looked about for the treasures the Yankees had left behind.

UNION, SAM MOTT

On the south side of the railroad, the three regiments making up the 1st Brigade were hard pressed. Lieutenant Colonel Sam Mott was in command of the 57th Ohio.

The Confederate men were in the Alabama regiments under the command of Colonel John Coltart. They came forward in columns of regiments. To Mott's surprise, the columns seemed to be four or five regiments deep. His eyes were to be believed because in addition to the sharpshooters performing as skirmishers, Colonel Coltart had the entire brigade moving on the greatly reduced number of men in the field fortifications south of the train tracks. These attacking forces moved as individuals. They didn't seem to need the reassurance of feeling the next man's elbow. They were glad to be part of a group, but it seemed you would have to kill them all to get them to stop. Mott reflected that early in the war, the only way to get soldiers to go forward was as a collected and connected mass. Men were more comfortable now with all the fury and hell around them. Coltart's brigade was sliding off to its right so the full brunt of the attack didn't fall only on the slender ranks of the 55th and 57th Illinois.

In the aftermath of the first assault, Mott realized that there was little or no shooting coming from his right. He soon understood the Federal forces there had been routed. More urgent than that was the unsettling reality of some 500 or so Rebel troops in a well-formed line of battle were moving fast into his own unprotected right and rear. Then, more troops were pouring out of the railroad cut. Mott yelled for the 55th and 57th Illinois regiments to change front to the right so that his Union force were no longer facing to the west toward Atlanta but north and northeast toward the fast-moving Alabama soldiers of Sharp's brigade. Notwithstanding Mott's intentions and orders, it was too late to change front, as the ragged, bearded, begrimed Alabamians were beyond his right flank and resolutely in his rear. Ragged volleys from the attackers felled men in blue uniforms and dissolved their ability to stand and fight. With or without orders, the embattled 2nd Brigade fell back toward Harrow's 4th Division to their left. They, too, moved back toward the line of trenches and rifle pits established on the 20th and 21st and that they had left only this morning.

Small unit leadership was available that day, but at the brigade and division level, the leadership on the blue side of the line was in flux and disarray. When General McPherson was killed earlier that day, a series of events relating to the command structure of the Army of the Tennessee commenced. Logan became the army commander and left a vacancy as commander of the Fifteenth Army Corps. That position was filled by Brigadier General Morgan Smith. The failure to protect the railroad cut must be laid at his feet because he was personally aware of the lack of defenses prior to the battle.

Beyond that, with Morgan Smith's promotion, the divisional command became vacant and then was filled by Lightburn. Lightburn had been the commander of the 2nd Brigade. Colonel Wells Jones took over the brigade upon the elevation of Lightburn. Jones had previously commanded the 53rd Ohio within the 2nd Brigade. These machinations, although done in a nearly automatic manner, left one new colonel and one nearly new colonel as brigade commanders in the 2nd Division.

Just two days before, the commander of the 1st Brigade had been Giles Smith, and now, Giles Smith had been selected to become the new divisional commander of the 4th Division. Giles Smith's vacancy was taken by Colonel James Martin. While the promotion activity took place smoothly enough, it nonetheless affected the 2nd Division of the Fifteenth Army Corps in a substantial and meaningful way. Assumption of command when one is merely in camp is busy enough but to do it in the face of a fierce assault compounds problems and creates a less than ideal command structure. If the location of Dodge's Sixteenth Army Corps on the left rear of the army was a stroke of good fortune for the army, the miserable command chain in the 2nd Division was very nearly its counterweight.

Martin, who had taken Giles Smith's vacancy, had not been with his entire brigade behind the field fortifications south of the railroad and was not now, but rather he had moved off with half his brigade to support the 4th Division to his left. His supporting movement left Mott as the acting brigade commander of the remaining three regiments, the 111th Illinois and the 55th and 57th Ohio, which were essentially in the center of the extended Union line. The 2nd Brigade's force north of the railway had dissolved because at the level above that of regiments, only new and untried leadership existed. Only eight regiments composed the front that was the 2nd Division's responsibility.

The two brigades along the railroad were at a disadvantage that afternoon. The soldiers, noncommissioned men, and junior officers all acted in a creditable fashion. The veterans showed that mature soldiers know what to do and how to do it. Nonetheless, their leaders failed them. By about 4:30 in the afternoon, the Union line was in shambles and had retreated toward its starting point earlier in the day. The flood tide of the Confederate assault had crested, leaving the flotsam and jetsam of the attack all along the former 2nd Division front. That whole line was now in Southern hands. A powerful punch had collapsed an entire section of Union line, and events were now in place to exploit this remarkable development.

CHAPTER ONE HUNDRED

Union | CHARLES WALCUTT & MORTIMER LEGGETT

Walcutt's 2nd Brigade, 4th Division,

Fifteenth Army Corps

July 22, 1864

4:00 p.m.

UNION, CHARLES WALCUTT

Walcutt had command of his original five regiments, his brigade, and the other two sent to him by General Harrow, his division commander. They were arranged in the shape of a backward "7." The two newly acquired regiments, the 70th Ohio under Major Bill Brown and the 26th Illinois then operating under Captain Bloomfield, were on the cap of the "7" shape, facing to the west and holding the trenches just vacated by the men of the 2nd Brigade. The men of the 2nd Brigade were arranged along the leg of the "7," running east and west at a right angle to the main line of battle. This position in effect refused the left of the Fifteenth Army Corps. In addition, it buttressed the right of the embattled Seventeenth Army Corps and allowed the 2nd Brigade to provide a hammer of firepower to the anvil of Leggett's 3rd Division.

Smith's Texans of Cleburne's division had attacked several times through that gap between the west-facing Seventeenth Army Corps and the south-facing Sixteenth Army Corps under Dodge. Now they had swung around to attempt to take the steep east side of Bald Hill. With each unsuccessful attempt, they retired to the belt of trees at the base of the hill. By turning their attention to the hill, the Southerners presented a tempting target to Walcutt's brigade. Walcutt's western soldiers and a section of 24-pound howitzers poured an enfilading fire into this pocket as Smith attempted to rally and reorganize his exhausted and valiant troops. The hard, metallic smell of fresh blood and mangled bodies mingled with the stink only dirty, sweating men can produce. Over it all hung the pall of smoke created by the rapid discharge of rifles and smoothbore cannons. There was the rank smell of men's bowels set free from gut shots that killed but first shook a man to his roots with hours of unrelenting pain. The little gorge with its grove of trees was a killing ground.

The attack on the north end of the Fifteenth Army Corps spread down the line by a brigade-sized echelon, like an uneven butternut-colored snake. At the end of that long, surging line were the green militia troops of Gustavus Smith. Walcutt then saw other Union troops fall back to the field works they had left earlier in the day after the attack through the railway cut dislodged them. This made some sense, in that if done successfully, it would present a front to the attacking Southerners rather than a flank. Units moving to one's right encouraged blue soldiers to retreat as well.

UNION, MORTIMER LEGGETT

From his vantage point on Bald Hill, Leggett could see the 4th Division of the Fifteenth Army Corps to his immediate right falling back. He could also see the 4th Division of the Seventeenth Army Corps beginning to falter in its steadfastness to his south. He knew he needed Walcutt's brigade to be steadfast and to continue to deliver its hammer blows on the Texans at the base of the hill. Those Texans, despite the battering crossfire, were still alive and dangerous. If the crossfire diminished, those hard Texans would swarm up the hill.

Leggett managed to find Walcutt in the melee and stood by him as a staff officer from Harrow's 4th Division headquarters stumbled forward.

"Walcutt, sir, General Harrow wants you to return to our line of this morning." The young staff officer was breathing hard, and his words were difficult to understand. On request, he repeated Harrow's order to fall back.

At that point, Leggett said, "Colonel Walcutt, this order must be a mistake. My orders are to hold this hill at all costs. You can see that it is the key to the battlefield. Blair, Logan, and Sherman have ordered the hill to be held at any hazard. You must remain here. You hold my right flank. My left is under tremendous pressure, and it is hard to say where my front or rear is. Without you, we are lost, and the whole left of the army is gone."

Walcutt hesitated only long enough to confirm with one more searching look that all Leggett had said was true. "General, I think you're correct. My boys and I will stand with you as long as your division can stand firm." Turning to the staff officer, Walcutt explained the situation and told him to tell General Harrow that Walcutt would not follow Harrow's order and he would take responsibility for everything that transpired after. This was an uneasy position to remain in. On his own right, an attack was underway. His brigade was like an island in a mighty flood.

Leggett prayed silently to himself, "God bless that young man and all those rifles." Leggett was gratified. This east-west line formed the strong breakwater of the Union line here on the south end of the field. Notwithstanding its importance, it was a position of extreme exposure. The enemy were pushing hard. They had won some victories in this contest and were looking for more.

This young man, Walcutt, had taken a position in the face of superior orders to the contrary. It was a bold stroke by a bold leader and rare personal courage. To some degree, it was just like the independent individual-oriented Army of the Tennessee. Leggett's force easily could be rolled up if not for Walcutt's gallant determination and willingness to make a hard decision.

CHAPTER ONE HUNDRED ONE

Union | THOMAS SWEENY

FIELD HEADQUARTERS OF THE SIXTEENTH ARMY CORPS,

ARMY OF THE TENNESSEE

JULY 22, 1864

4:10 P.M.

"Well I'll be a pie-eyed son of a bitch," one-armed Sweeny said under his breath. "I will say one thing about Mr. Dodge. When he is asked for his best, hardest fighting brigade, damned if he doesn't pick Colonel Mersey's of my division."

Logan had ridden over on his big, black horse to the left and rear of the Army of the Tennessee line shortly after receiving orders placing him in command of the army and asked for a fighting brigade. There had long existed an easy, almost civilian rapport between the three major generals—Logan, Blair, and Dodge—who led corps in the Army of the Tennessee. All three were volunteers, two were or had been members of Congress, and all knew the results were what counted. As a result, each loaned troops to the other two generals when one of them was hard pushed and needed help. It was exactly this off hand, seemingly cavalier attitude that was almost in defiance of the orderly way the old army operated that sent Sweeny into a fit of anger.

"They damn well should know better. It's no way to run an army," Sweeny thought. *"If I were in charge, things would undergo a massive change. At least McPherson had been a regular. Logan with all his 'hurry up' will just make things worse."*

Of course, Logan wasn't just asking Dodge. He was the new commander and could order it if that was what was required. But Logan hadn't ordered. He had asked, as was the well-developed habit between Logan and Dodge.

"Dodge, we are in a bad way over on the right. The Fifteenth Corps has been pushed back and is in danger of giving way. I purpose to take Martin back with me. Give me the best brigade available." Logan had spoken conversationally, but his restless energy was pulsing, and even those who didn't know Logan could tell he was ready to go.

"Take Sweeny's 2nd Brigade. They are mostly Illinois men under Mersey. You know they can move and fight. Good luck to you. I think we have whipped the Rebs good here, so your back door will be safe."

"Sweeny, go tell Mersey to get ready and to move out with General Logan. Go tell Colonel Martin to move his brigade, as he is needed back at home."

Sweeny had moved off. Sweeny might not like any of those fellows, but this time, Dodge made a good command decision even though Sweeny was not pleased that his command would be reduced by one of its two brigades. He knew Mersey's three Illinois regiments had a long day already, with marching two miles to charge the enemy, routing them, and taking two stands of colors. Now, they would have re-trace their path back across the railroad tracks. Maybe when this was finished, those boys could get some well-earned rest.

CHAPTER ONE HUNDRED TWO

Union | JAMES MARTIN

1st Brigade, 2nd Division, Fifteenth Army Corps

July 22, 1864

4:15 p.m.

It had been a very busy and frustrating day for thirty-seven-year-old Colonel James Martin. Just the day before yesterday, the 20 of July, he had been the commander of the 111th Illinois Infantry Regiment. In fact, he had been in the same position since September 19, 1862 when the unit had elected him as colonel. Now, he had come to command the 1st Brigade. Martin had not yet made the change in his mind. He still felt like he belonged to his old regiment.

The frustration of the day, in part, lay in his new activities as brigade commander. He was very pleased to have been selected to lead the brigade and knew it came as a result of having performed in an admirable way in past military matters. Yet he used to do things that seemed important, such as commanding the skirmishers out in front of the 1st Brigade's lines. That had clearly been important work and serving as the tripwire for the army behind him gave him a keen sense of importance and value.

On this day, as brigade commander, he had led his three regiments in what seemed a useless march. First, Martin had been ordered at about 2:00 p.m. to take the brigade reserve—the 116th and the 127th Illinois and the 6th Missouri—and report to Harrow, the 4th Division's commander. Harrow's command lay south of Martin's own 2nd Division. With Martin at the head of the column, he had sought out Harrow. Harrow soon directed him to a position. It had seemed to Martin that no sooner had he arranged the three regiments than a second order arrived that required the brigade report to Dodge and support the small force of the Sixteenth Army Corps.

The three regiments reached the Sixteenth Army Corps after some marching. Dodge's command had been hotly engaged by at least two divisions of Hardee's corps, and the sights and sounds of the aftermath of the battle were much in evidence. As Martin stood to the rear of the Seventeenth Army Corps, he could see down the hill over by the open field to the tree line the Southerners had sallied from. He could see men moving among the dead, who lay sometimes in rows like the detritus on a shore after a storm. Elsewhere, men bent to provide aid to the wounded and dying.

It seemed to Martin that the Sixteenth had been well positioned to deny the Confederates access to the rear of the Union army. Was it luck or design? Thus far, his new command had proved they could move about in the hot sun and get where they were told to go. His contribution had contributed only raising clouds of red dust and creating parched throats. His men still had their full load of ammunition that they had carried all day as they marched about, shooting at no one. Upon his arrival, Martin had reported to Dodge, who was standing with McPherson's successor, Logan. Martin had stood with the more senior officers for a short time, but finding he was not really needed, he excused himself to rejoin his men, who were resting a short distance away. Martin was politically astute enough to enjoy rubbing shoulders with Logan and Dodge, but frankly he hoped his brigade would find useful work before this afternoon was over.

For some time, the noise of combat could be heard. It came from the direction of the Seventeenth Army Corps, which he assumed was still anchored to Bald Hill, and then, a new overlay of sounds drifted south from up around the railroad track, the general area he had been ordered from earlier that afternoon.

A rider then came in and made straight for the knot of senior offices. He saluted Logan and began his hurried report. In a few minutes, he saw one-armed Sweeny leave the party and move rapidly down to the point at which the line of the 2nd Division changed direction and formed a right angle.

An aide left the command group and grabbed the reins of two horses. One was the black one favored by Logan. Logan, full of energy and resolve, mounted and moved directly toward Martin. Martin came to attention, saluted, and then inclined his head to listen to what Logan said.

"The lines of the Fifteenth have been broken in more than one place. You and your brigade should take the shortest route and rejoin the rest of your command. I will be moving out momentarily with one of Sweeny's brigades and will take them north of the 2nd Division. It will be clear what you will need to do once you arrive. Martin, take your men on the double, and have them ready to do their best. I know I can count on your boys from Illinois."

Martin saluted as Logan called back, "Good luck, Jim. Make Illinois proud."

Martin hurriedly called the three regimental commanders together and issued simple, direct orders. It was clear to the soldiers that at the end of their next march, they would be actively engaged in repelling the enemy from the very place they had marched away from two hours or so ago.

CHAPTER ONE HUNDRED THREE

Confederacy | HENRY CLAYTON

CLAYTON'S DIVISION

NORTH OF THE GEORGIA AND WESTERN RAILROAD

JULY 22, 1864

4:20 P.M.

From the standpoint of the men under Clayton on the left end of Cheatham's corps, the battle seemed to rage from just over to their right all the way to the end of the line way down. Stewart's three division corps was spread out along the north side of the city, awaiting the hoped-for rout of the Union Army of the Tennessee. Hardee's and Cheatham's corps were to drive it toward the Chattahoochee River. Facing Stewart were the Federal troops of the Army of the Cumberland under General George Thomas.

Clayton's division was the leftmost of the three loose divisional fronts of Cheatham's corps and consequently the leftmost portion of the Army of Tennessee until the fortified line of ditches crossed Peachtree Road that led north from Atlanta to Buckhead. Smoke and noise seemed to boil up, starting with the next division to their right. Artillery, ranging from rifled guns to the smoothbores, combined with musket fire to produce a hard roar that rose and fell in time with some erratic score. As yet, they were not engaged. They knew it was to be a general engagement, and apparently, they were to be the last troops thrown forward. The ball had opened several hours ago, and now it seemed it was finally their turn on the dance floor. As best they could tell, the fight had rolled toward them from way around to their right and beyond.

The exact size and composition of one's enemy is never completely known. In this case, it was all a mystery to General Hood. What was unknown to Hood was even less well understood by Hood's three subordinate corps commanders. At the division level, the situation was at best tactical, and little more than a hint of the anticipated outcome was known. For General Clayton, this matter was restricted to the front his troops had before them as they stared at the rolling, rough terrain to the east. They knew the Yanks were deep in the trenches, which only yesterday they had left when ordered back into the inner line of Atlanta's defensive works. The objective was about a mile away, and the route lay through low, swampy ground that seemed to be nearly impassable. To the right of this low, wet ground was better ground that continued until it was cut by the single track of the railroad to Decatur. The terrain to the south of the railroad was to be taken by their sister division under the command of General Brown. Brown's division seemed to be engaged all across its front.

Clayton had received his orders from General Cheatham. It seemed clear to Clayton that in this regard Cheatham, new to his corps command, was a mere conduit for the orders from one-legged Hood, as there seemed to be nothing bearing Cheatham's personal stamp on the instructions. The four brigades of Clayton's division did not anticipate an attack from the dug-in infantry to their front. If this would be the case though, the brigades were going to form up inside the fortifications of Atlanta. They would then sally forth and form a two-brigade front arranged with Baker's brigade in the front left and Stovall's brigade to its right. Behind them in a second formation would be the troops of Gibson's brigade, and to its right would be the men of Clayton's old brigade. On order, the four brigades would dress and close to their right as the regiments began to line up for the attack.

However, it was far more likely that Clayton's division would be attacking the dug-in Union troops. Leading a combat division into battle against an entrenched and determined enemy was new to Clayton. It was not the most auspicious way to begin as a division commander, but Clayton was confident in his leadership skill and in the division. It was a pretty good division and should do well.

Clayton assembled his force by brigade. Colonel John Higley, commander of the 40th Alabama, was in temporary command of Baker's brigade, and this force was placed on the left of the assault line. To Higley's right, Clayton placed Stovall's Georgia brigade, which remained under the command of Colonel Abda Johnson of the 40th

Georgia. Within Johnson's force were the nearly 500 men of the 1st Georgia State Line under the command of newly promoted Lieutenant Colonel John Brown, the younger brother of fiery Governor Joe Brown of Georgia. Here the line was broken and the next brigade, Gibson's brigade, formed up and was canted over from the Georgia brigade, but not really behind it. On the left of the Gibson's brigade were the four Alabama regiments of Clayton's former command, which were now under Colonel Bush Jones.

Clayton said, "Colonel Johnson, move forward. Keep the sun to your back and drive the enemy back and occupy their lines."

Then he added, "Colonel, you know that Brown is now commanding Hindman's old division. He's out there ahead of you and to your right. If possible, catch up with him and make a connection on your right with Brown's troops."

"Yes, sir," came Johnson's reply.

"I'll have Colonel Jones with those Alabama boys right behind you. You can count on 'em. They used to be mine."

"Hope so, sir. It looks hot out there."

"Go on now. Move those piss-ant Georgia boys out now."

"Yes, sir."

Next, Clayton moved over to the left of his front line to speak to Higley.

Movement from the enemy line caught the eyes of several of the riders. "General," one keen-eyed staff officer said. "There's a considerable force moving out there from our left to our right. That force of Yanks could make it pretty warm for our flank."

Clayton, always quick, turned to Major John Eldridge, his division artillery officer. "Major, let's get your three batteries started up. Play on those blue troops moving yonder. Break 'em up."

Eldridge gave a hurried half salute and rode hard to his three batteries, which contained twelve field pieces. Soon, the four ordinance rifles and the Napoleons began to sling ordinance over the advancing butternut brigades and into the ranks of blue soldiers moving to their flank.

With Eldridge on his way, Clayton directed Higley to send his four Alabama regiments obliquely to the left to confront the Union counterattack. He hoped this combined infantry and artillery strike would dampen the stirred up Union soldiers.

Next, Gibson's brigade was ordered up and out to link up with Brown's division to its right. On order, the brigade moved forward behind the 14th Battalion Louisiana Sharpshooters, acting as skirmishers. Moving essentially due east, the brigade marched off to lend support to Baker's brigade under Higley, which had preceded them.

CHAPTER ONE HUNDRED FOUR

Confederacy | JOHN M. BROWN

STOVALL'S GEORGIA BRIGADE, CLAYTON'S DIVISION

EAST ALONG THE NORTH SIDE OF THE RAILROAD

JULY 22, 1864

4:30 P.M.

The men of the 43rd Georgia were out in front of the other five regiments of what was known as Stovall's brigade and were deployed as skirmishers for the brigade and half of the division. Some of the men enjoyed the individual freedom of being on the skirmish line. It seemed more in keeping with their nature than moving in lock step shoulder-to-shoulder with the man next to them. Some were sure that even though they were out front, it was less dangerous than with the massed troops to their rear. Out here, they could find a little cover and move to the left and right. Only well-aimed individual rifle fire was likely to find a mark. Behind the 43rd Georgia in a battle line from left to right were the 42nd Georgia, 1st Georgia State Line, 32nd Georgia, 40th Georgia, and 41st Georgia. They were in a traditional double line and had a front that reached nearly 300 yards. Anyone with an eye to recent military history would know that line nearly approximated the length of an 1862 regiment.

At the head of the 1st Georgia State Line was twenty-year-old Lieutenant Colonel John Brown, brother of Governor Joe Brown. He had taken a wound in the shoulder during a short but intense skirmish on June 18 that had been just a little more than a month earlier. It had been a painful wound, and it was still of considerable hurt to him under normal circumstances. This was not normal: it was hot and dusty. But, he had forgotten everything but his responsibilities in his new leadership role.

As the brigade moved east with the sun behind them, they chanced upon Brigadier General John Brown, who was immediately to their right. As soon as Johnson of the 40th Georgia arrived at his side, Brigadier General Brown began to use his considerable speaking skills to explain the situation they both now confronted. Brigadier General Brown explained that his division needed immediate support, especially over on the right side of the railroad. He directed Johnson's brigade to cross the roadway and the railroad tracks and to come to the assistance of his hard-pressed troops. The tracks bent away to the left so that Johnson's brigade could cross the tracks at nearly a right angle and proceeded to move forward.

As Johnson's brigade marched, it was clear to all the men that they were a second wave or follow on element, as the ground they moved on was covered with dead and wounded men. In addition, other detritus of war was scatted about: knapsacks, haversacks, blankets, and weapons. Occasionally a man would halt and retrieve a weapon that might prove on inspection to be better than the one he currently carried.

As the brigade moved closer, it became increasingly clear that they were proceeding toward a battery of at least four guns—Battery A of the 1st Illinois. The battery was producing tremendous amounts of smoke and noise as the hidden guns fired out of a low, wide bank of smoke. Muzzle flashes could sometimes be seen as bright orange stabs of color were followed by hard, hot, heavy noise of canister. The order rang out to take cover. Men hit the earth and began to reload their Enfield rifles. This was a difficult job to perform while on their backs or sides. Among the men down was young Lieutenant Colonel Brown. His was not a voluntary drop to the ground, but rather as a result of a wound to his thigh.

Senior Regimental Captain Albert Howell hurried his men to reload. Then with no apparent thought for his safety, he sprang up yelling, "Follow me, boys. Let's take those works." The men of the 1st State Line rose up and ran forward in a mad charge along the ground near the railroad cut and into the battery area. Some men in blue uniforms, who were begrimed by the action, ran from the approaching Confederates while others were too tired to move and slowly raised their hands in surrender. The two 12-pound Napoleons on the south side of the tracks were now in the hands of the 1st State Line and others from Stovall's brigade. It was now past 5:00 p.m., and the members of the

43rd Georgia began to sort themselves out and to prepare for whatever repercussions were to come.

From about 300 yards to the Union rear, a six-gun battery began putting steel into the ranks of the victorious Confederates. The left of Johnson's line had struck the Union line first and were some forty to sixty feet ahead of the regiments on their right. The regiments came on in a sort of echelon fashion, and as the enemy lines combined, bitter hand-to-hand fighting took place. The noise and smoke from the battery, the smells, and disturbed earth produced the stench of sweat and death. Bayonets, gun butts, knives, swords, or anything that could be swung or used with deadly force was in use on both sides of the line.

On the right of the line, Lieutenant McGinnis of Company C of Johnson's old 40th Georgia watched in fascinated horror as a bayonet on the end of a 10-pound Springfield rifle was plunged into the chest of the man next to him. McGinnis was unarmed but bent forward and picked up an entrenching spade. Then, like his Scottish warrior ancestors of old, he began to slash around him with the small, sharp shovel. Lots of commanders talked about the use of cold steel and the use of the bayonet, but to actually be so engaged at such close quarters was personal and far less romantic. The arching blade struck first the Yank with the rifle and bayonet, nearly removing the Yankee's head from his neck, and then into the side of a second Union soldier. McGinnis dropped to his knees, chest heaving and legs weak.

Johnson's brigade had clashed with the Union 57th Ohio, 55th Illinois, and the remains of the 111th Illinois that had earlier been in support of the Union skirmishers. These three Union regiments had been on the receiving end of Sharp's troops' earlier attack up the undefended railroad cut. Now as Johnson's men attempted to regroup in and around the captured guns and earthworks, the men of those three Union regiments were likewise halting in their retreat and beginning to swing around to reform for a counterattack.

CHAPTER ONE HUNDRED FIVE

Confederacy | PRIVATE ROBERT BRASWELL

57th Georgia, Mercer's brigade, Walker's division,
Hardee's corps, Army of Tennessee
In reserve and in support of Cleburne's division
on Flat Shoals Road
July 22, 1864
4:45 p.m.

Thoughts of all kinds crowded into seventeen-year-old Robert Braswell's mind as he sat leaning against a sapling surrounded by his friends and comrades of the 57th Georgia. He was young and in excellent physical condition, but he was worn out. His mind was spinning even as his exhausted body wanted to go to sleep. Robert was certain his two brothers, Billy and Samuel, were dead. Late on July 20, just two days ago, he had been close enough to watch Steven's brigade step off on the west side of Peachtree Road toward the Union units that were just coming across Peachtree Creek. Robert had slipped over after his supper the previous evening to see and spend time with his older brothers. Word was that General Stevens had been killed. Robert knew from personal experience that there had been hard fighting as three of Hardee's four divisions had swept down from their position and up the hill past Andrew Collier's house and into the devastating storm of lead from the dug-in Yankees of Newton's division.

Robert knew his brothers had not returned after the battle was over. He had looked and asked everyone he could the next day, and he knew Billy and Sam had not been on the long march of last night. In his mind, he struggled with his fears. Maybe they were merely wounded or captured or in some manner separated from their unit. He prayed for their safety and well-being. He knew a lot of boys had died in that poorly planned and executed attack, and as more time passed, he became increasingly certain that his brothers were among them.

Robert figured he must be at least ten miles south of Atlanta. That meant he was as close to Fort Valley, his home, his mother, and that beautiful, young girl Laura Love as he had been in quite a while. Home couldn't be more than a hundred miles away right now. In all the confusion, he knew he could slip away when night fell and be well on his way home by the time they called roll in the morning. It was easy to think about but impossible for him to undertake.

His exhausted mind raced. He remembered being in the creek bottom today, watching the other regiments simply getting shot up as they tried to get up the hill. It couldn't have been more than 400 to 500 yards across relatively open ground. Even within the natural protection of the depressed creek bed, they had taken hits. Men had died or were wounded. The attack on his part of the field wilted away after only an hour or so had passed. Then his regiment, as part of the brigade, had worked their way out of the dense forest, avoiding the millpond they had entered on the way in, and had moved to the road they had traveled the night before. They had then marched west and north past Hardee's headquarters and then sort of north again until they stopped. Now, men lay exhausted and about used up, just as Robert was. Word was that they were going to attack some hill as part of Cleburne's division. If he had to fight, fighting under Cleburne's leadership was about as good as it got in a poor situation.

The Army of Tennessee seemed to be catching hell. It came from the Yankees and from Richmond, Virginia. They had been shot at and repulsed by the blue bellies. They had lost General Johnston and now had Hood. Robert had seen Hood. The poor fellow had to be helped into the saddle because his leg was gone. It was hard to see how such a man could really run an army. Since Hood had taken command, Robert had suffered his worst two days in the army. From his personal point of view, the army had endured a pretty bad two days as well.

CHAPTER ONE HUNDRED SIX

Confederacy | ARTHUR MANIGAULT & BUSH JONES

INSIDE THE LINES FORMERLY HELD BY THE UNION 2ND DIVISION, NORTH OF THE RAILROAD

JULY 22, 1864

5:00 P.M.

CONFEDERACY, ARTHUR MANIGAULT

The excited, victorious troops of Manigault's brigade occupied all of the trench line from north of the railroad past the brick two-story house to the low, swampy area that separated the 1st and 2nd Divisions of the Fifteenth Army Corps. Manigault's men had completely routed five veteran regiments and captured four guns from the 1st Illinois and the four 20-pound Parrotts from Battery H of the 1st Illinois. Regiments were jumbled together, and firing was still going on as men leveled their rifles at the fleeing Yankee soldiers. Others scrambled to remove the spikes from the Parrott rifles so they could be placed in Southern service. Wounded were moaning or staring off into space. There were a few dead, and some captured Yankees were milling about. The horses from both batteries were dead in large heaps, still harnessed to the limbers and caissons. To some, the death of the horses seemed a greater loss than the loss of the soldiers.

The area his men had captured was familiar to General Manigault and his troops as they were again in the trenches they had created earlier in the week and then had abandoned on the night of July 21, less than twenty-four hours ago. The abatis of felled trees had been reversed, as had the face of the entrenchments themselves. About 500 yards to the east, the Ohio regiments that had been so quickly routed were now reforming after having been rallied near their old defense line.

Now one of the failures of senior leadership asserted itself: Manigault then received an order to leave the hard-won trenches and return to the city. With no enthusiasm and with much disbelief, the South Carolina and Alabama regiments began to move out and back over the ground they had just liberated. There was some grumbling at the turn of events. It is difficult to successfully assault entrenched troops supported by artillery. Here, such an assault had been done at considerable cost, and then, it was thrown away. About 1,400 yards back toward the city, a second order was received that rescinded the earlier order to withdraw.

The brigade halted its western movement, faced about, and set off to reclaim that ditch in the dirt for the second time in less than twenty-four hours. Some ragged Union resistance had filtered back to their forward line by this time. The Southern troops fell on them with a vengeance, and after a hot contest, the blue Yanks were pushed out for the second time.

For the first time, Union batteries on both the left and right of Manigault's brigade began to find their range and score hits. The long arm of the Union was effective, firing from both the 4th Division, located south of the railroad, and from the 1st Division, which was north of the captured field fortification and was placing steel and explosives on target. Although there were many captured Union pieces, they were not operational, and consequently, the Southerners had no artillery support. The Confederates were now forced to endure the shellfire without returning it.

The brigades commanded by Manigault and Sharp had breached the enemy line and captured artillery and enemy soldiers but were now in need of reinforcements. Requests for such additional manpower were sent with some regularity back to the division command. Both Sharp and Manigault had their hands full. Neither could advance, and Union resistance from the consolidating efforts of officers in the Fifteenth Army Corps seemed to be stiffening. Leaving what they had gained at such a high price seemed a horrible wrong, but without more men and weapons in the fight, retreat came to be seen as the only real choice. As these thoughts were racing through Manigault's brain, the lead elements of Holtzclaw's brigade of Clayton's division suddenly appeared on the scene.

Colonel Bush Jones approached Manigault and quite formally asked, "Sir, my complements. Where would you suggest my regiments could provide the most assistance?" Manigault, taken aback, decided on the spot that Jones was the coolest, most collected fellow he had ever met.

CONFEDERACY, BUSH JONES

Jones' brigade was made up of four regiments of Alabama troops. These regiments were the 18th, 36th, and 38th Alabama as well as the combined 32nd and 58th Alabama. All and all, the brigade was a veteran outfit. It was well led, and the men and units were as comfortable in combat as men could become. Normally referred to as Holtzclaw's brigade, it had more often than not been commanded by Colonel Bush Jones. These opportunities came during the periods during which Holtzclaw was trying to recover from injuries and sickness.

To the right of Manigault's troops were the six Mississippi regiments of Tucker's brigade under the command of Colonel Sharp. These two Southern brigades had control of a half-mile or so of fortifications that ran from south of the railroad north to beyond the big brick house. Between the troops, they had captured some eight guns in all and routed a full Union division and parts of two more for at least some distance. From the Confederate left came the first shellfire from the hill where the Howard House sat. All the available artillery was being moved to provide enfilade fire on the trenches held by the hot, dirty, hard men of Manigault's brigade. These guns, some twenty in all, were under the personal direction of a redheaded major general from Ohio, Uncle Billy Sherman. In addition, soldiers from Wood's 1st Division were massing beyond the swampy area to counterattack.

From Manigault and Sharp, Colonel Jones learned that the Union forces were massing on the left. He could tell for himself that well-directed cannon fire was screaming down the Confederate position with considerable effect. The fire was heavy and galling. Colonel Jones calmly ordered a rapid change of front and formed his brigade nearly at a right angle to that of Manigault's. The regiments altered their position from facing east to one in which they would face north. They pivoted on the lead or rightmost company so they would no longer be parallel with Manigault's captured lines but perpendicular to it. The 38th Alabama was still on the right, but the orientation of the entire line had shifted some ninety degrees. The new line was loose, extended more than 600 yards, and had the effect of refusing Manigault's left.

Colonel Jones had ridden the line and moved off to supervise the establishment of the new position when he discovered that his rightmost regiment was now committed to an assault. Jones rode hurriedly to the east and found that the irrepressible Major Ruffin, after only the slightest urging from Manigault and Sharp, had charged some 200 yards to roust the enemy from these works. Ruffin, always ready to take on the enemy alone or with his command, had moved against the Federals like a hungry dog after meat. They had been joined quickly by the 36th Alabama.

Jones ordered his other two regiments forward to maintain the integrity of his command. The terrain prevented the command from remaining intact, however. Nonetheless, the attack was successful and the two rightmost regiments held their ground for five minutes. Then, to his surprise, Jones discovered that the same brigades he had been supporting were now being withdrawn. He ordered his brigade to retire as well, in the process losing many to capture.

Ruffin's Alabamians had advanced to a portion of the enemy line nearly 200 yards from Manigault's left. Considerable distance separated the two gray forces. One could not support the other. The 38th and 36th Alabama were, in effect, an island now attacked from the front and right by the men in blue from the 2nd Brigade of the 2nd Division. To Jones' front and left, Jones' brigade was now subjected to fire from advancing infantry and artillery fire from the men of the 1st Division, who were in motion to support the confusion that had engulfed the 2nd Division.

All this was simply too much to bear. Valor and competence is, in the end, no match for large numbers of skilled veteran troops with a simple, clear directive in mind. Jones' brigade had provided shock support at exactly the right moment. They had functioned as a robust reserve should in support of Manigault and Sharp. Yet the tide of battle turned, aided by confusion, bad judgment, and uncertainty in the Southern command at the division level. By the end, all three brigades had withdrew from the high watermark of their success and gone back toward the grim defenses of the city.

CHAPTER ONE HUNDRED SEVEN

UNION

DeGress Battery

North end, the right of the 2nd Division of the Fifteenth Army Corps

July 22, 1864

4:45 p.m.

The guns the 30th Ohio and 37th Ohio, who had been hammered at by Sharp's men earlier, were to support and protect, and they did until they were again taken as Sharp's Alabama regiments started to trickle back after the Southerners momentarily withdrew. The hard red piece of geography occupied by the guns, limbers, and caissons of the battery was bordered to the north by that large, low swampy area.

The fortified line first dug by Confederates formed a sort of arch that eased away toward the west so that Union troops north of the Troup Hurt house seemed to be flanking the attacking Southern forces. To the Confederates, the line seemed concave and stretched along over their left shoulders. Manned by infantry and artillery, the top of the line provided an opportunity for enfilading fire into the left and rear of the attacking Southern troops. The opportunity was even greater since the enfilading fire was directed from high ground so that the Union gunners could actually see the enemy troops.

This was exactly the situation presented to Major Clemens Landgraber. The six guns of the 2nd Missouri and the 4th Ohio had originally been positioned about 800 yards north of the DeGress Battery, which lay to the south and across the 250 yards of low, damp land that separated the 1st and 2nd Divisions. Landgraber had moved his pieces outside of the breastworks and fired into Manigault's attacking brigade as they swarmed past Widow Pope's white house and onto the four guns of the DeGress Battery. That same swarming Confederate tide had driven the

Union veterans out of their trenches and back toward the line they had held earlier that same day as well as dislodged the brigade that had been the infantry support for the 2nd Missouri Battery. When the brigade fell back to the higher, less-contested ground near the Howard House, the 2nd Missouri was isolated. Nonetheless, Landgraber wheeled his guns around to face south and kept up a steady fire into the area around the captured big guns of the 1st Illinois Light Battery H.

The victorious Southerners were now directing their rifle fire at the unsupported battery. It did not take Landgraber long to decide to order the horses and limbers forward and to fall back to the comfort of the nearly 2,000 men in the 1st and 2nd Brigades of the 1st Division, who were now reforming on the hillside just to the north. Once on the grounds of the so-called Howard House, the guns once more went into battery and began firing shell and spherical case shots into the enemy lines north of the railroad.

Just as the Federal troops had given way before the butternut onslaught, the units began to gather themselves to reengage. Brigadier General Charles Woods commanded the 1st Division. Having withdrawn in a mannerly fashion, Woods was ready when he got orders from his new corps commander to attack in concert with others to retake what they had lost. Woods ordered his entire seven-regiment force forward. This force included his old command, the 76th Ohio, which was now commanded by Woods' older brother, Colonel William Woods.

The troops moved back along the same path they had retreated over. The division went forward in two well-formed lines of battle, sort of straddling the entrenchments they had recently vacated. The 2nd Brigade with its three regiments attacked in front of and on the flank of the enemy in the trench, and the 1st Brigade went forward to deliver a blow in the enemy's rear and flank. This movement to regain their lines was taking place at the same time Colonel Bush Jones was changing his front in support of Manigault and Sharp. Supporting Jones' brigade were the four Alabama regiments of Baker's brigade under Higley, which were moving up on Jones' left.

The Federals who had been dislodged from their field fortifications by Manigault's and Sharp's brigades had withdrawn in a disorganized manner back toward Decatur. These were the soldiers of Lightburn's 2nd Brigade of the 2nd Division, and although temporarily beaten, they had not been completely routed or defeated. They still had fight left if they were properly led. They were now being reformed and sorted out to be useful in driving the Rebels out of the captured works. As these regiments were being shaken out, the lead elements of the regiments of Mersey's brigade—the 2nd Brigade of the 2nd Division of Dodge's Sixteenth Army Corps—were even now arriving on the scene. These were the men of the 81st Ohio, the 66th Illinois, and 12th Illinois who had successfully participated in routing Bate's and Walker's joint two-division assault four or so hours ago. These were also the same Federal veterans who had first blunted and then overwhelmed the initial attack by Hardee's corps over on the southeast corner of the Union line.

With uniforms made black with sweat and faces gaunt with exertion, these Federal troops were pushing rapidly forward to the place they were needed. In the fray was Logan, whose style of leadership demanded he lead from the front. Unlikely as it was for an army commander to be at the tip of the spear as he prepared for a counterattack, that was where he was to be found. As Logan came forward on the black warhorse called "Slasher," men yelled his name. Logan's acknowledgement seemed to be personally directed at each man he passed. His direct, charismatic connection encouraged the men he led in such a way as to multiply their combat effectiveness. They knew they could win with "Black Jack" as their leader.

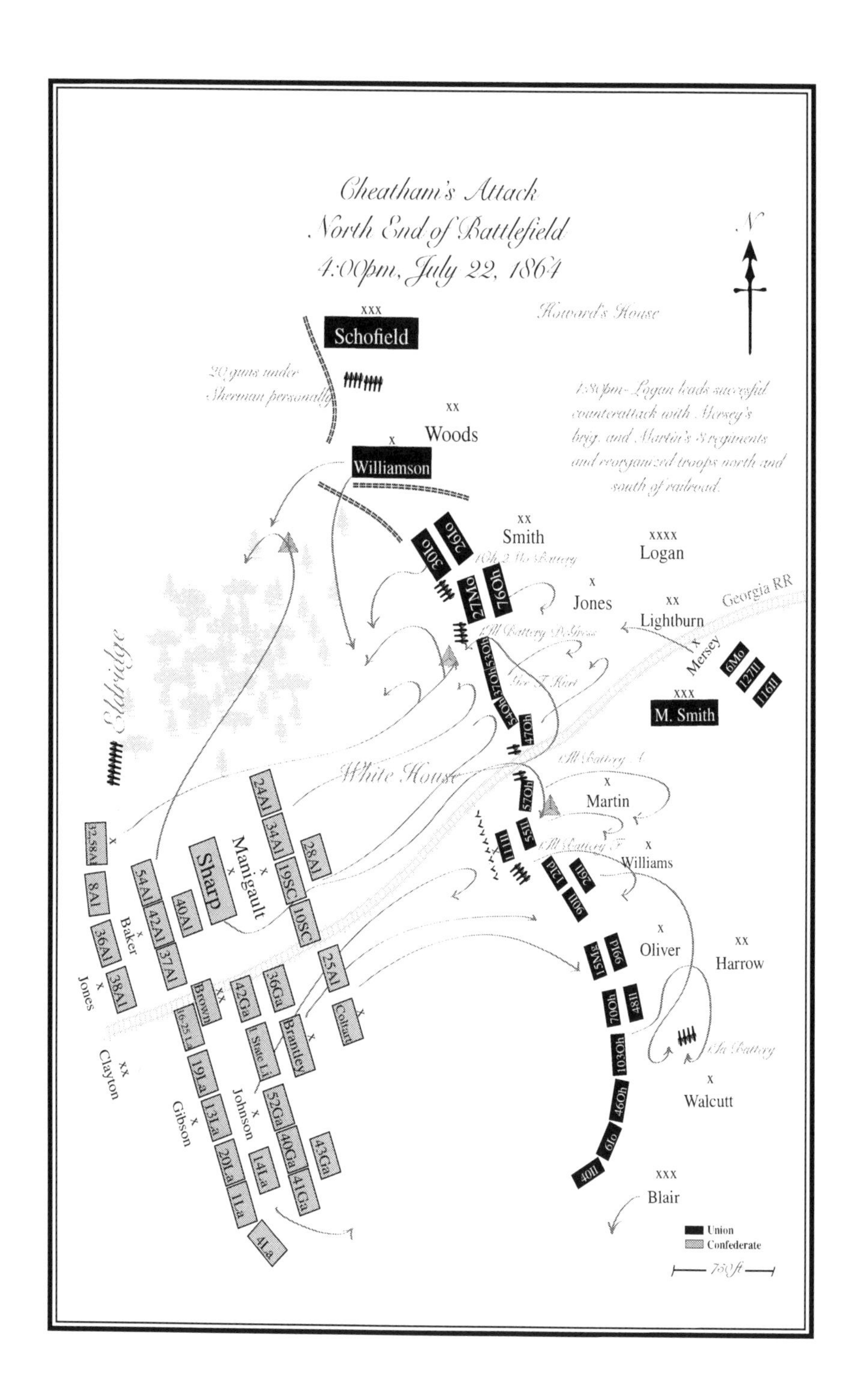

Cheatham's Attack
North End of Battlefield
4:00pm, July 22, 1864
N
Howard's House
XXX
Schofield
20 guns under
Sherman personally
XX
Woods
X
Williamson
4:30pm- Logan leads sucessful
counterattack with Mersey's
brig. and Martin's 8 regiments
and reorganized troops north and
south of railroad.
XX
Smith
30Io
26Io
XXXX
Logan
27Mo
76Oh
X
Jones
XX
Lightburn
Georgia RR
X
Mersey
6Mo
127Il
116Il
XXX
M. Smith
Eldridge
White House
X
Martin
57Oh
55Il
111Il
X
Williams
24Al
34Al
28Al
Manigault
Sharp
19SC
10SC
32,58Al
8Al
54Al
42Al
40Al
37Al
36Al
38Al
Baker
Jones
25Al
36Ga
42Ga
Brown
16-25La
Coltard
Brantley
Clayton
19La
13La
20La
1La
4La
Gibson
Johnson
52Ga
40Ga
41Ga
43Ga
14La
X
Oliver
15Mi
99Id
70Oh
48Il
103Oh
46Oh
6Io
40Il
XX
Harrow
X
Walcutt
XXX
Blair
Union
Confederate
750ft

CHAPTER ONE HUNDRED EIGHT

Union | JOHN LOGAN

GENERAL HARROW'S 4TH DIVISION

JULY 22, 1864

5:00 P.M.

All along the line General Logan had ridden, troops had halted their work to raise hands, weapons, hats, and fists in the air and called his name, "Black Jack, Black Jack!" It was great for them to rally. Being there among them created a personal form of electricity. It pulled men to him by some magnetism and sent them away refreshed or recharged with a greater sense of mission and their part in it. He was unclear about the source of this thing, but he knew that on this day, he was the right man in the right place. Perhaps someone else could have been more successful, but he was here and clearly more than able to fill the hole left by McPherson's death.

Logan's enthusiasm and willingness to risk all was infectious and ran along with him. Men ready to quit were now ready to reform and retake what they had earlier abandoned. Personal leadership and leading by example was working. Even his big black horse seemed to detect the excitement in the circumstance and behaved in a manner befitting the steed of a medieval Marcher Lord. Military chaos, danger, potential defeat of the Army of the Tennessee, and the huge tactical loss for Sherman all loomed before him. Logan believed he could do all that was required, almost by will alone, and he would.

CHAPTER ONE HUNDRED NINE

Union | LUCIEN P. GREATHOUSE

SOUTH OF THE RAILROAD AS THE 4TH DIVISION OF THE FIFTEENTH ARMY CORPS COUNTERATTACKS

JULY 22, 1864

5:00 P.M.

Astride a big, yellow horse sat twenty-two-year-old commander of the 48th Illinois, Brigadier General Lucien Greathouse. The big horse had been at work since early this morning. His workday had run through the noonday heat and into the late afternoon. The horse was covered with the sweat and its froth like nearly every other living thing on this hot afternoon. Although Greathouse was unaware of his promotion to brigadier general, the orders were even now on their way. The promotion order would be delivered on July 24, 1864.

In the morning of July 22, pickets had set out to report to Colonel John Oliver, the brigade commander, that the Union lines both north and south of the railroad were under severe assault. The positions earlier held by the 70th Ohio and the 15th Michigan were in danger of being overrun. The 48th Illinois and the 99th Indiana were sent back across the same ground they had charged over several hours earlier.

After a hard fight on the south of the railroad, the men of the Federal 2nd Division and the 1st Brigade of Harrow's 4th Division had now begun to fall back as Cheatham's men overran the areas. At the same time, Logan returned toward the wreckage of the Union line at the railway gap with the brigade, under the command of Mersey, of Sweeny's 2nd Division of the Sixteenth Army Corps. Knowing that Mersey's hot and recently bloodied brigade was in good hands and competent to deal with the fight on the north side of the railroad, Logan was distracted to see the substantial disarray south of the railroad.

With his predisposition for action compelling him and the big black horse moving him, Logan saw a knot of mounted officers off to his left. In seconds, he joined them and evaluated the chaos before him.

"Harrow," Logan barked. "What in hell does this mean?"

Explaining quickly, Harrow replied, "Sir, the 2nd Division over there on my right was overwhelmed and retreated. Their lines were broken. For me to have kept Williams' brigade in place would have allowed the enemy to hit them from the rear. I moved them back here to our old lines to reform."

Logan said, "Those works must be retaken or the whole Army of the Tennessee is gone to hell. They *must* be retaken. Bring those batteries up here now and shell those damn Johnny Rebs out of those holes. Do it now, man! Do you hear?!"

As late afternoon came, the 4th Division, including the 48th Illinois, were preparing to counterattack and regain their advance lines. Troops were tired, hot, thirsty, bloody, and dirty. Smoke from the two batteries assigned to the 4th Division was thick on the still afternoon air. The world seemed consumed in smoke, fire, and noise. Greathouse on his yellow horse knew his troops always fought best when he was in the front leading them. They always followed, and success was always theirs. The yellow horse jumped forward as the spurs on Greathouse's non-regulation leather boots encouraged him.

Harrow's roar to charge, which was echoed by brigade, regimental, and company officers, ignited the blue troops forward, and charge they did. As his horse went forward, Greathouse unsheathed his long saber. Turning his head over his left shoulder, he yelled the order to charge at the top of his lungs to his men and rode rapidly toward the entrenched boys in butternut. As his horse carried him close, a Rebel yelled, "Surrender, you damn fool! Can't you see you are beaten?"

Greathouse, full of the fire of combat and gallantry, yelled back, "Beat? Hell, we have only just come into the fight." As he began to stand in his stirrups, a minie ball struck him dead center in the chest, and he was dead before his body struck the ground. He had been on this earth for fifteen days, one month, and twenty-two years.

CHAPTER ONE HUNDRED TEN

UNION

DeGress Battery

North end, the right of the 2nd Division of the Fifteenth Army Corps

July 22, 1864

4:45 p.m.

Colonel Martin, commanding the three regiments of 1st Brigade of the 2nd Division of the Fifteenth Army Corps, had been well south of the railroad supporting General Harrow's 4th Division. He then received orders from Logan to move his three regiments back toward the railroad and the area of operations they had left earlier in the day. By returning, they would be positioned to help repel the aggressive forces of Deas, Brantley, and Sharp. All of this Federal activity by the Fifteenth Army Corps was enhanced by the relatively narrow front established by the Confederates, Logan's willingness for direct and personal leadership, the presence of veteran troops, and the semblance of an interior line.

As a result of the formidable bulge created by the two divisions of Southerners who had engulfed the DeGress Battery, the Hurt House, the road, and the railroad cut, the Confederate troops created an incursion of about 3,500 feet in the Federal line. This lodging was now about to be assaulted by forces amounting to some twenty regiments. A veteran Union force of seven regiments would strike from the north, or left, of the Confederate line. It was joined by the reorganized regiments of Lightburn's 2nd Brigade, which would strike from the east. The three regiments of Mersey's 2nd Brigade, which was now in line of battle, would strike the Rebels from the southeast. These regiments were then joined by the three regiments belonging to the brigade under Martin. This was an ad hoc but nonetheless powerful and nearly irresistible force that simply overwhelmed the enemy with mass, violence, firepower, determination, and calculated coordination. It functioned in the informal, easy way the Union's premier western army had learned and developed over the years of its existence.

The Union forces moved forward from the base of the hill the Howard House sat on. The eight guns from Landgraber's division artillery supported them. In addition, there were five batteries from the Twenty-Third Army Corps now being served by fresh gun crews, adding substantial volumes of steel on target. These guns under Sherman himself would endeavor to prevent any reinforcements from coming to the aid of the butternut left and to provide additional support to the counterattack by the men of the 1st Division. The moving regiments ranged from west to east as follows: 4th Iowa, 9th Iowa, 30th Iowa, and the 27th Missouri—all in one line of battle. Behind the first line came a second line made up of the 25th Iowa, the 26th Missouri, and the 76th Ohio. Some 2,000 men, a strong veteran force, were on the move.

This force moved easily until it found the low, swampy ground. The terrain acted to break up the neat regimental lines. The Confederate force responded to the threat confronting their left flank by pouring heavy fire into the assaulting Federals. The low ground was difficult to traverse, but it provided cover for the 1st Division, not unlike that provided to Manigault's brigade when they had begun their assault on the 2nd Division north of the railroad. The swampy bottom carried a streambed that was wet, soft, and bramble filled. The Union soldiers forced their way through and emerged on the Southern side, where their officers hastily realigned the battle lines.

The 1st Brigade struck the Rebel line at the point where the DeGress Battery was located, and the 9th Iowa took possession of it. The 4th Iowa was sent into the ravine west of the line, where it shortly ran into the buzz saw that was the 650 men of the 54th, 42nd, and 37th Alabama.

Higley's brigade poured relentless fire down into the natural trench that was occupied by the 300 men of the 4th Iowa. The advantage of the natural defense provided a certain equality between the opposing forces.

Yet the Southern forces had gone as far as they could. Their movement to the left had stretched its resources to a point that no reserve or reinforcement existed for Cheatham's corps. In effect, Higley's and Jones' brigades had been the shock reserve. They had successfully punched out the salient and sustained it for a while, but there were no troops behind them. Orders came for the Confederates to retreat. Tired, hot, and thirsty, the butternut troops began to fall back the long mile or so to the fortifications of Atlanta. Wounded who could move on their own struggled. Some fell, and some had friends help them in their painful withdrawal. Dead, dying, and others littered the field. No Union pursuit followed. The blue forces were exhausted and, in their hearts, satisfied by the restoration of the status quo ante.

CHAPTER ONE HUNDRED ELEVEN

Confederacy | WILLIAM HARDEE & SAM WATKINS

SOUTH OF BALD HILL

JULY 22, 1864

5:05 P.M.

CONFEDERACY, WILLIAM HARDEE

The life-and-death struggle for Bald Hill was still killing men on both sides. Hardee knew the battle was over on the right. He believed there was still a chance to make all the day's losses still count if the stubborn Yankee resistance on the hill could be overwhelmed. Cleburne represented most of his aspirations for anything that might resemble a victory.

Union forces were still in combat with the enemy. The intermingled units had been pushed, shoved, kicked, and punished backward 300 to 500 yards from the fishhook position held early this morning. Some regiments found themselves in the fifth or sixth defensive position of the day. For some, the move backward toward the hill had been orderly, under orders, and in a manner that maintained the integrity of the companies and regiments. For others, the movement had been more a rout with fear as the commander. It had been every man for himself. For some, death resolved any questions about the way they should perform their duty. For others, wounded and insensible with pain, baking under the heat of the July sun and overcome by circumstances, the hell was just beginning.

General Hardee had earlier issued orders and slowly remnants of his forces combined.

Colonel Walker's relatively fresh brigade, which had mostly been marching all day, returned from the far right with tales of swamps and blackberry thickets. The Tennessee division commanded by George

Maney, who had been over on the left all day, also returned now that Wright's brigade under the command of Colonel John Carter had returned to the fold. Lowrey's men had marched and counter marched through a terrain that was nearly a swamp. His left had lost contact with his right, and the thickness of the woods was such that even in the bright light of day, Lowrey couldn't see more than a hundred yards of his lines at a time. During the charge that had taken place earlier in the afternoon, each of his regimental organizations had lost more than fifty percent of their effective strength, some 578 men.

In addition, he had remnants of Granbury's Texans under the wounded Brigadier General James Smith. This brigade had lost all but one of its regimental officers and had sustained heavy losses as a result of its combat on July 21 and 22. On top of this, he had patched together what remained of Mercer's Georgia brigade under Lieutenant Colonel Guyton and Gist's South Carolina and Georgia soldiers, who in the absence of Gist was now operating under Colonel James McCullough. Granbury's Texans, Mercer's Georgians, and Gist's South Carolina and Georgia soldiers would not be directly involved in the assault but would rather form a reserve, which could be called on if any opportunity presented itself for exploitation by these all but worn-out soldiers. Hardee also gathered as much of his field artillery as he could to provide close support to his attaching infantry columns.

On and around Bald Hill, the Union soldiers had a still evolving defensive system. The original north-south line held by Leggett's 3rd Division of the Seventeenth Army Corps now had an arm that ran perpendicular toward the east. This line was occupied by the two brigades commanded by Hall and Potts that have been so roughly handled for the previous four or five hours. Wangelin's 3rd Brigade of the 1st Division was newly tied into the south-looking eastward extending line. Extending from the south of the hill were two lines of troops facing Atlanta to the west, and covering their backs were more soldiers from Seventeenth Army Corps, who were facing west. The attacking Southerners of Hardee's corps would strike this formidable line.

About 5:00 p.m., Hardee ordered his two divisions forward. Cleburne, with his personality in full display, led the way. Maney had his full division for the first time that day, and his men began their attack from the southwest and struck the west side of the Union forces. Coming up at the same time was the brigade led by Govan. Govan's boys hit the same Union line from the southeast. Resistance was initially great from the Federals, but being caught in the middle of two enfilading crossfire, the Union troops were moved out of their trench. The Union soldiers retreated under pressure and slowly were driven back up the trench line toward Bald Hill to their north. Along the way, men were killed, wounded, and left behind to be caught up by the men from Maney's and Cleburne's divisions.

Maney's troops swarmed just at the point where the eastward and perpendicular Union line intersected the north-south line. It was at this apex that Battery D of the 1st Illinois, a four-gun battery of 24-pound Howitzers, was positioned. The boy captain, Edgar H. Cooper, commanded the guns. In addition, the six guns of the 15th Michigan Light Battery H, which consisted of six three-inch ordnance rifles, were just east of Cooper's big guns, providing a hard point to the new line. As Union troops converged, the new line gained gravity and strength. Experienced gun crews served these ten guns, and their rate of fire was quick. It seemed each gun exploded every ten to fifteen seconds. Smoke, flash, and fire made assaulting the corner and line an uncomfortable experience. The range into the troops of Cleburne and Maney, which were now more or less combined, was close. With each explosion, huge holes were ripped into the grey and butternut lines.

CONFEDERACY, SAM WATKINS

Sam Watkins of the 1st Tennessee, part of Maney's old brigade now under Colonel Cornelius Walker, was close to Maney when he said in a near formal manner, "Soldiers, you are ordered to go forward and charge that battery. When you start that charge, I want you to do it as if you were upon the wings of the wind. Shoot down and bayonet the cannoners and take those guns at all hazards."

Cleburne had been in the forefront of Govan's troops just to the right of the 1st Tennessee and shouted, "You hear what General Maney said, boys. If they don't take it, then by the eternal God, you have got to take it."

One of General Cleburne's former fellow countrymen from the 10th Texas yelled back, "Faith, General. We'll take up a collection and buy you a battery, by Jesus."

With the talking done, the fighting recommenced with passion. Up and down the line, the Rebel yell and the Texas cattle calls rose from parched throats and sang out of powder-blackened faces. Close combat, man-to-man, ensued. The lines made up of the 3rd Division of the Seventeenth Army Corps were solid, and the troops manning that trench line knew they had no place left to go. They fought bayonet to rifle butt, ball to fist.

Sam Watkins would later recall that before he fell, he felt like the hot flame of hell had been turned loose on him. Smoke from a thousand personal weapons created dirty, white billows that hung close to the ground. These individual balls of smoke grew, enhanced by the cumulus clouds generated each time one of the artillery pieces spoke. These growing clouds combined with the manmade thunder and lightning forged in the sun's heat to create a scene terrible and impossible to paint completely. Men, wet with sweat, scared, and in the grip of courage, fought on as though possessed.

On the blue side of this hell of shooting and noise, Force was commanding his dug-in, defending soldiers by being in as many places in the shortest period of time. He seemed to be wherever he was needed. As the fighting grew particularly desperate, General Force yelled for a flag. One of those hearing his cry was frightened into thinking that surrender was the next and most logical step. That young man came running to Force with a large white handkerchief.

As he approached Force with the proffered white flag, the commander erupted, "Damn you, sir. I don't want a flag of truce. I want an American flag." Soon, the proper flag was obtained and planted where it could be seen by most of the Federals on Bald Hill. The presence of the flag helped rally and stabilize the Union line. Brigadier General Force was soon thereafter hit in the head by a round that exited his eye. Blood rushed from his eye, head, nose, and mouth. Not dead but badly wounded, he nonetheless remained with his command. He was unable to speak, but his steadfastness was a catalyst to his men.

The battle raged, but that hastily prepared perpendicular line part way up Bald Hill somehow held. Maney's Tennesseans, Smith's Texans, and Govan's Arkansans had slugged it out with their larger, stronger opponent. They had given better than they got, but it was an impossible task to push the strong western men of the Seventeenth Army Corps any farther up the imposing hill.

As the sun began to sink and the first of the dusk began to show, the firing became sporadic as though by agreement. The cry of the wounded could now be heard, and the terrible realities on a personal basis were realized.

Hardee's effort—late in execution, fantastic in delivery, and very nearly a success—just had not been enough.

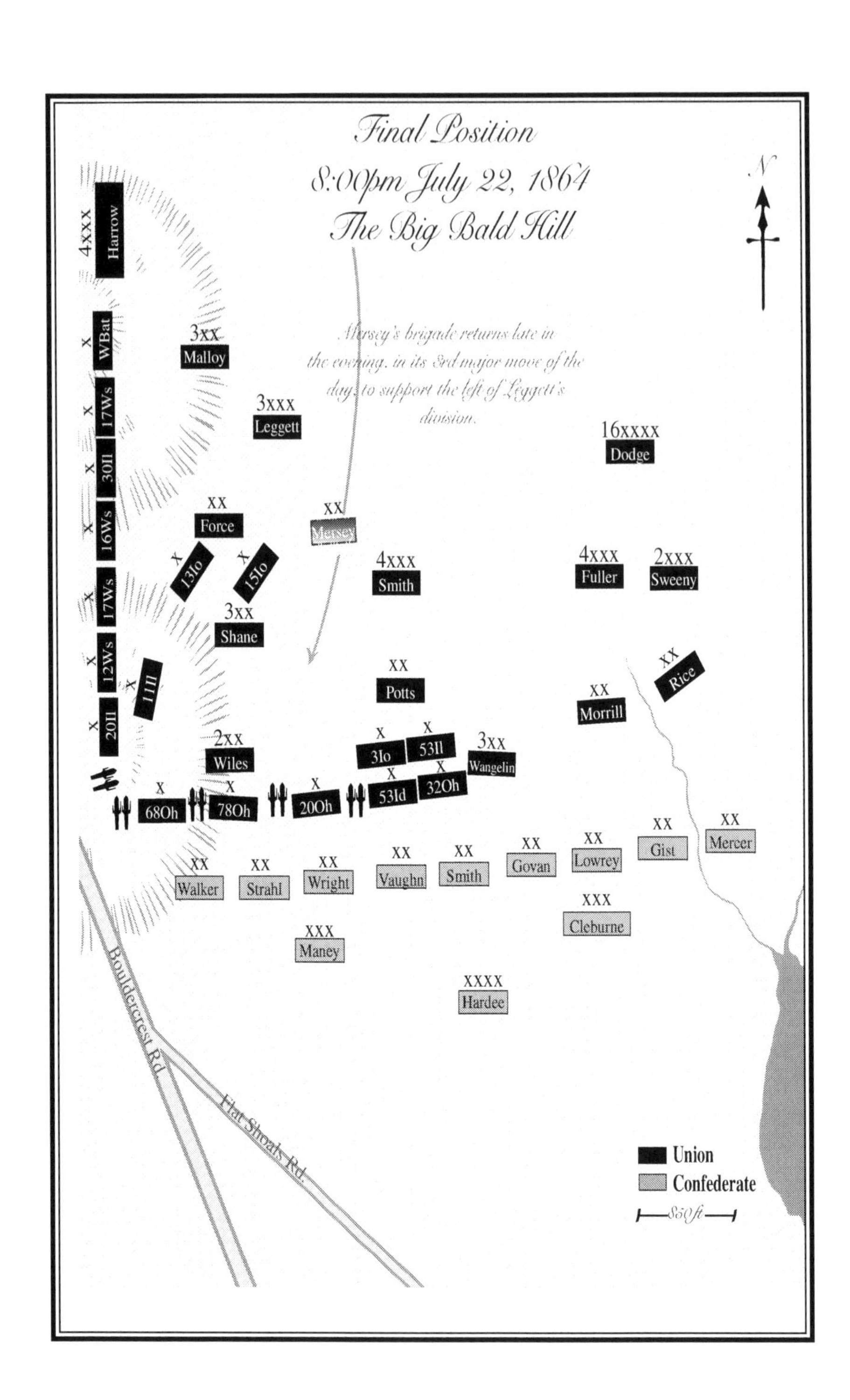
Final Position
8:00pm July 22, 1864
The Big Bald Hill
N
Mersey's brigade returns late in the evening, in its 3rd major move of the day, to support the left of Leggett's division.
4xxx
Harrow
x
WBat
3xx
Malloy
x
17Ws
3xxx
Leggett
x
30Il
16xxxx
Dodge
xx
Force
xx
Mersey
x
16Ws
x
13Io
x
15Io
4xxx
Smith
4xxx
Fuller
2xxx
Sweeny
x
17Ws
3xx
Shane
x
12Ws
x
11Il
xx
Potts
xx
Rice
xx
Morrill
x
20Il
2xx
Wiles
x
3Io
x
53Il
3xx
Wangelin
x
53Id
x
32Oh
x
68Oh
x
78Oh
x
20Oh
xx
Walker
xx
Strahl
xx
Wright
xx
Vaughn
xx
Smith
xx
Govan
xx
Lowrey
xx
Gist
xx
Mercer
xxx
Cleburne
xxx
Maney
xxxx
Hardee
Bouldercrest Rd.
Flat Shoals Rd.
Union
Confederate
850ft

CHAPTER ONE HUNDRED TWELVE

Confederacy | JOHN HOOD

HOOD'S HEADQUARTERS

JULY 22, 1864

10:30 P.M.

Hood's restless eyes read the message he had written. It was familiar to him, but he wanted to be certain the day's events were set forth in a correct manner.

Near Atlanta, July 22, 1864—10:30 p.m.

Hon J.A. SEDDON, Richmond:

The army shifted its position last night, fronting Peach Tree Creek, formed line of battle around the city with Stewart's and Cheatham's corps, General Hardee, with his corps, made a night march and attacked the enemy's extreme left at 3 o'clock to-day, drove him from his works, capturing 16 pieces of artillery and 5 stand of colors. Major General Cheatham attacked the enemy at 4 p.m. with a portion of his command, drove the enemy, capturing 6 pieces of artillery.

During the engagement we captured about 2,000 prisoners, but loss not fully ascertained.

Major-General Walker killed, Brigadier-Generals Smith, Gist and Mercer wounded. Our troops fought with great gallantry.

J.B. Hood,
General.

That would have to do. It seemed a great success, even if the result was not quite as hoped for. He would see where they were the next day. It had been a busy time since taking command, and it was time to get a little rest.

CHAPTER ONE HUNDRED THIRTEEN

Union | JOHN LOGAN

LOGAN'S HEADQUARTERS

JULY 22, 1864

LATE EVENING

It had been one of the busiest days and maybe the most important day of Logan's life. It had been a long day with lots of challenges, few of which had been familiar to him. In many ways, it was the kind of day to relish, especially after getting through it successfully. Logan sat smoking a cigar and reviewed his last message of the day.

HDQRS. DEPARTMENT AND ARMY OF THE TENNESSEE,
July 22, 1864.

Maj. Gen. W. T. SHERMAN, Commanding, &c.:
DEAR SIR: I have seen all the corps commanders since I left your headquarters and made the best dispositions I could of the troops of the Army of the Tennessee. I find one division of the Seventeenth Corps somewhat despondent, but think they will hold their position; have sent them three fresh regiments to support them in holding the hill that I think is the key-point to my whole position. Some prisoners, who have just come inside our picket-lines in General Dodge's front, report themselves from Hood's corps (now Cheatham's), which they report moving to our left, in order to attack in the morning; they say Atlanta is held by militia, and that Polk's old corps is on our extreme right, west

of Atlanta. This statement may not be true, but I am inclined to think it is true from all that I have learned from other prisoners. The note to you from General Schofield giving you the information that there was nothing but a small force of cavalry in Decatur to-day, would somewhat do away with my impression about the force were it not for Colonel Sprague's report to General Dodge. He reports that he was attacked by a large force, and had lost nearly 400 men killed, wounded, and captured, as General Dodge informs me. I give you this information all as I get it, that you may judge from all information that you may get as to where troops of the enemy are and what their intentions are.

Very respectfully,
JOHN A. LOGAN,
Major-General.

Logan could only hope that Sherman would think he was doing a good job with the paperwork side of running this army. It was clear he had done a good job of holding the position he had inherited after General McPherson's death. The volunteers who made up the Army of the Tennessee had held or rallied and were still in charge of the field at the end of the day. Even Sherman would agree the army had performed well.

CHAPTER ONE HUNDRED FOURTEEN

Confederacy | JAMES HAGAN

PRISONER OF WAR COMPOUND, ARMY OF THE TENNESSEE

NEAR THE DECATUR ROAD

JULY 22, 1864

NIGHTTIME

The last three days had been filled with turmoil, combat, marching, more combat, and more capture. So far, the Yankee soldiers had treated Hagan and his fellow captives well enough. These Union soldiers, despite a full day of combat, seemed to have an excess of food, water, weapons, and animals. It was a rich, pulsing force that was very different from the sharp-edged, hard army he had been a part of for so long.

On the evening of July 19, he had felt the tension in the air and had known change and a hard fight were soon to be his fare. He was still hungering for the box of sweets and food his wife was to send him, but during the chaos of the day, he hadn't had time to think about the box. In that fight for Bald Hill—though to First Sergeant Hagan's mind, the attack had not really gotten under way—he found himself, Captain Knight, Sergeant Pounds, Captain Carroll, Lieutenant Hall, Giddins, and Byrd surrounded by grim-faced Federal troops. As he was on his way to the Union rear, he saw Colonel Nisbet, the newly minted brigade commander, had also been captured.

Once in the assembly area, he had seen one of the Tomlinson boys had also been taken. While the fighting was over in this particular sector, there was still ragged firing from the southwest. The Yanks around him spoke of nearly being overrun, making a stand, and finally retaking what they had lost. Hagan thought that it was hard to know the truth. The Yanks didn't seem comfortable. They were staying put and not moving off the battle line.

Hagan contemplated his capture. No doubt, barring a freak accident, he should survive the war, and with luck, he would ultimately be able to return home and see his wife and the farm.

His three years as a soldier for the Confederacy was nearly at an end. He had entered the service in Big Shanty, Georgia, just a little north of where he was tonight. He had come into the service with Captain Knight and a hundred other young men from Berrien County, and now he was ending his active service with some of those same men. Lots of men had been lost along the way. He was alive and well, and that was all he could ask for.

CHAPTER ONE HUNDRED FIFTEEN

Union | H.H. GRIFFITHS

1ST IOWA BATTERY

BEHIND THE LINES OF THE FIFTEENTH ARMY CORPS, SOUTH OF THE RAILROAD

JULY 22, 1864

9:00 P.M.

All over what had been the battlefield, on both sides of the line, fires glowed. Animals moved. Men ate and slept. The wounded and dying set forth cries. Sweat mingled with the dark earth smells that arose from huge holes torn by random and well-aimed artillery. The stench of death was everywhere. Bodies not yet swollen and not always rigid lay in heaps of sudden lifelessness—eyes open and staring, surrounded by flies and other feasting insects. When men die and the control they exert on themselves and everything around them vanishes, their poor beaten bodies let go of what they can: feces, blood, and urine. The bodily fluids formed a magnet of life, providing juice to the flying and crawling bugs and began the many steps of returning each dead thing back to the earth.

The smells of smashed wild onions, crushed and broken pine limbs and needles, the stink of exploded powder, and the scent of evaporating urine in rough wool trousers were pervasive—a ripe, thick, harsh stink that reached into a man's brain through his nose and mouth. Once this aroma was breathed, it was the kind of smell that could always be recalled even years later, sometimes involuntarily when one's mind drifted back over what was, what could be, and, for many, what never would be.

Everything was made worse by the heat, which was not enough to cook the deads' flesh but was enough to release the essence of death into the immediate atmosphere. Death and heat seemed to lie like a dense cloud over the acres of broken, exhausted, angry men. Soon, corpses would harden and bloat. Mouths that earlier had eaten, kissed, and spoken would bake into grimaces, and eyeless sockets would loom in those wasted, broken faces.

Somewhat stiffly, the bone weary artillery officer of the Union 4th Division, H.H. Griffiths, walked through the limbers, caissons, and battery wagons. He was moving toward Lieutenant Gay, the commander of the 1st Iowa Battery, who was taking his ease around the campfire. To Gay and the men about the fire, he said, "Sharp fight today."

"Yes, sir. I think a sharp fight covers it."

"You and the battery did well today."

"Thank you, sir."

"Listen, I haven't had a chance to see your artificers, Charles Hough and Bill Dilts, yet. If I don't see them, thank them for me. They did a great job of carpentry on the coffin for Colonel Greathouse."

"Yes, sir. It all fits quite tightly. They did a good job, and the Colonel deserves it. Without Colonel Greathouse and his 48th Illinois and their rifles, we would have lost a couple of guns and a lot of men. They covered us when we were pulled out of there. The coffin isn't much, but it seems right to me that we can send him back home in a coffin made by the 1st Iowa. He was really just a boy."

Later, the coffin and its contents would begin its long journey back to Vandalia, Illinois.

CHAPTER ONE HUNDRED SIXTEEN

Union | GRENVILLE DODGE

IN THE REAR OF THE FIFTEENTH ARMY CORPS

ALONG THE DECATUR ROAD

JULY 22, 1864

10:35 P.M.

Disorganization was slowly being overcome on the Union side as men found their way to regiments that had earlier disappeared. Consolidation, food, coffee, and a sense of relief bolstered the Union defenders.

But even now, sporadic gunfire could be heard. Most of the gunfire came from the south side of Bald Hill, where trenches ran nearly east and west at a ninety degree angle from the main line. In some instances, the troops in blue held the north side of an earthwork, and the butternut-clad men of the south held the other side. Across the line, Cleburne's soldiers clung grimly to the high watermark they had achieved with a general sense that victory over the stubborn Yankee foe had nearly been theirs.

Further to the east, the men of the Seventeenth Army Corps continued to improve the line they had defended and had accomplished what many had believed to be impossible only hours before. They tied their lines into those held by men of the Sixteenth Army Corps and mingled with the soldiers of Wangelin's brigade from the 1st Division of the Fifteenth Army Corps to successfully hold off the Confederate soldiers.

Hungry and exhausted, men from the Fifteenth Army Corps held the line they had first taken early this morning, which stretched from north of Bald Hill across the Decatur Road and the railroad, past the Hurt House, and toward the hill where Schofield's Army of the Cumberland lay in untested trenches.

The smell of the battle was still in the air, but without the sun, the grimmest aspects were concealed from all but the most intent eyes. Small sounds of agony, pain, and frustration mewed along the red clay ditches as men came to realize they were still alive. The three men—Logan, Blair, and Dodge—who gathered near the big oak had escaped a near thing today.

Generals Logan, Blair, and Dodge had fought the Army of Tennessee for nine hours as hard and fast as the butternut-and-gray corps of Cheatham and Hardee had forced them to. The emotional high, which had been heightened by cups of coffee and some occasional whiskey, and the unexpressed joy of life in the middle of so much death and destruction had peaked and was rushing toward fatigue.

Logan, having run the Army of the Tennessee all afternoon from one crisis to the next, had been in his natural element. "We licked 'em today, didn't we?" he said to the other two major generals. "By God and thunder, we held and beat them bad today!"

It appeared that he was still ready to go, almost as though he hoped another break would occur so he could lead the way, plug the gap, and win the war on his black horse with his exalted troops.

With less enthusiasm, Blair and Dodge looked at each other as though they shared a secret. Sometimes, Logan was so full of himself it was almost an embarrassment. Logan still talked and moved and explained how it had all come about as Dodge and Blair thought to themselves that they damn well knew how it had come about and knew the cost had been great.

Logan said, "Dodge, it was great that you had those brigades over there, just where the Rebs were going to attack. Almost seemed as though they had just marched up."

Dodge replied, "John, let's not get carried away. McPherson, God rest his soul, had ordered me near that place. I was on my way to tie into Frank's left and give him a little help. Really just never got to the right place. But in a sense, I suppose we did."

Blair spoke up, "You both know I could have used the help, and I got more than I bargained for today. But I guess it was for the good of all that you were where you were. Patrick Cleburne was more than a handful. If he'd had another brigade, I shudder to think that he might have taken that Bald Hill back. John, thanks for sending that brigade of yours over to the hill this evening. Tired as everyone is, they will be a great help."

Speech always seemed to restore Logan's energy. He took a long pull from a nearby canteen. Refreshed and lubricated, he spoke again, "Look here, our boys are exhausted and worn out. Isn't that right? Frank? Dodge? Wouldn't it be best to tell Sherman we could use a little relief? Couldn't he let us have some of the fresh boys from Schofield's Twenty-Third Corps?"

Logan was becoming more animated now and was pushing both his friends and now his subordinate corps commanders to join him in his expression of need. Logan argued, "That's the right thing to do, isn't it? Dodge, you are junior here, but more to the point, Uncle Billy likes you best. You are an engineer, and he doesn't think about you the same way he sees Frank and me. Damned if I don't think Bill Sherman hates congressmen worse than newspapermen. Go tell him we need some help. He will buy it better from you."

Dodge rose to his feet, and with a half-smile said, "I'm not sure there is much to choose from between congressmen and reporters, so I guess I understand Sherman pretty well."

Dodge and a few of his staff moved off, mounted their tired horses, and rode forward to find General Sherman. They rode toward the hill to the north to Sherman's headquarters. They rode into the yard and found Sherman in his tent. It was growing late, but here at the Headquarters of the Military Division of the Mississippi, a fair amount of bustle was still evident. Lantern light was prevalent, unlike the dark lines of Bald Hill.

As Dodge approached, Sherman glanced up. He seemed surprised to see Dodge, but he didn't seem at all displeased. Sherman, though always busy, retained his high energy even if he seemed somewhat worn by the events of the day. After all, he had been in the fight; he had organized the field guns on the hill and bossed them personally. Nonetheless, he half rose and said, "General Dodge, good to see you." As he spoke, he extended his right hand to grasp Dodge's left.

Sherman said, "Shame about McPherson. I counted on him for more than just to run the Army of the Tennessee. Great friend. I always thought I would be the one to die in this conflict and assumed he would take my place. Grant feels the same way." McPherson couldn't really be replaced. He was a great cadet and a true professional officer—Sherman's right arm.

"Yes, we lost a good and great man today. He will be sorely missed by every man in our little army," Dodge agreed and then spoke again.

"General, I hate to bother you. I know you were not expecting me, but General Logan and Blair sent me to see if you could provide us with some relief from the Army of the Cumberland or from Schofield's Army of the Ohio."

Sherman, who had been restlessly pacing, turned on Dodge, "Dodge, you whipped them today!"

"Yes, sir."

"Can't you do it tomorrow?" Sherman asked swiftly.

"Yes, sir."

Sherman looked at Dodge as though their oral exchange was now as complete as it had been brief.

"Good evening, General Sherman," Dodge said softly as he half saluted and turned back to his horse and staff. As he mounted and commenced his ride back to where Logan and Blair waited, he said to himself, "I will not repeat this errand again."

As the small group of Union horsemen rode away, Sherman mused. He guessed that he could have explained it to Dodge. It seemed important especially in light of General McPherson's death to have it said that the Army of the Tennessee had fought a great battle that day, needing no help and receiving none. It stood alone in the face of all Hood could throw at it. It stood and fought and whipped the best the South had to offer. Those boys were worn out, but he suspected that Hood would not have the ability or desire to try again tomorrow after the hard beating he took. He felt safe for the Army of the Tennessee tonight and tomorrow. After that, they would see. Sherman turned to the draft of a report on his desk. It could go out on the wire tomorrow.

Near Atlanta, Ga., July 23, 1864

Maj. Gen. H.W. Halleck,
Washington, D.C.

Yesterday morning the enemy fell back to the entrenchments proper of the city of Atlanta, which are in a general circle of a radius of one mile and a half, and we closed in. While we were forming our lines and selecting positions for batteries, the enemy appeared suddenly out of the dense woods in heavy masses on our extreme left, and struck the Seventeenth Corps (General Blair's) in flank, and was forcing it back, when the Sixteenth Corps (General Dodge's) came up and checked the movement, but the enemy's cavalry got well to our rear and into Decatur, and for some hours our left flank was completely enveloped. The fighting that resulted was continuous until night, with heavy loss on both sides. The enemy took one of our batteries (Murray's of the Regular Army) that was marching in its place in column on the road unconscious of danger. About 4 p.m. the enemy sallied against the division of General Morgan L. Smith, which occupied an abandoned line of rifle-trenches near the railroad, east of the city, and forced it back some 400 yards, leaving in his hands for the time two batteries, but the ground and batteries were immediately after recovered by the same troops, re-enforced. I cannot well approximate our loss, which fell heaviest on the 15th and 17th Corps, but count it 3,000; but I know that, being on the defensive, we have inflicted equally heavy loss on the enemy. General McPherson, when arranging his troops, about 11 a.m., and passing from one column to another, unconsciously rode upon an ambuscade without apprehension and at some distance ahead of his stall and orderlies and was shot dead. His body was sent in charge of his personal staff back to Marietta and Chattanooga. His loss as that moment was most serious, but General Logan at once arranged the troops, and had immediate direction of them during the rest of the day. Our left, though refused somewhat, is still within easy cannon-range of Atlanta. The enemy seems to man his extensive parapets and, at the same time, has to spare heavy assaulting columns; bit to-day we will entrench our front lines, which will give me troops to spare to meet these assaults. I cannot hear of the loss of more than a few wagons, taken by the enemy's cavalry during his temporary pause in Decatur, whence all the trains had been securely removed to the rear of the main army, under cover of a brigade of infantry, commanded by Colonel Sprague. During the heavy attack on the left, the remainder of the line was not engaged.

W.T. Sherman,
Major-General.

CHAPTER ONE HUNDRED SEVENTEEN

Confederacy | JOHN HOOD

HEADQUARTERS OF THE ARMY OF TENNESSEE

JULY 23, 1864

EARLY MORNING

General Hood knew it was important to communicate with the government in Richmond. Although he knew only little more about yesterday's successful attack, he did have some reported statements to correct.

ATLANTA, July 23, 1864

Hon. J.A. SEDDON,
Richmond:

In the engagement of yesterday we captured 18 stand of colors instead of 5, and 13 guns instead of 22, as previously reported. Brigadier-General Mercer not wounded. All quiet to-day except skirmishing, and the enemy occasionally throwing shell into the city. The army is in good spirits.

J.B. HOOD.

CHAPTER ONE HUNDRED EIGHTEEN

In the future, historians would treat the actions of the Federal and the Confederate armies from Johnston's retreat over the Chattahoochee through July 22 as a series of loosely connected events rather than a whole action or process with a general guiding concept. Neither Johnston nor Hood ever enunciated an overarching strategy of how to win the war. They would fight when things seemed in their favor, and Johnston believed it advantageous to pull the Union army deeper and deeper into the South. Generally, the North planned and acted, and the South provided a response. The South sometimes anticipated, like the change of command to Hood, but not often.

Yet, a lot of what at first seems to be a series of unrelated events on further review takes on the shine of consistency and process. Not only is the geography close enough together to be one larger piece of dirt, but many activities take place at essentially the same time. The forces used are in some part the same. An act one place influenced or resulted in a reply elsewhere.

In the battle, the northern movements were in unison, maybe less than perfectly executed, but nonetheless accomplished. The clash along Peachtree Creek began at Moore's Mills and flowed to Howell Mill. Then, it jumped forward to Clear Creek and west with the Battle of Collier's Ridge. At the same time, in reaction to the Federal movement from Decatur, the Southern line continued to shift to the right. Fighting was going on north and east of the city, and that combat held both sides in place and prevented substantial, battle-winning support from being moved from one venue to the other.

There were some exceptions but there was no support of the size, strength, or ability required to change the outcome of the battle. Rather, the leaders used the principle of conservation or economy of force, i.e., deploying the least amount who were more or less able to do the immediate tactical job. Examples were the movement of Cleburne's division, the positioning of Smith's 3,500 Georgia Militia force, and Hardee's night march and attack. While they served an important role in the battle of Atlanta on the east side of town, Cleburne's division's departure from one spot and movement to another tied the first location to the second and to some degree integrated the activities. What would the result have been if Cleburne's division had stayed and been hurled against Newton's troops with Stephen and Walker rather than relying on Bate and Maney?

So, this thirteen-day period in July of 1864 marks an integrated, fluid battlefield—more complex as a result—and not a string of events unrelated to one another. The thirteen days of combat, with the last seven days being the most important, is known as the Battle of Atlanta.

EPILOGUE

The soldiers who stood their ground, ran for cover, or moved forward into a murderous hailstorm of spinning, half-ounce cones of lead did not march to Peachtree Creek or storm up the hill to Collier Road knowing that they were participating in the Battle of Peachtree Creek or the Battle of Atlanta. Many did not know the name of the watercourse or the name of the road men lost their lives along in pursuit of goals too difficult to understand or explain. The combatants did not know the distance to the Chattahoochee River or to Roswell, Georgia. They did not know the length of the defensive line, the height of the hillsides, the units assailing them, the route they marched, or their point of departure. The troops engaged did not know the name, psychology, or motivation of the enemy troop commander or anything about the new colonel running their own regiment. The numbers of dead and wounded were not known either, only that an individual himself was alive or was near death. The ignorance had a commonality that enveloped both the men in blue and the men in gray, who smashed into one another with little thought except to stay alive and kill that misguided yellowbelly aiming that long gun. The overall understanding of the battle we have now is a blessing these men didn't have. It may be that if the information available to us had been possessed by each actual participant, then the battle would have never occurred, and the present would be without that particular past.

The name of the murderous, blood-soaked, brutal days on the north and east sides of Atlanta would have to wait for a reporter or a journalist or a historian to coin a name for the awful activity that took place in what was otherwise an unremarkable field or woods. The formal invoice for the human misery and wreckage, imprecise and imperfect as anyone with a bit of knowledge would know, still had a ring of certainty when the "Battle of Atlanta" or the "Battle of Peachtree Creek" appeared in the dutifully written after-action reports that soon appeared.

The tallies men had for the number of men dead, wounded, and captured were a bit like keeping score and presumed one could discern a winner and loser from their review. The exact losses, in killed and wounded, from the combat taking place from July 18 through the July 22 are not known. The two forces have different definitions of casualties, and estimates of enemy losses are almost always exaggerated. But, the estimated numbers are that Major General Bill Sherman's three armies lost nearly 23,650 soldiers during the month of July in killed, wounded, and missing, which includes captured. The loss for the Army of Tennessee under Generals Johnston and Hood for nearly the full month of July totals around 10,841.

So who won? Was it the Federals, who had lost the most, or the Confederates, who lost the least? What had changed? By some, the army that retained the field the fight took place on is the victor. In the narrowest sense, this would make the Union army the winner, but Hood held Atlanta, and in the broadest sense, nothing much had changed. In fact, July 23 seemed a lot like the earlier, larger phases of the campaign. After those days in July, the city of Atlanta remained in Rebel hands. The bloodied Rebel Army of Tennessee was intact and within the fortifications and entrenchments surrounding Atlanta. The Confederates were dug-in in a strong defensive position, and the Union force was halted for the moment, awaiting the orders that consistently came—maneuver to the right. It was just one day pretty much like the one before and likely the one after.

This series of bloodlettings was not one of those monumental battles like Waterloo, where Napoleon's loss to Wellington ended his reign as Emperor of France and marked the end of his hundred-days return from exile. In regard to its decisiveness, the contest around Atlanta pales in comparison to Vicksburg or the hot July days in that small village in Gettysburg, Pennsylvania. Waterloo, Vicksburg, and Gettysburg all were cumulating events. The struggle for Atlanta, at least on July 23, was all merely process. Nonetheless the series of fights beginning with the River Line and proceeding through Roswell, Peachtree Creek, Ezra Church, the Siege, the Extended Line, and Jonesboro all somehow have fallen under the mantle of "The Battle of Atlanta."

In some ways, Hood's aggressive approach resulted in Sherman being drawn into fulfilling a major part of his mission. Sherman came to grips with the Southern army and came close to causing its destruction. It came, not as a result of offensive action by the Federals, but rather because they were attacked, they absorbed the sledgehammer blows, and they reacted. The industrial war-making ability of the South was still functioning in part afterward, but the sharp spear of nationalism—the army—had been damaged. It is fair to say the result came not by Sherman's design, but rather by accident. The general whose instincts were to maneuver and avoid the direct clash had success by essentially repulsing vigorous attacks by a determined, veteran, experienced, and lethal enemy.

The fight was far from over. It was not until early in the morning of September 2, 1864, that the Georgia Militia and Stewart's corps slipped out of Atlanta under the glare of fires burning everything not taken earlier by soldiers and citizens and under the tremendous explosions of locomotives and large supplies of ammunition. The mayor formally surrendered the city, and by 11:00 a.m., the first Federal troops entered the long-sought Gate City. In an effort to destroy Atlanta's war-making industrial base (that quickly flared out of control), Sherman also burned about thirty percent of the city in mid-November before his march to the sea.

There were many unresolved issues remaining in the Federal and Confederate armies, but the issue surrounding Hood and Johnston would continue even after the Atlanta Campaign. Hood continued his active, aggressive, direct form of warfare, which resulted in bleeding the Army of Tennessee into a pale specter of its previous robust, effective self. Hood resigned, and Johnston was recalled to his former command, which he surrendered on April 26, 1865. In 1874, Johnston completed his writing on the war, in which he went after Hood—disparaging him and his generalship. Hood refuted Johnston in "A Reply to General Johnston." Later, Hood was determined to write an expanded memoir to respond to the way first Johnston and then Sherman portrayed his conduct of the war. *Advance and Retreat* was not published until 1880 after Hood's death from yellow fever in 1879.

APPENDIX

1. MILITARY ORGANIZATION

An army is really only a headquarters. It consists of a commanding general, who is usually a major general, and his staff and escort. These men were basically communicators with the headquarters above and below. Communications are better if directed from below to those above, but more often than not—since politics are battles no maps are drawn for or no campaigns openly discussed—the communications go down the chain of command to subordinates.

Under the Union armies in the military hierarchy were corps. The Army of the Cumberland had three full infantry corps and one of cavalry. It was huge, well-led, and expertly administered. This army had about 40,000 troops. Next in size was the Army of the Tennessee with three infantry corps and nearly 30,000 men. The smallest was the Army of the Ohio, which was essentially a corps plus, as an army usually had two or three corps reporting to it.

Corps are headquarters, too, and they are also led by a commanding general, who is usually a major general, and his staff. Corps have two or more divisions subordinate to it. In Sherman's army, each corps had at least two divisions, and many, especially the heavy Army of the Cumberland, had three. Although the position of divisional commander calls for a major general, the command was often held by brigadier generals, who wear one star. In the Civil War, because of attrition, colonels sometimes commanded divisions. This often happened on the battlefield if the enemy sharpshooters were accurate and the commander was killed.

Army, corps, and division represent three layers of command hierarchy as the headquarters. The next lower layer is a brigade. These units are commanded by a colonel or a one-star general. Every division has two or more brigades.

Reporting to brigade headquarters are regiments, and regiments are commanded by colonels or lieutenant colonels. Regiments had numbers and carried a state name, signifying the home state of many of the men, such as the 6th Iowa or the 66th Illinois. In the beginning stages of the war, regiments were made up of about 1,000 men organized into ten companies, each with about a hundred men. Captains led companies, which were denoted by letters in the alphabet, such as Company A or B. Typically, these letters were A through K, but never J. Captains often raised a hundred soldiers from a town or county and were most often elected to their positions. Colonels leading regiments generally were elected from the group of captains, as was the assistant regimental commander, whose rank was that of a lieutenant colonel. Without elections, the governor of the state appointed the regimental and company grade officers.

Two or more companies of a hundred men made up a battalion. Battalions are groups of companies less than a regiment. Typically, a regiment had two battalions. The right wing—or first battalion—was under command of the lieutenant colonel. The left wing—or second battalion—was under command of the regiment's major. The Union army didn't have much to do with battalions, but occasionally, one would be so recognized.

A company was subdivided into two or more platoons, which were led by lieutenants.

Two or more squads made up a platoon and were led by sergeants. At the bottom, or the top, were the individual private soldiers. Troops in the field know the men in their company and most of the soldiers in their regiment. These were people they were raised with—their friends and neighbors. The soldier fought in companies and groups of companies, and these companies lined up in a prescribed way. They did it every time they formed a line of battle, so the men grew used to who was on their left and right.

A Federal corps, at the beginning of the campaign, had between 10,000 and 13,000 men. Accordingly, each division contained 3,000 to 4,000 troops. Brigades, with their two or more regiments, had from 1,500 to 2,500 men. Regiments started with about 1,000 men.

A light artillery battery would have upwards of a hundred men, depending on the number of guns in the battery. Most often, there were six guns in a Union battery and four in the battery of their Confederate counterpart. Each Union division had at least two of those six-gun batteries, lead by a captain. A battery was made up of two gun sections. In the Military Department of the Mississippi, run by Sherman, some 254 artillery tubes or guns were spread out over the many divisions and more than 100,000 men.

2. THE SCIENCE BEHIND THE FIRE OF RIFLED GUNS

Rifled guns like the 10-pound Parrott rifles of the 1st Iowa Battery were the most technologically advanced military equipment of the age. Death, noise, fire and fear belched from rifled guns when fired. The hot gases that force themselves first from the 3-inch muzzle of the 10-pound 1863 Parrott rifle are the result of a centuries long process of manufacture, trial and error, and discovery. In a more immediate sense, it is a near instantaneous chemical reaction. Gunpowder is made of three ingredients: charcoal, saltpeter, and sulfur.

Willow and poplar trees—three to four years old and grown to about one inch in diameter—is the source of the best wood for creating charcoal. Charcoal, by itself, will neither burn nor explode. Saltpeter or niter is the chemical compound known as potassium nitrate (KNO3), which is found as a natural salt in various locations. It is found at or near the surface of the earth, any place where animal matter decomposes. Niter, alone, will not burn. When refined into small, perfectly white grains, it is ready for combination. Sulfur is yellow and is used to add consistency to gunpowder, to make it less able to absorb moisture, and to enhance the intensity the fire it produces.

These three substances are combined by pulverizing and are mixed with water and formed into cakes. These cakes are pressed and screened to separate the mixture by grain size. Additional moisture is removed by glazing in a revolving drum, and then the mixture is dried, sifted, and finally placed in 100-pound barrels for shipment. Gunpowder is then produced by pounding mills with mortars and pestles or by iron or marble cylinders or rollers. For cannons, the largest grains are used. For example, ten grams of cannon powder contain only 150 grains while that used for rifles may contain up to 15,000 grains or 100 times as much. The larger grains permit a more rapid ignition but allow for a slower combustion than do the smaller grains.

Before mixing, the ingredients are weighted because they are combined by weight. Ten units of sulfur are added to fifteen units of charcoal and then combined with seventy-five units of niter. This produces a powder that is quick burning because of the presence of so much oxygen in the niter.

When subjected to a temperature of 600 degrees Fahrenheit, gunpowder undergoes an intense chemical change whereby powder grains melt and are changed into gases. This gas expands very rapidly and violently to between 600 to 1,000 times the volume of the original solid. This explosive reaction is confined initially in the small, dark chamber, at the base of the weapon it has reposed in. The ignition of the powder creates great heat and light as it moves from grain to grain, creating combustion—that evolution of the powder into a gas. The two actions work in concert with the pressure of the initial combustion, forcing the burning or ignition forward and through the bag of gunpowder more rapidly than if it were not present. In effect, the one-pound bag of powder undergoes ignition and combustion nearly in an instantaneous flash and generates a pressure on the rear of the projectile of something like 2,000 to 3,000 pounds per square inch.

The balloon of intensely heated nitrogen and carbonic acid gas slams into the rear of the iron bolt with such explosive pressure that the projectile overcomes its original inertia and begins to race forward down the interior of the tube. The comparatively soft wrought iron or copper base is flattened by the explosive hammer blow and its outer rim quickly expands to conform to the lands and grooves that make up the barrel's rifling.

The five grooves measure 0.1 of an inch below the corresponding raised surface of the interior of the gun tube, the lands. This rifling twists one complete turn every twenty-four feet. As the missile moves forward, it is passed by some of the gases. As a result of being explosively thrust forward and being simultaneously gripped at its end by the expanded soft metal cup, a clockwise rotation begins. This rotation quickly builds so that at the end of its 69.875 inch trip out of the mouth of the piece, the bolt has rotated seven inches to the right or one-fourth of the perimeter of the three-inch tube. With this rotation comes a rapid spin. At the time it leaves the tube, the missile is moving at about 1,800 feet per second or 1,227.3 miles per hour.

The super-hot gas ahead of and around the projectile heat the air in the barrel and at its mouth to such a degree that the air burst into flame. From the perfect black hole that forms the mouth of the piece issues a brief, intense flash of flame and expanding gases. At night, this produces a beautiful light and sound show.

From the center of the muzzle, the round itself—nearly ten pounds of spinning, hot metal—exits and begins its journey, freed from its iron confines. It sails to its final impact.

With the elevation of the muzzle at five degrees above the horizontal, the shell will spend only six seconds in flight before it strikes the ground 5,850 feet away. Immediately upon its release from the muzzle, the round begins slowing, as friction, gravity, and the spin of the earth all conspire to halt its flight and to cast it into the ground. During that brief period in the air, the projectile will have spun some 293 times. This spin accounts tor the superb accuracy of the weapon.

As thunder is to lightning, so is the noise of the explosion to the combustion that caused it. To the gunners, the noise is immediate, but to an observer a mile away, the sound of the discharge takes four to eight seconds to reach him. Within that time, the flight is generally over. The speed of light and that of sound, starting at the same point, achieve greatly disparate rates of acceleration and speed. Racing at 1,100 feet per second, sound catches up to the observer only after the object causing the noise has already hit the earth.

Generally, for pieces like the 10-pound Parrott, it takes thirty to forty seconds to load and fire. Over time, a gun might be fired once a minute. When pressed, good gun crews could get off two or three shots per minute and an exceptional crew could manage four shots per minute for a short period. The ability to load and fire four times per minute corresponds almost exactly with the loading and firing ability of an exceptional infantry soldier. Of course, in such an exhibition, it was easier to begin with the weapon already loaded so that the first shot comes at the beginning of the exercise.

3. BATTERY CREW AND FIRING FIELD ARTILLERY

A battery was the key organizational unit used for the field artillery. Six guns for a battery was fairly typical of the Federal army. The South generally made do with four guns to a battery. Each gun constituted a detachment, or a platoon. Each platoon had one gun, its caisson, and their limbers. It was commanded by a sergeant who proudly answered to the title of "Chief of the Piece." This term rolls poetically from the lips of others and is well received by the one being so addressed. Under the Chief of the Piece were two corporals. An entire gun crew had eight members, each of whom was identified by a number, except the "gunner," who ordinarily was also the Chief of the Piece.

Shot time often depended on the need to aim, the type of weapon, the ammunition being fired, the level of energy possessed by the gun crew, the intensity of the combat, the leadership available, and the skill of the crew. This was true whether the crew wore blue or gray.

In theory, each gun was to be separated by forty-two to forty-eight feet, meaning that a properly spaced battery would present a front of 240 feet or some 80 yards. A limber with an ammunition chest was supposed to be located eighteen feet to the rear of the gun.

With the command "Commence Firing!" the gunner would order, "Load!" Number 1 cannoneer sponged the tube with a combination sponge/rammer, a wooden pole with a woolen sponge soaked in water. The sponge would extinguish any sparks or burning material remaining from the previous shot.

Number 2 took a prepared round consisting of a powder bag and one form of projectile or another from Number 5 and placed it into the mouth of the piece.

Number 1 had already reversed the rammer/sponge and, now, using the rammer end, rammed or pushed the round home to the base of the gun.

Number 3 held his thumb over the vent while the ramming took place. His thumb was encased in leather. The purpose of this was to prevent any lingering un-extinguished spark in the tube from coming into contact with air and the powder bag, thereby causing ignition.

The gunner sighted the piece.

Number 3 used a trail spike to move the trail either left or right, as directed by the gunner.

Number 5, after being relieved of the prepared round by Number 2, returned to the limber for the next round from Number 6 or 7. Number 6 selected, cut, and affixed the colored fuses for shell or casement shot as needed. Number 5 returned to his station with the next prepared round.

The gunner could adjust the tube up or down using the metal elevating screw, which raised or lowered the rear of the gun as needed. Once satisfied with the elevation and direction, the gunner stepped clear of the piece by moving to the rear and side and ordered, "Ready!"

Number 1 and 2 stepped clear.

Number 3, using his vent prick, punctured the powder bag by forcing the metal prick down the vent and into the bag and then withdrawing it.

Number 4, standing behind the left wheel of the carriage at the other side of the breech from Number 3, hooked his lanyard to a friction primer, which he then seated and inserted into the vent.

Number 3 covered the vent with his left hand as Number 4 moved to the rear, taking care to leave slack in the lanyard.

The gunner ordered, "Fire!" Number 3 removed his hand and stepped clear of the right wheel while Number 4 yanked the lanyard.

The friction primer created sparks that ignite the fine musket-grain gunpowder, which in turn ignited the main charge. The gun fired, recoiled, and was manhandled back into its firing position.

At that point, the gun crew's orchestrated ballet begins again. It is a seamless choreographed dance with eight men, a limber, and a gun carriage with each man dodging a bucking recoil and trusting the other to follow the gunner's orders and perform his individual function without delay or direction. The firing exercise was dangerous to anyone behind a wheel, in front of the muzzle, or near an exploding tube or anyone misusing a friction primer. During a mere drill, this was danger enough. During battle, the enemy fire can create "hot" conditions in which no bummers, coffee-coolers, or other shirkers could exist.

4. THE INFANTRY RIFLE DRILL

To shoot a field weapon, soldiers had to perform about twenty steps, which for convenience had been broken down to twelve commands:

Load.
Handle cartridge.
Pour powder.
Seat round.
Draw rammer.
Ram.
Replace rammer.
Prime.
Shoulder.
Ready.
Aim.
Fire.

The commands became familiar to each soldier. The motions that his hand, arms, thumb, fingers, feet, eyes, and brain went through were as smooth on his part as the motion between the trigger and the hammer in the piece itself were.

The motions were honed down to be as efficient as a man could devise. Men had been loading muskets, now rifles, through the muzzle of the weapon since before they first stepped foot on American soil. Weapons were better, but the loading was essentially the same as when a soldier's grandfather had killed Redcoats during the Revolution.

Soldiers would stand with the stock between their feet, with their left hand holding the weapon out some eight to ten inches in their front and with their right hand near the top of their leather cartridge box, which was held by a wide leather belt on their right side. On the next command, a soldier's fingers would find, grip, and extract a paper cartridge that was tubular and was the exact same size as the open muzzle of his weapon. The soldier would bring it to his mouth and place it between his teeth. The top would be torn off to expose the black-grained powder. Then, carefully extending the lip of the paper tube inside the muzzle, he would tip it upright, and the contents would pour into the long barrel.

Then, the soldier would remove the remainder of the paper from the conical-shaped lead bullet—a minie ball—and place the generally well-lubricated round into the open muzzle.

If the weapon were clean, then the round eased into the opening, but if it were dirty from firing, the greasy powder mixture meant getting the round started was a chore. Older smoothbore weapons were easier to load and consequently could be loaded faster. Once seated so it would stay in place, the round was either well inside or mostly out. Some men originally used a short piece of wood as a "starter" to get the round into the barrel. Most developed a strong thumb, which could seat the ball into its resting place.

Once the round was seated, the soldier would draw his ramrod out of the narrow nest that lay under the barrel. This long, thin metal rod had a ridged and slotted cylinder on the end, which matched up perfectly with the exposed end of the round. Pushing down with the metal rod drove the lead round down the barrel to rest firmly and tightly on the black-powder charge. The slender ramrod made a distinctive sound as it touched the rifled sides of the barrel. The orchestrated symphony of the metal on metal made a pretty melody, which was pleasing to the ear.

Strong, experienced loaders could plunge or shoot the rod and the round with one easy flinging motion. Less able or experienced men tapped the round down using a more tentative, up-and-down, repetitive stroke of the metal rod. The treaded end of the rod provided some purchase when it was far enough down the muzzle to enable a soldier to grip it in lieu of the slender, slippery smooth surface of the rod itself. Naturally, the next step involved the removal of the rammer from the confines of the barrel, which was then stuck in its nesting tube or in the ground within easy reach of the trooper's right hand.

With the order "prime," the soldier's left hand would grip the weapon low enough on the length to bring the stock up to his waist. The weapon would then make a greater angle with his body than it had before. The right hand would pull back the hammer until the hammer clicked into half cock, creating a sweet and mechanical sound. His thumbnail or thumb and forefinger would flick or pull the expended brass percussion cap of the nipple. The soldier would then withdraw a shiny brass object that looked a bit like a top hat without the brim from the cap pouch on his belt. This object was a cap filled with fulminate, and it fitted nicely over the hole in the center of the nipple. The weapon would then be loaded and ready to fire.

At the command "shoulder," the soldier would put the weapon to his right shoulder. The left hand would act to steady and hold the weapon up. At "ready," the soldier would relocate his feet to align his body with the direction of fire and lower the end of the piece to be nearly vertical with his right side. His right hand would grip the underside of the narrow, wooden neck of the stock near the trigger guard, and his thumb would fully cock the hammer by drawing it back as far as possible until it set. Next, the weapon would be moved, and the head canted over so the man's right cheek lay against the smooth wood of the stock. The man's right eye that would be over the rear sight would find the front sight. The barrel would then come down as to align the rear and front sights on the target. Holding his breath with index finger inside the trigger guard and curved around the trigger, the soldier would slowly exhale and squeeze the trigger on the command "fire."

The butt of the stocks would hammer back into the pocket of the right shoulder. As the gun fired, white smoke would billow, and the sound of the nearly contained explosion would go off inches from each soldier's face. Generally, the discharge of the weapon came as a surprise, and sometimes, it didn't come at all.

SOURCES

It took me years to write *Seven Days in July*, and during that entire time, I never stopped reading about the war that nearly destroyed this nation and I never quit stopping to read the historical markers and walk accessible areas. In Atlanta, ghosts of warriors of long ago find little rest among the new buildings, which lie on the fields of battle and have triumphed over the earlier combatants.

I owe a debt to all the historians, authors, and map makers who put the facts, ideas, and questions into book form and lightened my personal journey through this period of history. Thank you. The books I have listed all made a contribution to my story and form the foundation of my knowledge. We know more about the war today than those who lived through it did because of the scholarship of many writers before me.

The books listed should be read for the best understanding about the times, the war, and the battles. They are invaluable. Where I deviate from the history they teach, let it be explained by an imperfect understanding or that my interpretation of the events required it—or a combination of the two.

Allardice, Bruce S. *More Generals in Gray*. Baton Rouge, LA: Louisiana State University Press, 2006.

Ambrose, Stephen E. *Nothing Like It in the World: The Men Who Built the Transcontinental Railroad, 1863-1869*. New York: Touchstone, 2000.

Arnold, James R. *The Armies of U.S. Grant*. London: Arms and Armour, 1996.

Barker, Lorenzo A. *With the Western Sharpshooters: Michigan Boys of Company D, 66th Illinois.* Huntington, WV: Blue Acorn Press, 1994.

Bell, James W. *Civil War Georgia Regimental Series No. 1.* Hodges, SC: Lindy Publications, 1990.

Boatner, Mark. *The Civil War Dictionary.* New York: Vintage, 1991

Buck, Irving A. *Cleburne and His Command.* Jackson, TN: McCowat-Mercer Press, 1959.

Carter, Samuel, III. *The Siege of Atlanta, 1864.* New York: St. Martin's Press, 1973.

Castel, Albert E. *Decision in the West: The Atlanta Campaign of 1864.* Lawrence, KS: University Press of Kansas, 1992.

Connelly, Donald B. *John M. Schofield and the Politics of Generalship.* Chapel Hill, NC: University of North Carolina Press, 2006.

Cox, Jacob D. *Sherman's Battle for Atlanta.* New York: Da Capo Press, 1994.

Daniel, Larry J. *Soldiering in the Army of Tennessee: A Portrait of Life in a Confederate Army.* Chapel Hill, NC: University of North Carolina Press, 1991.

Davis, George B., *U.S. Army, Leslie J. Perry, and Joseph W. Kirkley. The Official Military Atlas of the Civil War.* New York: Barnes & Noble Publishing, 2003.

Dodge, Grenville M. *The Battle of Atlanta and Other Campaigns, Addresses, Etc.* Denver: Sage Books, 1965.

Evans, David. *Sherman's Horsemen: Union Cavalry Operations in the Atlanta Campaign.* Bloomington, IN: Indiana University Press, 1996.

Farber, Daniel A. *Lincoln's Constitution.* Chicago: The University of Chicago Press, 2003.

Fleming, James R. *Band of Brothers: Company C, 9th Tennessee Infantry.* Shippensburg, PA: White Mane Publishing, 1996.

Flood, Charles B. *Grant and Sherman: The Friendship That Won the Civil War.* New York: Farrar, Straus and Giroux, 2005.

Foote, Shelby. *The Civil War: A Narrative. 3 vols.* New York: Vintage Books, 1986.

Forrester, Rebel C. *Glory and Tears: Obion County, Tennessee, 1860-1870.* Union City, TN: H.A. Lanzer Company, 1966.

Foster, Samuel T. *One of Cleburne's Command: The Civil War Reminiscences and Diary of Capt. Samuel T. Foster, Granbury's Texas Brigade, CAS.* Austin: University of Texas Press, 1980.

Glatthaar, Joseph T. *Partners in Command: The Relationships Between Leaders in the Civil War.* New York: The Free Press, 1998.

Goodwin, Doris K. *Team of Rivals: The Political Genius of Abraham Lincoln.* New York: Blithedale Productions, 2005.

Goss, Thomas J. *The War Within the Union High Command: Politics and Generalship During the Civil War.* Lawrence, KS: University Press of Kansas, 2003.

Grant, Ulysses S. *Ulysses S. Grant: Memoirs and Selected Letters.* New York: Library of America, 1990.

Griffith, Paddy. *Battle Tactics of the Civil War.* London: Yale University Press, 2001.

Hanson, Victor D. *The Soul of Battle: From Ancient Times to the Present Day, How Three Great Liberators Vanquished Tyranny.* New York: Anchor Books, 2001.

Hay, Thomas R. "The Atlanta Campaign (I)." *The Georgia Historical Quarterly* 7, no. 1 (1923).

---. "The Atlanta Campaign (II)." *The Georgia Historical Quarterly* 7, no. 2 (1923).

Headquarters and Department of the Army. *FM 100–5, Operations.* Washington, DC: Government Publications Office, 1986.

Hitt, Michael D. *Charged with Treason: Ordeal of 400 Mill Workers During Military Operations in Roswell, Georgia, 1864-1856.* Monroe, NY: Library Research Associates, Inc., 1992.

Ives, Washington. *Civil War Journal and Letters of Sergeant Washington Ives, 4th Florida, C.S.A.* Translated by Jim R. Cabaniss. N.p.: n.p., 2008.

Jenkins, Robert D., Sr. *The Battle for Buckhead: From Nancy Creek to Peach Tree Creek.* Dalton, GA: Mill Creek Press, 2010.

---. *The Battle of Moore's Mill: The First Battle for Atlanta.* Dalton, GA: Mill Creek Press, 2010.

Jones, James P. *Black Jack: John A. Logan and Southern Illinois in the Civil War Era.* Tallahassee: Florida State University, 1967.

Kennett, Lee B. *Marching Through Georgia: The Story of Soldiers and Civilians During Sherman's Campaign.* New York: Harper Collins Publishers, 1995.

Lee, Robert E. *The Wartime Papers of R.E. Lee.* Edited by Clifford Dowdey. New York: Bramhall House, 1961.

Little, Robert D. "General Hardee and the Atlanta Campaign." *The Georgia Historical Quarterly* 29, no. 1 (1945).

Longacre, Edward G. *Worthy Opponents: William T. Sherman and Joseph E. Johnston: Antagonists in War—Friends in Peace.* Nashville: Rutledge Hill Press, 2006.

Losson, Christopher. *Tennessee's Forgotten Warriors: Frank Cheatham and his Confederate Division.* Knoxville, TN: University of Tennessee Press, 1989.

Manigault, Arthur M. *A Carolinian Goes to War.* Columbia, SC: University of South Carolina Press, 1988.

McMurry, Richard M. *Atlanta 1864: Last Chance for the Confederacy.* Lincoln, NE: University of Nebraska Press, 2000.

---. *John Bell Hood and the War for Southern Independence.* Lexington, KY: University Press of Kentucky, 1992.

---. *Two Great Rebel Armies: An Essay in Confederate Military History.* Chapel Hill, NC: University of North Carolina Press, 1989.

Mctyre, Joe and Rebecca Nash Paden. *Historic Roswell Georgia.* Charleston, SC: Arcadia Publishing, 2001.

Miller, Charles D. *The Struggle for the Life of the Republic: A Civil War Narrative.* Edited by Stewart Bennett and Barbara Tillery. Kent, OH: Kent State University Press, 2004.

Moltke, Helmuth, Graf von. *Moltke on the Art of War: Selected Writings.* Edited by Daniel J. Hughes. Novato, CA: Presidio Press, 1993.

Newton, Steven H. "Formidable Only in Flight?" *North and South* 3, no. 4 (April 2000): 43-56.

Nosworthy, Brent. *The Bloody Crucible of Courage: Fighting Methods and Combat Experience of the Civil War.* New York: Carroll & Graf Publishers, 2003.

Parrish, William E. *Frank Blair: Lincoln's Conservative.* Columbia, MO: University of Missouri Press, 1998.

Patterson, Gerard A. *Rebels from West Point.* Mechanicsburg, PA: Stackpole Books, 2002.

Purdue, Howell, and Elizabeth Purdue. *Pat Cleburne: Confederate General.* Hillsboro, TX: Hill Jr. College Press, 1973.

Sandburg, Carl. *The War Years, 1861-1864. Vol. 2 of Abraham Lincoln: The Prairie Years and the War Years.* New York: Dell Publishing Co., 1954.

Scaife, William R. *Civil War Atlas.* Atlanta, GA: Civil War Publications, 1995.

Secrist, Philip L. *The Sherman Trail of Battle to Atlanta, 1864.* Macon, GA: Mercer University Press, 2006.

Shaara, Michael. *The Killer Angels: The Classic Novel of the Civil War.* New York: Ballantine Books, 1975.

Shanahan, Edward P. *Atlanta Campaign Staff Ride Briefing Book.* Atlanta, GA: Office of the Command Historian, 1995.

Sherman, William T. *Memoirs of General William T. Sherman.* New York: Da Capo Press, 1984.

Symonds, Craig L. *Joseph E. Johnston: A Civil War Biography.* New York: Norton, 1994.

Taylor, Thomas T. *Tom Taylor's Civil War. Compiled by Albert Castel.* Lawrence, KS: University Press of Kansas, 2000.

The Photographic History of the Civil War. 10 vols. Edited by Francis T. Miller and Robert S. Lanier. New York: The Review of Reviews Co., 1911.

United States War Department. *The War of the Rebellion: A Compilation of the Official Records of the Union and Confederate Armies.* 128 vols. Washington, D.C.: Government Printing Office, 1880-1901.

Walker, Scott. *Hell's Broke Loose in Georgia: Survival in a Civil War Regiment.* Athens, GA: University of Georgia Press, 2005.

Warner, Ezra J. *Generals in Blue: Lives of the Union Commanders.* Baton Rouge, LA: Louisiana State University Press, 1992.

---. *Generals in Gray: Lives of the Confederate Commanders.* Baton Rouge, LA: Louisiana State University Press, 2000.

Watkins, Sam R. *"Co. Aytch:" A Side Show of the Big Show.* New York: Touchstone, 1997.

Whaley, Elizabeth J. *Forgotten Hero: General James B. McPherson.* New York: Exposition Press, 1955.

Wilson, Douglas L. *Honor's Voice: The Transformation of Abraham Lincoln.* New York: Vintage Books, 1999.

Woodworth, Steven E. *Jefferson Davis and His Generals: The Failure of Confederate Command in the West.* Lawrence, KS: University Press of Kansas, 1990.

Made in the USA
Columbia, SC
25 May 2019